Radioactive Isotopes
in
Medicine and Biology

COMPANION VOLUME

RADIOACTIVE ISOTOPES
IN MEDICINE AND BIOLOGY
★ ★ Medicine

By

SOLOMON SILVER

2nd Edition

RADIOACTIVE ISOTOPES IN MEDICINE AND BIOLOGY

★ BASIC PHYSICS AND INSTRUMENTATION

EDITH H. QUIMBY, Sc.D.

*Professor Emeritus of Radiology, College of Physicians and Surgeons,
Columbia University, New York*

and

SERGEI FEITELBERG, M.D.

*Director, Andre Meyer Department of Physics, The Mount Sinai Hospital; Associate
Clinical Professor of Radiology (Physics), College of Physicians and Surgeons,
Columbia University, New York*

Second Edition

84 Illustrations

Lea & Febiger

Philadelphia   1963

615.84
Q6r
[v]

Library of Congress Catalog Card Number: 62–10610

Printed in the United States of America

Preface to Volume I of Second Edition

FOLLOWING publication of the first (one-volume) edition of this book, there were numerous requests for more complete coverage in the medical field, for material on non-medical laboratory techniques in biochemistry, physiology and biophysics, and for more detail in certain parts of the physics and instrument section. The publishers talked with many scientists using radioactive nuclides for a wide variety of purposes, and came to the conclusion that it was difficult to satisfy everyone with a single volume. They accordingly suggested to the authors that a 3-volume work should be envisaged. The first volume, basic physics and instrumentation, should be useful to isotope users in all fields; the second should deal only with medical applications, and the third with non-medical research techniques in biology and chemistry. The authors decided this was worth doing. Drs. Quimby and Feitelberg prepared the first volume, along the lines of their sections of the first edition, but with considerable amplification in some places, and with the inclusion of new data. Dr. Silver undertook the medical volume, which appears with its own preface. These two are published almost simultaneously. The third volume, being entirely new material and requiring a new author, will not be ready at the same time, but it was deemed preferable not to hold up the first two to wait for the third. Its appearance will be announced by the publishers.

As with the first edition, it is intended that this one shall serve as a basis for study, both by classes and individuals, but no claim is made to completeness. This would be impossible, in such a rapidly developing field. Nor has an effort been made to provide a complete bibliography; here again, it would be impossible to be up-to-date. Fundamental studies are listed and also some of the newer developments, but supplementary library work will be necessary for a thorough coverage of practically any broad topic.

Our course on clinical uses of radioactive isotopes has continued to be given twice a year; there are now about 500 graduates. We, the teachers, have learned much from our students. We have continued to have generous cooperation from our professional colleagues, to whom we wish to express our appreciation. Special acknowledgment is due to Dr. Marvin Williams, whose meticulous review of the first edition was particularly valuable in the

(5)

preparation of the second. Dr. E. E. Stickley has read a great deal of the proof and furnished valuable suggestions. Miss Ellen Ewald has prepared the new illustrations, and our secretaries, Mrs. Gerda Osborn, and Mrs. Eva Schaefer, have continued to give us invaluable aid with the manuscript. The encouragement of the publishers and their enthusiasm for this new approach have contributed very greatly to bringing it to completion.

EDITH H. QUIMBY

New York, N. Y.   SERGEI FEITELBERG

Preface to the First Edition

THE artificial production of radioactive isotopes was announced twenty-five years ago, and caused a tremendous sensation among physicists and chemists, but aroused little attention among physicians. However, within a short time physiologists found that the new substances provided powerful tools for metabolic studies, and then some more truly clinical applications became apparent. In 1939 radioactive phosphorus was used as a substitute for whole-body x-irradiation in the treatment of certain blood dyscrasias. About the same time the value of radioactive iodine in the study of thyroid function was demonstrated, and within another three years this material was used in the treatment of toxic goiter. Radioactive iron was simultaneously employed by other groups in various studies relating to red blood cells and iron reserves. By 1940 there was a considerable literature dealing with medical uses of artificially radioactive isotopes, but there was no suggestion that they would eventually provide standard diagnostic and therapeutic procedures. They were obtainable only from cyclotrons, usually at great cost, and frequently in such form as to require considerable chemical manipulation before they could be used.

The discovery of the chain-reacting pile or nuclear reactor changed this picture, but it was not until 1946, after the end of World War II, that even one reactor could be used to provide isotopes for non-military purposes. In July of 1946, the Atomic Energy Commission announced a limited availability of certain isotopes for medical use, at much lower costs than cyclotron products, and in the next six months about 100 shipments were made for medical research in 38 institutions. Ten years later a thousand medical institutions were authorized to obtain the materials, and doctors in some of them were using very large quantities of radioactive isotopes.

At the beginning of this period, each individual or group had to enter an almost uncharted field. Some information was available in the literature, but in general, procedures were developed independently; all studies were essentially on a research basis. However, as their value became known many physicians wanted to avail themselves of the new tools. There were demands for instruction courses and for textbooks; these were intensified by the fact that the Atomic Energy Commission required the physician to have a certain amount of training before issuing him an authorization to obtain radioactive isotopes from their reactor. Few people or groups felt that they had the time or the qualifications to give a comprehensive course, and the books that appeared dealt mainly with limited parts of the field. In any case, progress was being made so rapidly that a book was out of date almost by the time it was published.

In June of 1954, the present authors, with the generous cooperation of physicians and physicists throughout New York City, undertook to offer a four-week full-time comprehensive course in clinical uses of radioactive isotopes. The response was so enthusiastic that they were forced to present the course twice a year, once as originally planned, for non-residents of the city, and once on a basis of one afternoon a week for eight months, for those living within commuting distance. It has now been given eight times, naturally with modifications from year to year. This book is the outgrowth of our experience in lectures, laboratory exercises, and conferences with the approximately 225 students who have completed the course.

It has been written as three quite separate parts, each by the author who has the most to do with that field in teaching the course. But each author owes much to the collaborators who have given so freely of their time and interest. It is hoped that the book will serve as a basis for study both by classes and by individuals, but no claim is made to completeness. In fact, it is certain that considerable supplementary reading will be necessary for everyone who wants a really comprehensive survey of even the generally used procedures. References have been supplied for this purpose, but no effort has been made to assemble a complete bibliography. For any particular type of study, recent papers of the survey type, which are listed, will provide complete sets of references.

We wish to express our grateful appreciation to our colleagues in the presentation of the course, for their generous sharing of their information, and to those other friends who have freely permitted us to use their published material. A special acknowledgement is due to Miss Ellen Ewald, who prepared all the illustrations from sketches supplied by the authors. To our secretaries, Miss Judith M. Weinberg, Mrs. Katherine Johanny, and Miss Blanche Lipkowitz, who have typed and re-typed the manuscript, looked up references, and generally been indispensable, we give our thanks. The publishers' enthusiasm in getting the book under way, and their patient but persistent attention to its progress should receive a large share of the credit in bringing it to completion.

EDITH H. QUIMBY
SERGEI FEITELBERG
SOLOMON SILVER

NEW YORK, NEW YORK
SEPTEMBER, 1958

Contents

PART I.—BASIC PHYSICS

By EDITH H. QUIMBY

of beta rays. Scattering of beta particles. Self-scattering and
self-absorption of beta particles. Absorption and scattering
of photon beams.

Contents

PART II.—INSTRUMENTATION AND LABORATORY METHODS

By Sergei Feitelberg

Radioactive Isotopes in Medicine

Part I
BASIC PHYSICS

Edith H. Quimby

Introduction

1808. John Dalton (England) presented the first experimental basis for an atomic hypothesis.

1811. Amadeo Avogadro (Italy) distinguished between atoms and molecules.

1815. Wm. Prout (England) suggested hydrogen (protyle) as a basic component of all matter.

1869. D. I. Mendeleev (Russia) set up a periodic table of chemical classification of elements.

1895. Wilhelm Conrad Roentgen (Germany) discovered x-rays.

1896. Henri Becquerel (France) discovered radioactivity of uranium.

1897. J. J. Thompson (England) discovered that the electron is a constituent of all atoms.

1898. Marie and Pierre Curie (France) discovered polonium and radium.

1900. P. Curie (France) found that the rays from radium consisted of two kinds, of very different penetrating power and deviated in different directions in a magnetic field. These later became known as alpha (α) and beta (β) rays.

1900. P. Villard (France) discovered a third type of radiation from radioactive substances, called it gamma rays (γ), and stated it to be identical with x-rays.

1905. Albert Einstein (Switzerland) proposed the theory of equivalence of mass and energy.

1910. F. Soddy (England) identified isotopes and isobars in naturally radioactive substances.

1911. Ernest Rutherford (England) discovered the atomic nucleus.

1911. C. G. Barkla (England) demonstrated the existence of extranuclear electrons.

1911. Victor Hess (Austria) discovered cosmic rays.

1912. J. J. Thompson (England) demonstrated the existence of isotopes in stable elements.

1912. C. T. R. Wilson (England) invented the cloud chamber for studying ionization tracks.

1913. Niels Bohr (Denmark) proposed an atom model with a central positively charged nucleus and a system of negative orbital electrons.

1913. H. G. J. Moseley (England), from a study of x-ray spectra, developed the system of atomic numbers.

1919. E. Rutherford (England) produced nuclear transmutation by bombarding nitrogen with α particles. He identified one product of the transmutation as a proton.

1932. Harold Urey (USA) discovered heavy hydrogen or deuterium.

1932. James Chadwick (England) discovered the neutron (whose existence Rutherford had suggested in 1919).

1932. J. D. Cockroft and E. T. S. Walton (England) produced nuclear transmutation by artificially accelerated protons.

1932. C. D. Anderson (USA) discovered the positron.

1932. E. O. Lawrence (USA) invented the cyclotron.

1934. F. Joliot and I. Curie-Joliot (France) discovered induced radioactivity in light elements by bombardment with natural α particles.

1934. E. O. Lawrence (USA) produced artificially radioactive nuclides by bombardment with artificially accelerated particles.

1934. Enrico Fermi (Italy) produced transformation of nuclei by neutron capture.

1939. O. Hahn and F. Strassman (Germany) discovered nuclear fission.

1939. Lise Meitner and O. Frisch (Sweden) calculated the huge energy release to be expected in nuclear fission.

1939. Enrico Fermi (USA) suggested the possibility of a chain reaction in nuclear fission. This was experimentally verified in several laboratories in USA and France.

1939. "Manhattan Project" (USA) was organized for military development of atomic energy.

1940. E. M. MacMillan and P. Abelson (USA) discovered two "transuranic" elements, neptunium and plutonium, following the bombardment of uranium by slow neutrons.

1942. (USA) First self-maintaining nuclear chain reaction in a uranium graphite "pile" or reactor, was initiated in Chicago.

1945. Atomic bombs were exploded July 16th in New Mexico, August 6th and 11th over Hiroshima and Nagasaki, Japan.

1946. (USA) "Manhattan Project," becoming Atomic Energy Commission, announced availability of pile-produced radioactive isotopes for medical, industrial and scientific research. Three hundred shipments made during first year.

1956. Atomic Energy Commission (USA) made over 15,000 shipments of isotopes to more than 5000 institutions in the United States and 32 other countries, during this tenth year of isotope distribution.

A LIST OF USEFUL REFERENCE BOOKS

BEIERWALTES, W. H., JOHNSON, P. C. and SOLARI, A. J. *Clinical Use of Radioisotopes*, Philadelphia, W. B. Saunders Co., 1957

CALDER, RITCHIE. *Living with the Atom,* University of Chicago Press, 1962.

Chart of the Nuclides, 2nd Ed. (revised to 1961) Nuclear Research Center, Karlsruhe. Gersbach & Sohn, Verlag, Munich, Germany.

COMAR, C. L.: *Radioisotopes in Biology and Agriculture.* New York, McGraw-Hill Book Company, Inc., 1955.

CURIE, EVE: *Madam Curie*, New York, Doubleday Doran and Company, Inc., 1938.

CURIE, MARIE: *Pierre Curie*, New York, The Macmillan Company, 1923.

ELMORE, WILLIAM C. and SANDS, MATTHEW: *Electronics, Experimental Techniques.* New York, McGraw-Hill Book Company, Inc., 1949.

FERMI, LAURA: *Atoms in the Family*, Chicago, Chicago University Press, 1954.

FRIEDLANDER, G. and KENNEDY, J. W.: *Nuclear and Radiochemistry.* New York, John Wiley and Sons, 1955. (Revised Version.)

GAMOW, G.: *Mr. Tompkin Explores the Atom* (Popular). New York, The Macmillan Company, 1945.

General Electric Chart of the Nuclides, 5th Ed. (revised to 1956), Knolls Atomic Power Laboratory, Knolls, New York.

GLASSER, O., QUIMBY, E. H., TAYLOR, L. S., WEATHERWAX, J. L. and MORGAN, R. H.: *Physical Foundations of Radiology*, 3rd Ed., New York, Paul B. Hoeber, 1961.

HAHN, PAUL F.: *A Manual of Artificial Radioisotope Therapy.* New York, Academic Press, 1951.

————: *Therapeutic Use of Artificial Radioisotopes.* New York, John Wiley and Sons, 1956.

HALLIDAY, D.: *Introductory Nuclear Physics.* New York, John Wiley and Sons, 1950.

HECHT, S.: *Explaining the Atom* (Popular). New York, The Viking Press, 1945.

HINE, G. J. and BROWNWELL, G. L.: *Radiation Dosimetry.* New York, Academic Press, 1956.

HULL, G. F.: *Elementary Nuclear Physics*, Revised Ed. New York, The Macmillan Company, 1949.

KAMEN, M.: *Radioactive Tracers in Biology*, 3rd Ed., New York, Academic Press, 1957.

LAPP, R. E. and ANDREWS, H. L.: *Nuclear Radiation Physics.* 2nd Ed., New York, Prentice-Hall, 1954.

MORGAN, R. H. and CORRIGAN, K. E.: *Handbook of Radiology.* Chicago, Year Book Publishers, Inc., 1955.

NEEDHAM, J. and PAGEL, W.: *Background to Modern Science* (Popular). New York, The Macmillan Company, 1938.

POLLARD, E. C. and DAVIDSON, W. L.: *Applied Nuclear Physics*, 2nd Ed., New York, John Wiley and Sons, 1951.

QUIMBY, EDITH H.: *Safe Handling of Radioactive Isotopes in Medical Practice*, New York, Macmillan, 1960.

REICH, HERBERT J.: *Theory and Applications of Electron Tubes.* New York, McGraw-Hill Book Company, Inc., 1939.

RUTHERFORD, E., CHADWICK, J., and ELLIS, C. D.: *Radiations from Radioactive Substances.* Cambridge, England, University Press, 1930 (Reissued in 1951).

SIRI, WILLIAM E.: *Isotopic Tracers and Nuclear Radiations.* New York, McGraw-Hill Book Company, Inc., 1949.

SULLIVAN, W. H.: *Trilinear Chart of Nuclides.* Washington, D. C., Government Printing Office, 1957.

VEALL, N. and VETTER, H.: *Radioisotope Techniques in Clinical Research and Diagnosis,* London, Butterworth, 1958.

WERNER, Sidney C.: *The Thyroid.* 2nd Ed., New York, Hoeber-Harper, 1962.

Radioactive Isotopes in Medicine and Biology

1

Atoms

RADIOACTIVITY is a characteristic of certain atoms, hence the approach to the study of radioactive substances should begin at the atomic level.

History of Atomic Concept. The idea of atoms as basic particles of matter is very old, but through the ages the concept of their nature has undergone many modifications. At the beginning of the last century Dalton organized ideas then current in this field. It was accepted that all matter was built up of components called *elements*, of which there were a large but limited number. The smallest fundamental particles of each element were its *atoms;* atoms of a particular element were all exactly alike, and different from atoms of all other elements; they were indivisible and unalterable.

With the discovery of radioactivity by Becquerel in 1896 and of the electron as a constituent of matter by J. J. Thompson in 1897, it became evident that the atom must have structure and even be capable of undergoing some sort of breakdown. During the next 15 years various atomic models were suggested, to be crystallized in the Rutherford-Bohr picture about 1913. According to this, the atom is described as basically like a miniature solar system; there is a central *nucleus* containing most of the atomic mass and carrying a positive electric charge; this is surrounded by a system of orbital negative *electrons.*

Atomic Building-Blocks. At first the nucleus was believed to be a mixture of basic positively charged particles and electrons, since the net number of units of positive charge on the nucleus was less than the number of units of atomic mass. The number of orbital electrons was accepted as being the same as the excess of positive charges in the nucleus, after the nuclear electrons had balanced out a certain number of them. This model was theoretically difficult to justify, and a new particle was postulated which should be of essentially the same mass as the unit positively charged particle, but have no electric charge. The positive particle was called the *proton;* the uncharged one was the *neutron.* Later, as will be seen, both particles were experimentally identified.

In the currently accepted model, neutrons replace nuclear electron-proton combinations and the number of orbital electrons is the same as that of the nuclear protons, so that the complete atom is electrically neutral. Protons and neutrons are called *nucleons*.

Masses of nuclei, or of atomic components, are specified in terms of mass units, whose derivation will be discussed later (page 25). One mass unit is 1.6598×10^{-24} grams.*

  1 proton weighs 1.00759 mass units = 1.6724×10^{-24} gm.
  1 neutron   1.00898 1.6747×10^{-24}
  1 electron   0.0005486 9.1085×10^{-28}

Present Picture of Atomic Structure. The simplest atom is that of ordinary hydrogen, with one proton for its nucleus and a single orbital electron. Next comes helium, with two protons and two neutrons in the nucleus and two orbital electrons, and then lithium with three protons, four neutrons and three electrons, as indicated in Figure 1. The electrons of

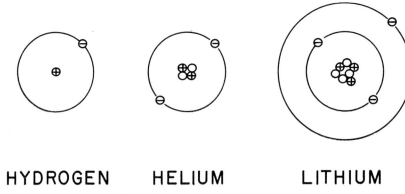

HYDROGEN HELIUM LITHIUM

Fig. 1. Structure of simple atoms.

hydrogen and helium travel in a single orbital region, but with lithium, the third electron starts a new orbit. Through the next seven elements (beryllium, boron, carbon, nitrogen, oxygen, fluorine, neon) the nucleus successively adds one proton and one or two neutrons, and an additional electron appears in the second orbit. Sodium, the eleventh element, starts a third orbit, which in turn fills up for succeeding elements; further orbits are added as the number of nuclear protons increases. All known elements fall into this type of build-up pattern.

Periodic Table. This periodicity offers an explanation for the classification by Mendeleev, who found in 1869 that when the known elements were listed according to their ascending atomic weights, certain properties recurred in regular cycles. Thus members of related chemical families

---

*The use of positive and negative powers of 10, as abbreviations for very large and very small numbers is standard procedure and will be employed throughout this book. For example, $3 \times 10^6 = 3,000,000$. $3 \times 10^{-6} = \dfrac{3}{10^6} = \dfrac{3}{1,000,000} = 0.000003$.

appeared in the same column, when the elements were arranged in eight groups, if hydrogen and helium were omitted and some places left vacant. This listing of the elements is known as the Periodic Table, and in its present form it is shown in Figure 2. Vacant spots in the earlier tables were assumed to correspond to undiscovered elements, and, in fact, by permitting deductions as to atomic weight and chemical properties of missing elements, led to their discovery.

If now the elements are arranged according to content of electron orbits, the same periodicity appears (Fig. 3). Thus the chemical behavior of an element seems related to the number of electrons in its outermost electron orbit. If that orbit is completely filled, the element is an inert gas, entering into no chemical combinations whatever. If it has only one electron, the element is chemically very active (hydrogen, lithium, sodium). Mendeleev's periodic table contained some uncertainties, but the orbital periodic table is complete and accurate up to the heaviest known elements.

Isotopes. A question which troubled early students of the atom was why atomic weights were not whole numbers. An early (1815) suggestion by Prout that all atoms were built up out of hydrogen had to be discarded for this reason, although, as will be seen, he was not far wrong. Later (1886) Crookes suggested that possibly atoms of a single element need not be identical, and that the atomic weight was that of a mixture of somewhat different atoms. This was heresy and little attention was paid to it. In 1910 J. J. Thompson developed an apparatus using electric and magnetic fields for accurate determination of relative nuclear charges and masses, and a year later Soddy showed experimentally that certain elements were in fact composed of atoms chemically identical but physically differing slightly in weight. He proposed the term *isotopes* for such atoms. Isotopes, then, are atoms of the same chemical element, but having atomic weights differing from each other by small whole numbers.* If the chemical properties depend on the number of orbital electrons, this must remain the same for isotopes of a particular element, and mass differences must be due to different numbers of nuclear neutrons. Diagrams of some isotopes are shown in Figure 4.

It now becomes evident that atoms of an element are not completely identified by the chemical symbol, but that the number and type of the nuclear components should also be indicated. Therefore the notation has been adopted which is used in Figure 4. The chemical symbol carries a subscript denoting the number of nuclear protons (or of orbital electrons). This is the *atomic number* and chemically characterizes the element. There is one element and only one for every number from 1 to 102.† The symbol also carries a superscript denoting the total number of nuclear mass particles, protons plus neutrons. This is the *mass number* and physi-

---

* Actually it is the *mass numbers* which differ by small whole numbers.

† For elements found naturally, atomic numbers go from 1 to 92: the others are manmade and will be discussed later.

Period	Group I	Group II	Group III	Group IV	Group V	Group VI	Group VII
1	1 1.008 **H** 2 1						
2	3 6.940 **Li** 2 2	4 9.013 **Be** 1 4	5 10.82 **B** 2 3	6 12.011 **C** 2 4	7 14.008 **N** 2 4	8 16.000 **O** 3 3	9 19.00 **F** 1 4
3	11 22.991 **Na** 1 5	12 24.32 **Mg** 3 4	13 26.98 **Al** 1 7	14 28.09 **Si** 3 4	15 30.975 **P** 1 6	16 32.07 **S** 4 4	17 35.457 **Cl** 2 9
4	19 39.100 **K** 2 7	20 40.08 **Ca** 6 6	21 44.96 **Sc** 1 12	22 47.90 **Ti** 5 5	23 50.95 **V** 2 7	24 52.01 **Cr** 4 6	25 54.94 **Mn** 1 11
4	29 63.54 **Cu** 2 11	30 65.38 **Zn** 5 10	31 69.72 **Ga** 2 10	32 72.60 **Ge** 5 11	33 74.91 **As** 1 14	34 78.96 **Se** 6 16	35 79.92 **Br** 2 21
5	37 85.48 **Rb** 2 21	38 87.63 **Sr** 4 16	39 88.92 **Y** 1 18	40 91.22 **Zr** 5 11	41 92.91 **Nb** 1 19	42 95.95 **Mo** 7 9	43 (99) **Tc** 0 21
5	47 107.88 **Ag** 2 23	48 112.41 **Cd** 8 15	49 114.82 **In** 2 26	50 118.7 **Sn** 10 21	51 121.8 **Sb** 2 31	52 127.6 **Te** 8 22	53 126.9 **I** 1 22
6	55 132.9 **Cs** 1 21	56 137.4 **Ba** 7 15	57-71 **Rare Earths**	72 178.5 **Hf** 6 9	73 180.95 **Ta** 1 14	74 183.9 **W** 5 13	75 186.2 **Re** 2 19
6	79 197.0 **Au** 1 21	80 200.61 **Hg** 7 17	81 204.4 **Tl** 2 20	82 207.2 **Pb** 5 23	83 209.0 **Bi** 1 19	84 (210) **Po** 0 24	85 (216) **At** 0 20
7	87 (223) **Fr** 0 8	88 226.05 **Ra** 0 13	89 (227) **Ac** 0 10	90-102 **Actinides**			
Rare Earths (Lanthanides)	57 138.9 **La** 2 12	58 140.1 **Ce** 4 14	59 140.9 **Pr** 1 11	60 144.3 **Nd** 7 7	61 (145) **Pm** 0 14	62 150.4 **Sm** 7 8	63 152.0 **Eu** 2 15
Actinides	90 232.0 **Th** 0 12	91 (231) **Pa** 0 13	92 238.1 **U** 0 14	93 (237) **Np** 0 12	94 (242) **Pu** 0 16	95 (243) **Am** 0 11	96 (247) **Cm** 0 13

FIG. 2—Periodic Table of the Elements (after Mendeleev).

Atomic No.	At. Weight	Symbol	Stable Isotopes	Radioactive Isotopes
2	4.003	He	2	1
10	20.183	Ne	3	4
18	39.994	A	3	5
26	55.85	Fe	4	6
27	58.94	Co	1	11
28	58.71	Ni	5	6
36	83.80	Kr	6	19
44	101.1	Ru	7	9
45	102.91	Rh	1	18
46	106.4	Pd	6	15
54	131.3	Xe	9	20
76	190.2	Os	7	14
77	192.2	Ir	2	16
78	195.09	Pt	6	13
86	(222)	Rn	0	16

Atomic No.	At. Weight	Symbol	Stable Isotopes	Radioactive Isotopes
64	156.9	Gd	7	9
65	159.2	Tb	1	17
66	162.5	Dy	7	12
67	164.9	Ho	1	13
68	167.2	Er	6	8
69	169.4	Tm	1	8
70	173.0	Yb	7	10
71	175.0	Lu	2	11
97	(249)	Bk	0	7
98	(251)	Cf	0	11
99	(254)	E	0	11
100	(253)	Fm	0	8
101	(256)	Mv	1	0
102	(254)	No		1

Upper Left—Atomic Number Upper Right—Atomic Weight of Normal Isotopic Mixture
Lower Left—No. of Stable Isotopes Lower Right—Number of Radioactive Isotopes (as of 1960)

Atomic Number	Element	Electrons in Orbits						
		K	L	M	N	O	P	Q
1	H	1						
2	He	2						
3	Li	2	1					
4	Be	2	2					
5	B	2	3					
6	C	2	4					
7	N	2	5					
8	O	2	6					
9	F	2	7					
10	Ne	2	8					
11	Na	2	8	1				
12	Mg	2	8	2				
13	Al	2	8	3				
14	Si	2	8	4				
15	P	2	8	5				
16	S	2	8	6				
17	Cl	2	8	7				
18	A	2	8	8				
19	K	2	8	8	1			
20	Ca	2	8	8	2			
21	Sc	2	8	9	2			
22	Ti	2	8	10	2			
23	V	2	8	11	2			
24	Cr	2	8	13	1	(Note Irregularity)		
25	Mn	2	8	13	2			
26	Fe	2	8	14	2			
27	Co	2	8	15	2			
28	Ni	2	8	16	2			
29	Cu	2	8	18	1	(Note Irregularity)		
30	Zn	2	8	18	2			
31	Ga	2	8	18	3			
32	Ge	2	8	18	4			
33	As	2	8	18	5			
34	Se	2	8	18	6			
35	Br	2	8	18	7			
36	Kr	2	8	18	8			
37	Rb	2	8	18	8	1		
38	Sr	2	8	18	8	2		
39	Y	2	8	18	9	2		
40	Zr	2	8	18	10	2		
41	Cb	2	8	18	12	1	(Note Irregularity)	
42	Mo	2	8	18	13	1		
43	Tc	2	8	18	14	1		
44	Ru	2	8	18	15	1		
45	Rh	2	8	18	16	1		
46	Pd	2	8	18	18	——	(Note Irregularity)	
47	Ag	2	8	18	18	1		
48	Cd	2	8	18	18	2		
49	In	2	8	18	18	3		
50	Sn	2	8	18	18	4		
51	Sb	2	8	18	18	5		
52	Te	2	8	18	18	6		
53	I	2	8	18	18	7		
54	Xe	2	8	18	18	8		

Fig. 3.   Partial table of electron configuration of the elements

cally characterizes the particular isotope. Some elements, such as phosphorus and iodine, have only one stable isotope. Many have two or
three, and some have several; tin has ten.

Isotopic masses are specified in terms of the $_8O^{16}$ atom as 16.00000.
These values are slightly different from chemical atomic weights, which
are based on the total isotopic mixture of oxygen (containing small amounts

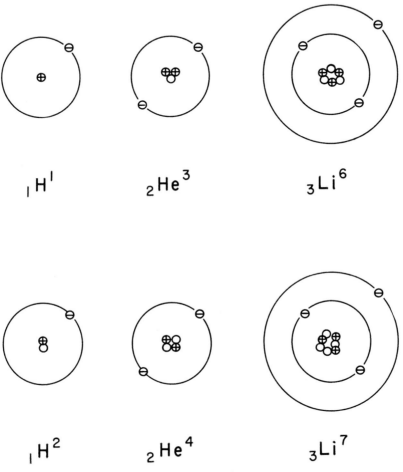

FIG. 4. Atomic structure of some isotopes.
(Nucleus of $_1H^1$ is the *proton*, of $_1H^2$ the *deuteron*.)

of $_8O^{17}$ and $_8O^{18}$) as 16.00000. The physical unit thus is about 0.02 per cent
less than the chemical. One *mass unit* is $\frac{1}{16}$ of the mass of $_8O^{16}$ or 1.6598 $\times$
10^{-24} grams. It appears that the standard will be officially shifted to $\frac{1}{12}$
of the mass of the $_6C^{12}$ atom. If this occurs, values of constants herein
given will be changed by only a few hundredths of one per cent; any calculations in this book will not be affected.

Nuclear Nomenclature. In addition to isotopes, there are also *isobars*, atoms having the same number of mass particles but different numbers of protons, and hence different atomic numbers. Another grouping is that of *isotones*, atoms having the same number of nuclear neutrons; they have both different mass numbers and different atomic numbers.

The definitions and classifications just discussed may be summarized as follows:

Atomic Number—number of protons in nucleus—symbol Z
Neutron Number—number of neutrons in nucleus—symbol N
Mass Number—number of mass particles in nucleus—symbol A

$$(A = N + Z)$$

Neutron Excess—excess of neutrons over protons $(N - Z)$.

For $_1H^1$ and $_2He^3$ there is no neutron excess, but a deficit; in each case $N - Z = -1$. For elements of atomic number $1 - 20$, one isotope has $N = Z$, or $N - Z = 0$. After helium all elements have at least one isotope for which $N - Z$ is greater than 0.

The symbol used for a particular nuclear species, or *nuclide* is
$_Z$Chemical Symbol^A ($_{11}Na^{23}$).

Isotopes—atoms having same Z's, different A's (hence, different N's)
$_{17}Cl^{35}$, $_{17}Cl^{37}$

Isobars—atoms having same A's, different Z's (hence, different N's)
$_{28}Ni^{64}$, $_{30}Zn^{64}$

Isotones—atoms having same N's, different Z's and A's
$_{18}A^{40}$, $_{19}K^{41}$, $_{20}Ca^{42}$

Isomers—atoms having same Z's and A's but different energy states in the nucleus. (This will be discussed later, page 95).

Classification of Stable Nuclei. There are known to be 274 stable nuclides of 81 elements; they are classified as follows:

Z even, N even—162
Z even, N odd — 56
Z odd, N even — 52
Z odd, N odd — 4 ($_1H^2$, $_3Li,^6$, $_5B^{10}$, $_7N^{14}$)

As Z increases N increases a little faster, so that above $Z = 20$ there are always more neutrons than protons. A chart of all known stable nuclides according to neutron and proton content is shown in Figure 5. It is seen that they are grouped along a smooth curve, with neutron content increasing steadily with regard to proton content.

Dimensions of Atoms and Nuclei. The dimensions of atoms and of atomic nuclei are very small. Diameters of outer orbits are of the order of 10^{-8} cm. Diameters of nuclei themselves are of the order of 10^{-12} to 10^{-13} cm. Thus an atom is almost all empty space; the actual part of its volume occupied by the nucleus and the electrons is extremely small. The simile of a fly and a few gnats in a large cathedral is suggestive. The very small nucleus must have an extremely high density; in fact, it is of the order of a hundred million tons per cubic centimeter!

Nuclear Forces. The nature of forces holding the nuclear components together has been the subject of much speculation. Protons would be expected to repel each other according to classical electrostatic behavior of charged particles. Evidently the nuclear forces contain an additional factor besides electrical and gravitational components. The presently accepted idea is of so-called *exchange forces* based upon the existence within

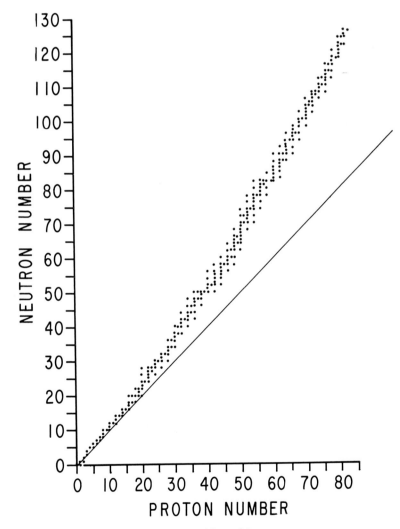

Fig. 5.   Proton-neutron plot of known stable nuclei.
Note the gradual increase in ratio of neutron numbers to proton numbers. The 45° line indicates a neutron-proton ratio of 1.

the nucleus of small sub-atomic particles called *mesons*. Such particles are known to exist. The pi mesons, or *pions*, have a mass about 276 times that of the electron; some have positive charges and some negative, some are uncharged. It is suggested that two nuclear particles share such a pion so that it is sometimes part of one and sometimes of the other, that is, they *exchange* it back and forth. Symbolically the force between a proton and a neutron can be described as

$$p_1 + n_1 \rightarrow n_2 + \pi^+ + n_1 \rightarrow n_2 + p_2,$$

where the p's denote protons, the n's neutrons and π^+ the shared pion. The original proton emits a positive pion and becomes a neutron. The pion is quickly absorbed by another neutron which thereby becomes a proton. Thus the proton and the neutron have *exchanged* the pion. Similarly a neutron turns into a proton by emitting a negative pion, whereas two protons or two neutrons may share a neutral pion. These exchanges take place at excessively high frequencies, so that the pion never really escapes from either particle, or they are "bound together." It is not within the scope of this book to elaborate further on this topic. The nature of the nucleus will be further discussed in Chapter 5, p. 53.

REFERENCES

FRIEDLANDER, G. and KENNEDY, J. W.: *Nuclear and Radiochemistry*, Chapter 2, New York, John Wiley and Sons, 1955, (Revised Version).

GLASSER, O., QUIMBY, E. H., TAYLOR, L. S., WEATHERWAX, J. L. and MORGAN, R. H.: *Physical Foundations of Radiology*, 3rd Ed., Chapter 2, New York, Paul B. Hoeber, Inc., 1961.

LAPP, R. E. and ANDREWS, H. L.: *Nuclear Radiation Physics*, 2nd Ed., Chapters 4 and 7, New York, Prentice-Hall, 1954.

NEEDHAM, J. and PAGEL, W.: *Background to Modern Science*, Chapters 1, 2, 3, and 5, New York, The Macmillan Company, 1938.

POLLARD, E. C. and DAVIDSON, W. L.: *Applied Nuclear Physics*, 2nd Ed., Chapter 1, New York, John Wiley and Sons, 1951.

SEMAT, HENRY: *Introduction to Atomic and Nuclear Physics*. 3rd Ed., New York, Rinehart, 1958.

STROMINGER, D., HOLLANDER, J. M. and SEABORG, G. T.: Table of Isotopes, Rev. Mod. Phys., *30*, 585, 1958.

WELCH, Periodic Chart of the Atoms, Ed. Meggers, W. F., 1959.

2

Radioactivity

Historical. The discovery of x-rays by Wilhelm Conrad Roentgen in 1895 stimulated the imagination of physicists in many countries. Henri Becquerel, in France, observed that x-ray tubes fluoresced brilliantly when emitting x-rays, and wondered whether substances which fluoresced under sunlight might also emit invisible radiations. Fortunately among the first materials he tested were some uranium compounds, and in 1896 he announced that these did in fact give off radiations, and furthermore that fluorescence had nothing to do with the phenomenon. Mme. Marie Curie took up the study of these substances, coining the words "radioactive" and "radioactivity" to describe the process. She investigated systematically the known elements and compounds, and found that all compounds of uranium and thorium possessed this property, and no other substances. She found also that some of the natural ores of uranium were much more active than the element itself, and so concluded that they must contain a hitherto unknown and very radioactive element.

At this point her husband, Pierre Curie, became so interested in her work that he gave up his own researches to join her, and they worked together until his untimely death in 1906. In 1898 they announced the discovery of not one, but two new radioactive elements, which they named *polonium* and *radium*.

The radiations emitted by these radioactive substances possessed the same properties as x-rays, of darkening photographic plates and of discharging electrically charged bodies. It was early observed that most of the rays were very unpenetrating, and could be stopped by a sheet of paper. A large part of those passing through the paper could traverse a few millimeters of wood or paper, but no more. A very small part of the original beam was very penetrating, traversing considerable thicknesses of metal.

Nature of the Radiations. At first the rays were thought to be all alike, differing only in penetrating power, and little was known of their nature. However extensive series of researches by Becquerel, Pierre Curie, and Villard showed that there were three quite distinct types of ray. This may be demonstrated by a simple experiment, as in Figure 6. When a beam of moving, electrically charged particles is passed between the poles of a magnet, their paths are bent into circles whose radii depend on the strength of the field, the magnitude of the charge, and the kinetic energy of the particles. The direction of the deflection depends on the sign of the charge. In the figure, the magnetic field is perpendicular to the page, with the south pole above and the north pole below. The very unpenetrating radiation is deflected clockwise, and the paths are circles of rather large radius, indicating that these are positively charged particles, and rather heavy. The moderately penetrating radiation is deflected in the opposite direction and the paths are much more strongly bent. These are therefore lighter, negatively charged particles. The heavier component was called the alpha (α) radiation, or more properly, α particles; the lighter, beta (β) radiation, or β particles. The undeflected component obviously does not

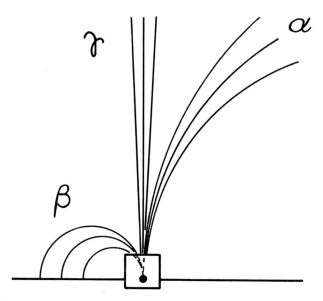

Fig. 6. Diagrammatic representation of deviation of alpha and beta rays in a magnetic field, while gamma rays are not affected. The field is perpendicular to the plane of the paper, the south pole being above and the north pole below.

consist of charged particles; its real nature was demonstrated by Villard, who showed that these rays were identical with those emitted by an x-ray tube. They were called gamma (γ) rays. Both x- and γ-rays are called *photons*.

Further study showed that the alpha particles have a mass about four times that of the hydrogen atom, and two unit positive charges. They are really nuclei of helium atoms, stripped of their orbital electrons and travelling with speeds of 8 to 15,000 miles per second. The beta particles have a mass about $\frac{1}{1800}$ that of the hydrogen atom, a single negative charge, and travel with speeds up to almost that of light. They are actually electrons. The gamma rays are electromagnetic radiations of the same sort as x-rays. These radiations will be considered further in Chapter 6.

Atomic Disintegration. It had been found that radioactivity was a property of the *atoms* of the radioactive elements. For a given quantity of such an element, the radiation was always the same, regardless of the chemical composition of the compound under study. Therefore it appeared that the actual atoms must be breaking down in some manner, to eject material particles. It has been mentioned in the previous chapter that this was the starting point for the development of ideas of atomic structure.

The radioactive elements which were discovered at first were all very high up in the atomic table, $_{92}U^{238}$, $_{90}Th^{232}$, $_{88}Ra^{226}$, $_{84}Po^{210}$. Their nuclei obviously contained large numbers of particles and apparently were too complicated to be completely stable. It is now known that every element with atomic number greater than 83 or mass number greater than 209 possesses the property of spontaneous emission of radiation, or is radioactive. These nuclei contain in a very tiny volume large numbers of charged and uncharged particles, all in motion and hence exerting electric, magnetic, gravitational, and intranuclear forces upon one another. It is not surprising that at some time a configuration is produced which is unstable, so that the nucleus breaks down.

This breakdown or *disintegration* is not, however, complete destruction. It consists always of the expulsion of a relatively small charged particle (α or β, never both simultaneously) accompanied by energy. The remaining nuclear components then rearrange themselves and settle down (temporarily or permanently) as the nucleus of an atom of a different element. The removal of an alpha particle decreases the nuclear charge by two units and its mass by four. The removal of a (negative) beta particle increases the positive nuclear charge by one unit; the mass is essentially unchanged:

$$_{Z}X^{A} - _{2}\alpha^{4} = _{Z-2}X^{A-4},$$
$$_{Z}X^{A} - _{-1}\beta^{0} = _{Z+1}X^{A}.$$

If the product element has Z greater than 83 or A greater than 209 it will in turn be radioactive. Thus the disintegration of radium is followed by a series of further disintegrations:

$$_{88}Ra^{226} - \alpha = _{86}Rn^{222},$$
$$_{86}Rn^{222} - \alpha = _{84}RaA^{218},$$
$$_{84}RaA^{218} - \alpha = _{82}RaB^{214},$$
$$_{82}RaB^{214} - \beta = _{83}RaC^{214},$$

and so on through four further transformations until the final stable product is reached, $_{82}Pb^{206}$. Radioactive series will be considered in more detail in Chapter 7.

Artificial or Induced Radioactivity. Before considering the behavior of naturally radioactive substances in detail, the field should be expanded to those elements in which radioactivity is induced artificially.

In 1919 Rutherford demonstrated the disruption of stable nitrogen nuclei by bombarding them with natural alpha particles, with the production of hydrogen and a heavy isotope of oxygen. (See Chapter 3, p. 44 for details). This was not an induced radioactivity; the instant the bombardment stopped the production of new particles stopped. However, in 1934 the Curie-Joliots discovered that when they bombarded aluminum with alpha particles a radiation appeared which continued after the removal of the source, and which died away in the same manner as radiation from known radioactive substances. They had actually produced a radioactive isotope of phosphorus by introducing extra mass and charge into the aluminum nucleus.

Since that time artificially produced radioactive isotopes of every stable element have been prepared. The subject of induced radioactivity will be considered in detail in subsequent chapters. At present it is sufficient to know that such substances do exist, and that their disintegration follows the same rules as those applying to the natural radioelements.

Characteristics of Radioactive Disintegration. Nuclei of any particular radioelement always disintegrate in the same way. It is apparently not possible, for instance, for radium sometimes to emit an alpha particle and sometimes a beta. There are a few instances in which a nuclide appears to have more than one mode of disintegration, such as, for instance, emission of both positive and negative beta particles; in these cases a fixed percentage of the material disintegrating always goes by each path. Furthermore, the energy accompanying the disintegration of atoms of a particular nuclide is always the same. It will be seen later that alpha particles from a specific nuclide either all have the same energy, or fall into a very few monoenergetic groups. The beta particles present a continuous range of energies up to a definite maximum, but this *spectrum* is constant for one nuclide. The gamma rays, if there are any, are also emitted in one or a few monoenergetic groups. (This whole topic is treated in more detail in Chapter 7.) This *constancy of type and energy of radiation emitted* is one specific characteristic of radioactivity.

The other specific characteristic is *constancy of rate of disintegration*. The amount of any radioactive element is always gradually decreasing; this gradual decrease is the result of many sudden disintegrations of individual nuclei. In any measurable quantity of an element there is always an enormous number of atoms (6×10^{23} per gram-molecular weight). During any instant, a relatively small fraction of these achieve instability and disintegrate. For every radioactive element, *a fixed percentage of all the atoms present disintegrate per unit of time.* There is no way of knowing *which* atoms will disintegrate in a given interval, but statistically it is possible to know *how many* will change. Actual rates vary enormously among various radioactive elements; in some cases only a small fraction of 1 per cent of all the atoms decays or disintegrates in a century, in others a high percentage is transmuted per second. Most of those of interest in medicine fall far within these two extremes.

Mathematical Expression of Disintegration Law. This type of decrease can be described mathematically. If N represents the number of radioactive atoms present at any instant, $-\dfrac{dN}{dt}$ represents the decrease in this number during a very short interval of time. This decrease is a fixed percentage of all the atoms present. Hence

$$-\frac{dN}{dt} = \lambda N, \qquad\qquad 2{-}(1)$$

where λ is the decay constant, or the fraction transformed per unit time, when the time unit is chosen short enough so that only a small fraction of the total number of nuclei disintegrate in that interval. λ is then the fraction *per second*, *per day*, etc., it expresses a *rate* of disintegration. This differential equation can be integrated,

$$N_t = N_o e^{-\lambda t}. \qquad\qquad 2{-}(2)$$

N_t is the number of atoms remaining from an initial number N_o after a period t; λ is the decay constant for the unit of time in terms of which the interval t is expressed; e is the base of natural logarithms, 2.71828. This is the expression of an "exponential decay law." The decay constant is characteristic of the nuclear species and cannot be changed by any means known at present. Great variations in temperature, pressure, chemical state, magnetic, electric, and gravitational fields, have been completely without effect.

Half Life and Average Life. Instead of using the decay constant it is possible to express the rate of radioactive transformation by specifying the period during which half of all the atoms initially present will disintegrate. This *half period* or *half life* can be obtained from a knowledge of the decay constant. In equation (2), N_t at the end of a half period is $\frac{1}{2} N_o$. The half period is indicated by T. The equation then becomes

$$\tfrac{1}{2} N_o = N_o\, e^{-\lambda T}. \qquad\qquad 2{-}(3)$$

Solving this equation by natural logarithms,

$$\ln \tfrac{1}{2} = -\lambda T,$$

$$\text{or } \lambda T = \ln 2,$$

$$\text{whence } T = \frac{0.693.}{\lambda} \qquad\qquad 2{-}(4)$$

Thus the decay constant and the half period bear a fixed relation to each other; if one is found by any means, the other can be calculated.

During the first half period, half of all the atoms initially present will decay, in the second half period, half of those remaining at the end of the first, or one-fourth of the original amount, and so on. Thus at the end of two half periods, three-fourths of the original will be gone; after seven half periods less than 1 per cent will remain.

Other useful periods are the nine-tenths and the one-tenth periods. Ninety per cent of the atoms survive longer than the nine-tenths period; ten per cent longer than the one-tenth period. These values $T_{\frac{9}{10}}$ and $T_{\frac{1}{10}}$

can be obtained from the decay formula in the same manner as $T_{\frac{1}{2}}$ using the appropriate fraction in equation 2—(3).

$$T_{\frac{9}{10}} = 0.15 \; T_{\frac{1}{2}} \qquad\qquad\qquad\qquad 2\text{—}(5)$$

$$T_{\frac{1}{10}} = 3.3 \; T_{\frac{1}{2}} \qquad\qquad\qquad\qquad 2\text{—}(6)$$

In general, if N_t represents the number of atoms remaining after time t, $N_o - N_t$ represents the number which have decayed, or

Number of atoms decayed, $N_o - N_t = N_o \, (1 - e^{-\lambda t})$.   2—(7)

Another useful concept is that of the *average life* of all the atoms of a particular radionuclide.   Just as insurance statistics can specify the average life expectancy of all members of a particular group of individuals, so radioactivity statistics can specify the average life expectancy of all atoms of a certain element.

Let N_o represent the original number of atoms, and N_{t_1} the number at any time t_1, where $N_{t_1} = N_o e^{-\lambda t_1}$. During a very short interval after t_1 the

number disintegrating is $\dfrac{dN_{t_1}}{dt}$. This is the number of atoms of lifetimes

between t_1 and $t_1 + dt$, or, if dt is vanishingly small, the number of lifetime t_1.

$$\frac{-dN_{t_1}}{dt} = \lambda \, N_{t_1} = \lambda \, N_o e^{-\lambda t_1}$$

or

$$-dN_{t_1} = \lambda \, N_o e^{-\lambda t_1} dt. \qquad\qquad\qquad 2\text{—}(8)$$

The *total* lives of the atoms in any group are the number in the group multiplied by the age of each, or, for the group of age t_1, $dN_{t_1} \times t_1$. The summation of groups for all values of t_1 from zero to infinity gives the total lives of all the atoms in the system.   This sum, divided by the total number of atoms, gives the *average life of any atom.*

$$\int_0^\infty t \; dN_t = N_o \lambda \int_0^\infty t \; e^{-\lambda t} \; dt = \frac{N_o}{\lambda}. \qquad\qquad 2\text{—}(9)$$

$$\frac{N_o}{\lambda} \div N_o = \frac{1.}{\lambda} \qquad\qquad\qquad 2\text{—}(10)$$

Thus *the average life is the reciprocal of the decay constant.*   Since the decay constant has been shown to be $\dfrac{0.693}{\text{half life}}$, the average life is $\dfrac{T}{0.693}$ or $1.443\,T$.

It is usually denoted by the Greek letter τ.

The average life is a quantity based on statistical analysis.   It does not represent the lifetime of most of the atoms, as is sometimes erroneously supposed.   Actually during this period, which is 1.443 T, the number of atoms initially present, N_o, will be reduced to $1/e \times N_o = 0.37 \, N_o$, as will be seen by introducing $1.443 \, T$ for t in equation $2-(2)$.

Half periods or decay constants of radioactive nuclei are listed in many places. Data concerning some of the more useful ones will be found in the appendix. By use of the decay constant and equation $2-(2)$ the amount of any radioactive material remaining at any time can be calculated. It is often convenient to plot "decay curves" for individual isotopes as shown

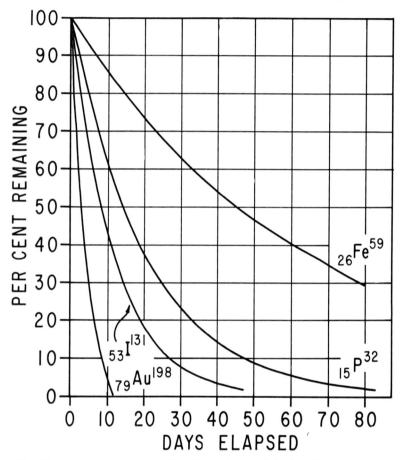

FIG. 7A. Decay curves for some radioactive isotopes, plotted on linear graph paper.

in Figure 7. The curves of Figure 7A, plotted on linear graph paper, require the determination of a considerable number of points, and the drawing of a smooth curve through them. The use of semi-logarithmic paper, as in Figure 7B, simplifies the procedure. It is a property of exponential expressions of the type $N_t = N_o e^{-\lambda t}$ that their graphs on semi-logarithmic paper are straight lines. For this reason it is only necessary to establish two points on the curve and draw a straight line through them.

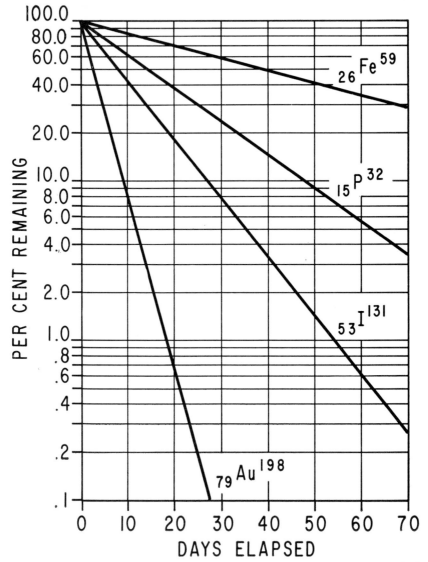

FIG. 7B. Decay curves for the same radioactive isotopes plotted on semi-logarithmic graph paper.

Activity. In practical work with radioactive nuclides the number of atoms N is not directly measured, nor usually is the rate of change $\dfrac{dN}{dt}$. What is actually measured is something proportional to the number of disintegrations per unit time, that is, something proportional to λN. This is usually termed the *activity*, and denoted by A. The actual value of A will depend on the measuring system employed, but if this is kept constant

A is obviously directly proportional to N. Hence a plot of experimentally determined values of A will give values of λ and T for the nuclide in question, from which such curves as those of Figure 7 may be prepared.

Units of Quantity of Radioactive Isotopes. The unit of quantity of radioactive material is the *curie* (c). This is the quantity in which nuclei disintegrate at the rate of 3.7×10^{10} per second. The millicurie (mc) and the microcurie (μc) are respectively the thousandth and the millionth part of a curie, or the quantities in which nuclei disintegrate at the rates of 3.7×10^7 and 3.7×10^4 per second. Obviously there is no simple relationship between curies and total number of atoms or weight of material. A nuclide with a short half period will not require such a large reservoir of its atoms to supply them at the needed disintegration rate as one with a long half period. However, it will be shown below that either the number of atoms or the weight per curie can be readily calculated when the half period and the atomic weight are known.

Total Number of Radioactive Atoms. The actual *number* of atoms of a nuclide is seldom specified; it is rather the *quantity* in terms of the units just mentioned. (Actual calibration or measurement of such quantities will be discussed in a later chapter.) If Q_o and Q_t represent the quantities of a nuclide with decay constant λ, initially and at time t, obviously

$$Q_t = Q_o\, e^{-\lambda t}.$$

The relationships among the various constants Q_o, Q_t, t, λ, T, and τ are shown in Figure 8. Any point on the curve represents the quantity Q_t of radioactive nuclide at time t. The quantity by which this will be diminished in the next instant is give by $\lambda Q_t = \lambda Q_o\, e^{-\lambda t}$. The sum of all these small decrements, from t = O to t = ∞, is, of course equal to Q_o, and is represented by the area under the curve.

The actual number of atoms, N_o, in a quantity Q_o mc can readily be calculated. For 1 mc, in the first second 3.7×10^7 nuclei disintegrate. That is, in the expression $\dfrac{dN_o}{dt} = \lambda N_o$, if λ is the decay constant per second, $\dfrac{dN_o}{dt} = 3.7 \times 10^7$.

Whence

$$\lambda N_o = 3.7 \times 10^7 \text{ per mc.} \qquad\qquad 2\text{--}(11)$$

And

$$N_o \text{ per mc} = \frac{3.7 \times 10^7}{\lambda} = 3.7 \times 10^7 \times 1.443\, T \qquad 2\text{--}(12)$$

where T is the half period in seconds.

In other words the total number of atoms in a curie is the number disintegrating per second times the average life in seconds. The constant which is usually known is the half life T in days. τ in seconds $= 1.443T \times 86,400$. Whence the number of atoms per curie is

$$3.7 \times 10^{10} \times 86,400 \times 1.443\ T = 4.6 \times 10^{15}\ T. \qquad 2\text{—}(13)$$

The weight of one curie depends on the number of atoms per curie and the weight of each one. Since one gram atomic weight of the element contains 6×10^{23} atoms (Avogadro's hypothesis), the weight of one atom of atomic

weight $G = \dfrac{G}{6 \times 10^{23}}$ gm $= \dfrac{G \times 10^3}{6 \times 10^{23}}$ mg.

Whence the weight of one curie of the element is

$$\frac{4.6 \times 10^{15} \times T \times G \times 10^3}{6 \times 10^{23}}\ \text{mg} = 7.65\ T\ G \times 10^{-6}\ \text{mg} \qquad 2\text{—}(14)$$

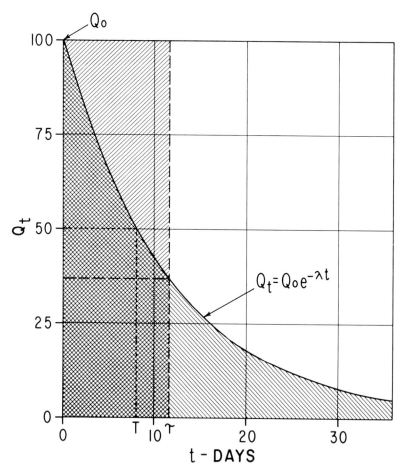

Fig. 8. Curve showing relationships among various constants involved in disintegration expressions.

For example, for I^{131}, T = 8.1, G = 131,* weight of 1 curie = $7.65 \times 8.1 \times 131 \times 10^{-6} = 8 \times 10^{-3}$ mg.

Weights of some common nuclides, in milligrams per millicurie, are given in Table 1.

Table 1. Weights of One Millicurie of Some Radioelements

Nuclide	Half Period	Weight—Mg per mc
Na^{24}	15.0 hours	0.000114
I^{131}	8.1 days	0.0081
P^{32}	14.3 days	0.0035
Sr^{89}	54 days	0.0368
Ca^{45}	164 days	0.0566
C^{14}	5570 years	187.0

Determination of Decay Constants. The method of determining the decay constant for a radioactive element whose rate is neither very long nor very short, is to prepare a sample which can be maintained in a fixed form for the necessary period, and make measurements on it at successive intervals. It is not necessary to determine the absolute quantity at any time; relative values are sufficient. These relative values are plotted, the half period determined, and the decay constant calculated. For example, a series of daily measurements of a sample of radioactive gold were as follows:

Hour	Counts per Minute
0	5600
24	4330
48	3340
72	2580
96	2000
120	1540
144	1190
192	710

These values, plotted in Figure 9, indicate a half period of 64 hours or 2.7 days. The decay constant is then $\dfrac{0.693}{64} = 1.08$ per cent per hour. Thus each day there is about twenty-five per cent less than on the preceding day.

For elements of every long or very short half period, successive measurements within a reasonable time are not practicable, and other methods have been devised. These will be found described in the literature.

A mixture of two or more isotopes of different decay rates will give data which will not fall on a straight line. However, by plotting and analyzing the complex decay curve, decay constants for the components can often

* G and A are not strictly identical. A is always a whole number, the total number of mass particles in the nucleus, while G is the actual atomic weight of the particular nuclide. In practice they are not very different and the use of A in the formula is justified.

be determined.   A sample supposed to be I[133] with a half period of 20.8 hours gave the following readings:

Day	Counts per Minute	Day	Counts per Minute
0	800	6	66
1	414	8	52
2	235	10	42
3	144	12	36
4	101	14	30

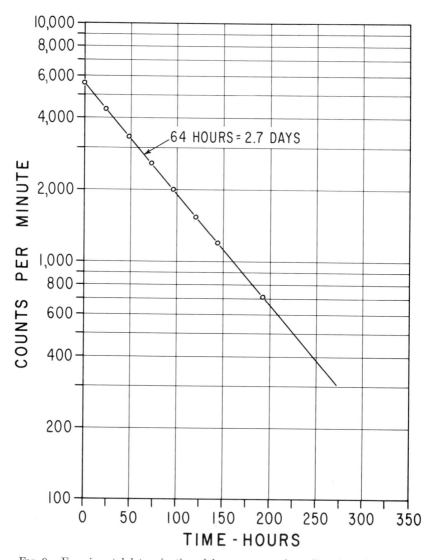

FIG. 9.   Experimental determination of decay constant for radioactive gold, $_{79}Au^{198}$.

These values, plotted in Figure 10, give the solid curve. The last part of this is a straight line, which can be extrapolated backward as shown by the dotted line, and indicates an exponential decay with a half period of just over 8 days, corresponding to I^{131}. For each day, the I^{131} contribution indicated by this dotted line should be subtracted from the measured value. The results are the crosses shown in the figure; a straight line drawn through these indicates exponential decay with a half period of about 0.9 day, corresponding to I^{133}. Apparently the material was a mixture of these

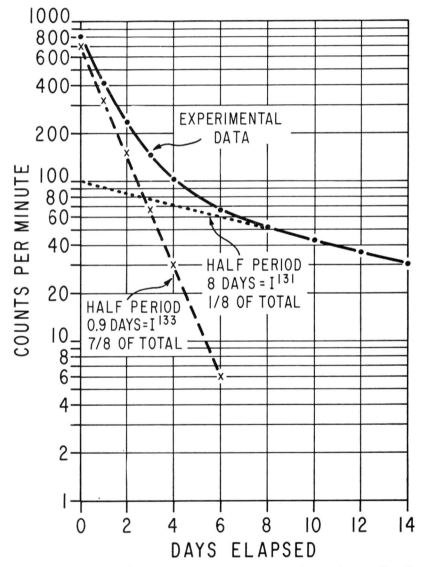

FIG. 10. Analysis of complex decay curve obtained from mixture of two radioactive isotopes.

two isotopes of iodine; at the initial reading one-eighth of the total counts were due to the longer-lived component.

In addition to curves prepared by the individual worker, usually by calculation from published data rather than from individual measurements, large-scale curves for the most common radioelements are commercially available, and some new slide rules with special scales for isotope decay are now on the market.

A convenient formula for quick approximation of the quantity of isotope remaining at any time may be developed from equation 2—(2). Since $\lambda = \dfrac{0.693}{T}$, and $e^{0.693} = 2$, the equation may be written

$$N_t = N_o \times 2^{-t/T} = \frac{N_o}{2^{t/T}} \qquad\qquad 2-(15)$$

In a particular case, assume T to be 2.7 days (Au^{198}) and the time in question, t, = 8 days. $t/T = 3$, and the quantity remaining is the original quantity divided by 2^3 or 8, namely one-eighth of the original amount. Again, assume T to be 14 days (P^{32}) and t one week. Then

$$N_t = \frac{N_o}{2^{\frac{1}{2}}} = \frac{N_o}{\sqrt{2}} = 0.71\ N_o.$$

When $2^{t/T}$ is not obtained by inspection it can be calculated by logarithms. However, for practical purposes it is often sufficient to approximate it.

For instance if $t/T = \frac{3}{4}$, this is between $\frac{1}{2}$ and 1. $\dfrac{N_o}{2^{\frac{1}{2}}} = 0.71\ N_o$ and $\dfrac{N_o}{2} = 0.5\ N_o$. So $N_t = \dfrac{N_o}{2^{\frac{3}{4}}}$ is approximately half way between $0.5\ N_o$ and $0.71\ N_o$.

Using $0.6\ N_o$ would be a satisfactory approximation. (The correct value is $0.595\ N_o$.)

For values of t which are small in comparison with the half period, an exponential expansion of $e^{-\lambda t}$ gives a useful formula.

$$e^{-\lambda t} = 1 - \lambda t + \frac{(\lambda t)^2}{2} - \ldots \qquad\qquad 2-(16)$$

$\lambda t = \dfrac{1}{\tau}\,t$, so the formula becomes

$$e^{-\lambda t} = 1 - \frac{t}{\tau} + \frac{(t/\tau)^2}{2} - \ldots \qquad\qquad 2-(17)$$

Since t is small in comparison with the half period, it is also small in comparison with the average life, and therefore $(t/\tau)^2$ and all higher powers are so small as to be negligible. Then the approximate formula becomes

$$e^{-\lambda t} = 1 - \frac{t}{\tau}, \qquad\qquad 2-(18)$$

which may be used if t is less than about $1/10\tau$. Thus in the case of $T = 87$ days $(S-35)$, $\tau = 124$ days, and the quantity remaining after one week (7 days) is $1-7/124 = 1-0.056 = 0.944$ of the initial amount.

Carrier, Specific Activity. A particular radioactive sample may consist entirely of the radioactive isotope in question, or it may contain stable isotopes of the same element. In the first case, the radioactive material is said to be *carrier-free*. In the second, if the stable and radioactive isotopes are in the same chemical form, it is said to be *with carrier*.

The term "carrier" arose from radiochemistry. Where chemical precipitations are carried out involving very small quantities of material, as is the case with a few microcuries of a short-lived isotope, it is sometimes impossible to carry the reaction to completion. Almost all compounds are soluble to some extent, and minute quantities of radioactive material may remain in the solution. By adding a relatively large amount of the stable isotope in the same chemical form, essentially all of the mixture can be "carried" down.

In some biological work, the total quantity of the element involved must be kept small, if normal physiological conditions are to be maintained. In this case, carrier-free radioactive material is highly desirable. An example of this is in the study of thyroid function with radioactive iodine. The body's normal daily intake of iodide is of the order of 100 to 200 micrograms, and administration of more than a few additional micrograms might alter the delicate physiological balance in the function of the thyroid gland. Accordingly carrier-free radioactive iodine is essential. On the other hand, in such studies as determination of fluid volume by isotope dilution the existence of carrier is seldom important unless it is chemically toxic.

The *specific activity* of an isotope preparation is usually stated as the number of millicuries of radioactive isotope per gram of the total mixture of radioactive and stable isotopes of the element in question. In carrier-free material the specific activity is, of course, the highest possible; in isotope catalogs such material is simply denoted by CF. When stable isotopes are also present, specific activity may vary from thousands of millicuries per gram to any small fraction of this proportion.

REFERENCES

FRIEDLANDER, G. and KENNEDY, J. W.: *Nuclear and Radiation Chemistry*, Chapter 1, New York, John Wiley and Sons, 1955, (Revised Version).

GLASSER, O., QUIMBY, E. H., TAYLOR, L. S., WEATHERWAX, J. L. and MORGAN, R. H.: *Physical Foundations of Radiology*, 3rd Ed., Chapter 14, New York, Paul B. Hoeber, Inc., 1961.

HALLIDAY, D.: *Introductory Nuclear Physics*, Chapters 1 and 2, New York, John Wiley and Sons, 1950.

LAPP, R. E. and ANDREWS, H. L.: *Nuclear Radiation Physics*, 2nd Ed., Chapter 6, New York, Prentice-Hall, 1954.

POLLARD, E. C. and DAVIDSON, W. L.: *Applied Nuclear Physics*, 2nd Ed., Chapter 6, New York, John Wiley and Sons, 1951.

3

Disruption of Stable Nuclei—Induced Radioactivity

First Artificial Transmutation. As mentioned in the preceding chapter, in 1919 Rutherford demonstrated the disruption of ordinary nitrogen nuclei as a result of their bombardment by alpha particles from naturally radioactive material. A diagram of his simple apparatus is shown in Figure 11.

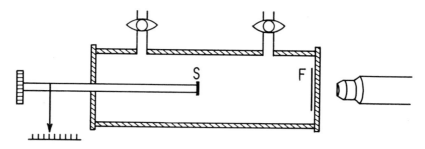

FIG. 11. Diagram of apparatus used by Rutherford to demonstrate disintegration of nitrogen nuclei by alpha particle bombardment.

Particles coming from the source at S traversed the gas in the tube, and on striking the fluorescent screen F, gave rise to scintillations which could be observed as individual points of light, by means of the telescope. The source was mounted on a movable support with a scale. When the gas in the tube was oxygen, no scintillations were observed at a distance greater than a few centimeters. When hydrogen was used, the distance was about four times as great, but again there was a definite limit. However, when pure nitrogen was introduced into the tube, some scintillations were observed at distances up to 40 centimeters. Study of the deflections of the paths of these long-range particles in electric and magnetic fields demonstrated that each had a single positive charge and unit mass; they were *protons*.

The nature of the complete transformation was not obvious. It might be a shattering of the nitrogen nucleus, although only one type of fragment was observed. It might just be a breaking off of part of the nucleus, or it might be a new kind of "nuclear chemical reaction." The matter was finally settled by actual photographs of the reaction taken by means of the Wilson cloud chamber (See Chapter 6, p. 77). Figure 12 is a reproduc-

(44)

tion of such a photograph taken by Blackett.   The heavy white lines are tracks of two sets of alpha particles from the Thorium $(C + C')$ source. In the center of the picture an alpha particle has hit a nitrogen nucleus. The long thin track extending to the left is made by the proton; the short stub is made by the remaining nuclear fragment.   Evidently there are only two fragments.   Since there must be conservation of total charge and

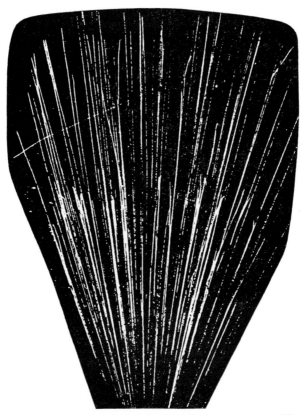

FIG. 12.   Cloud track photograph of alpha particles traversing air.   The heavy white lines are tracks of two sets of alpha particles from the Thorium $(C + C')$ source.   In the center of the picture an alpha particle has hit a nitrogen nucleus.   The long thin track extending to the left is made by the released proton, the short stub by the new heavy oxygen nucleus.   (Courtesy of P. M. S. Blackett and D. S. Lees, and of the Royal Society of London.)

mass, it is apparent that the heavier particle must have atomic number 8 and mass number 17.   It is therefore a heavy isotope of oxygen, and the nuclear reaction can be written

$$_7N^{14} + {}_2He^4 = {}_8O^{17} + {}_1H^1.$$

As soon as Rutherford announced this discovery, the procedure was repeated in other laboratories and alpha particles were used to bombard many elements. It was found that atoms of all elements with atomic numbers from 4 to 19 (beryllium to potassium) with the exception of oxygen, could be made to disintegrate; in all cases one product was a proton. The natural alpha particles did not have sufficient energy to get inside heavier nuclei than these.

A further disadvantage in these experiments was the relatively small number of alpha particles available for bombardments. Rutherford had estimated that only one alpha particle in a million of those passing through nitrogen gas resulted in a disintegration. The desire for sources emitting larger numbers of particles more energetic than natural alphas led to the development of powerful electrical instruments for accelerating charged particles. The *cyclotron*, the most useful of these in isotope production, will be described later in this chapter.

Discovery of the Neutron. In the course of alpha particle bombardment of various substances, the neutron, whose existence was postulated by Rutherford as described in Chapter 1, was discovered. Three groups of physicists in three countries contributed to this. In 1932, Bothe and Becker in Germany, shot alpha particles into beryllium, $_4Be^9$, and found a very penetrating radiation given off. They supposed that the alpha particle had entered the beryllium to make $_6C^{13}$ and that the extra energy had been given off as penetrating gamma rays. The Curie-Joliots in Paris studied this radiation, and found that after it was passed through paraffin there was *more* activity instead of *less* as there should have been. They identified protons in the radiation coming from the paraffin, but could not account for them. Then Chadwick, at Cambridge University in England, put forth the assumption that what came from the beryllium was a particle, with mass about the same as the proton, but no charge. Such an electrically neutral particle could go a long way through matter; it would not be affected by nuclei unless it really collided with them. In paraffin, which is very rich in hydrogen, the neutral particle, making head-on collisions with the hydrogen nuclei, would knock them out as protons. Many experiments since that time have verified the existence of the *neutron*. The correct equation for Bothe and Becker's reaction (excluding energy transfer) is

$$_4Be^9 + _2\alpha^4 = _6C^{12} + _0n^1.$$

Discovery of the Positron. About this time another particle was discovered in cosmic ray research, that was destined soon to play a part in nuclear physics; this was the *positron*. It has been seen (p. 30) that when charged particles traverse a magnetic field their paths are bent into circles. Many cloud chamber photographs had been made of tracks of electrons following such curved paths. In 1932, Anderson, in southern California, in a cloud chamber record of cosmic rays, found a track curved in the "wrong" direction. The particle making it had apparently the same mass as the electron, but a positive instead of negative charge. Since then, positrons have been frequently photographed, and have been found to be emitted in some radioactive disintegrations.

Artifically Produced Radioisotopes. In fact, the first artificially produced radioactive isotope was a positron emitter. By 1934 many elements had been disintegrated under alpha particle bombardment, but in all cases the products were stable, as were the hydrogen and oxygen of Rutherford's first experiment. Once the alpha particle source was removed, no further particles or radiations were observed. In that year the Curie-Joliots, bombarding aluminum with alpha particles, discovered something new. They observed neutrons emitted during the bombardment. But after the alpha source was removed, the irradiated aluminum foil continued to emit some kind of radiation, which decreased exponentially with time! Apparently they had created a radioactive substance, with a half period of three and a quarter minutes:

$$_{13}Al^{27} + _{2}\alpha^4 = _{15}P^{30} + _{0}n^1,$$

and

$$_{15}P^{30} \rightarrow _{14}Si^{30} + _{+1}\beta^0.$$

Immediately after the announcement of this discovery the hunt was on for new radioactive isotopes, or possibly for other new nuclear phenomena. By this time several types of accelerators for charged particles had been developed but the cyclotron was, and still is, the most useful in the isotope field. It can supply bombarding particles in tremendously greater numbers than any source of naturally radioactive material and with greater energies than the natural alpha particles.

The Cyclotron. The first cyclotron was built by E. O. Lawrence in 1932. The essential parts of the instrument are shown in Figure 13. The acceleration chamber consists of two hollow, semi-circular parts called Dees, because of their shape. Top, bottom, and outer circumference are closed, but the inner straight faces are open. These straight faces are parallel and slightly separated. The Dees are coupled into a very high frequency electrical system so that they are oppositely charged and the charge on each is alternately positive and negative, changing sign about 10^7 times per second. The whole chamber, in a shield that can be evacuated to a very low pressure, is placed between the pole pieces of a large electromagnet. At the center of the space between the Dees some arrangement is made for releasing protons or deuterons (Point S). Consider a proton released at S just at the instant that Dee A is at its peak negative charge, and B at its peak positive. The proton, being positively charged, will be repelled by B and attracted by A, and will enter the interior of A, with a definite velocity due to the potential difference between A and B. The electric charge on the Dee remains on the outside; the interior is field-free, so that once the particle is inside the charge ceases to act. However, the magnetic field does act on the moving, charged particle, bending its path

into a circle.   If the particle travelling in this circular path arrives back at
the space between the Dees just at the instant that their charges have been
reversed, it will again be accelerated across the gap, and will enter B with
a higher velocity than it had while in A.   Therefore, the radius of its new
circular path will be larger.   However, since it is moving faster, it will
again arrive at the gap at the instant of charge reversal, receive an additional impulse, and re-enter Dee A at still higher velocity.   If each individual impulse is 200 kev,* by the time the particle has made 50 revolutions,

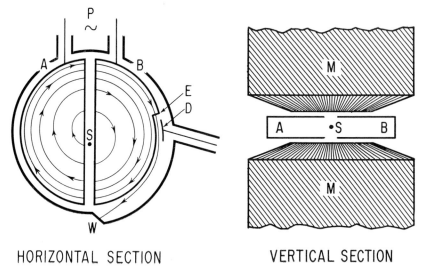

HORIZONTAL SECTION   VERTICAL SECTION

FIG. 13.   Diagram of central part of cyclotron.
A and B, Dees; S, ion source; P, alternating potential; D, deflecting plate; E, exit
slit; W, window; MM, magnet poles.

with two accelerations in each, it will have reached a total energy of 20
Mev.   By this time it will be far out toward the periphery of the Dee.
An exit slit is provided at E, with a charged deflector plate D to pull the
particle out of the circular path; it can then escape though the window W.
    The stream of high energy protons or deuterons emerging though the
window can be used as nuclear bombarders for any target introduced into
their path.   If neutrons are desired as bombarders, they can be produced
by deuteron bombardment of beryllium:

$$_4\text{Be}^9 + {}_1\text{d}^2 = {}_5\text{B}^{10} + {}_0\text{n}^1.$$

The beryllium target is placed in the deuteron beam, and a neutron beam
emerges on the far side of the beryllium.

    * One electron volt (ev) is the energy acquired by an electron in falling through a
potential difference of one volt.   Here the individual potential differences are each 200
kilovolts, and the final energy is twenty million electron volts.   See Chapter 4, p. 51 for
further discussion of energy units.

Thus the cyclotron provides positive or neutral particles, at any desired energy (within limits) and in relatively large quantities, for use in nuclear bombardment, disruption, and radioactive isotope production.

Machines to accelerate electrons to high energies have also been developed. Except in very special circumstances the electrons themselves, even at the highest available energies, are not able to produce nuclear transmutation. However, the x-rays produced by these energetic electrons in the betatron or synchrotron can sometimes bring about nuclear reactions. The phenomenon is not of practical importance in the production of isotopes, but has been valuable in studying energy relations.

REFERENCES

FRIEDLANDER, G. and KENNEDY, J. W.: *Nuclear and Radiation Chemistry*, Chapter 4, New York, John Wiley and Sons, 1955, (Revised Version).

GLASSER, O., QUIMBY, E. H., TAYLOR, L. S., WEATHERWAX, J. L. and MORGAN, R. H.: *Physical Foundations of Radiology*, 3rd Ed., Chapters 9 and 14, New York, Paul B. Hoeber, Inc., 1961.

LAPP, R. E. and ANDREWS, H. L.: *Nuclear Radiation Physics*, 2nd Ed., Chapters 12 and 13, New York, Prentice-Hall, 1954.

MORGAN, R. H. and CORRIGAN, K. E.: *Handbook of Radiology*, Section 4, Chicago, Yearbook Publishers, Inc., 1955

POLLARD, E. C. and DAVIDSON, W. L.: *Applied Nuclear Physics*, 2nd Ed., Chapters 4, 5, and 7, New York, John Wiley and Sons, 1951.

4

Nuclear Reactions

AT the present time over a thousand nuclear reactions are known; hundreds of radioactive nuclides have been prepared artificially. Transmutation is brought about by bombardment of nuclei with positively charged alpha particles, deuterons, or protons, with uncharged neutrons, and with photons (x-rays) of pure energy. These phenomena will be discussed in detail, but first, certain general considerations should be developed.

The Energy of a Reaction. In a chemical reaction, heat is either used up or given off; the reaction is called endothermic or exothermic. The complete reaction equation contains an expression for the heat of the reaction. For instance, instead of writing simply

$$C + O_2 = CO_2,$$

the complete form is

$$C + O_2 = CO_2 + 94{,}000 \text{ calories.}$$

That is, when one gram mol of carbon and two of oxygen combine to form carbon dioxide, 94,000 calories of heat are evolved. Similarly, in a nuclear reaction, energy is either used up or given off; the term analogous to "heat of reaction" is "nuclear energy change." The complete equation for Rutherford's first nuclear reaction should be

$$_7N^{14} + {}_2He^4 = {}_8O^{17} + {}_1H^1 + Q,$$

where Q represents the energy change. In a particular reaction, Q may be positive or negative. Positive Q means energy release; the reaction is *exoergic*. Negative Q, energy absorption, means *endoergic* reaction.

Exoergic reactions, those releasing energy, have attracted great attention. The energy liberated in a reaction with a large positive Q value is the "atomic energy" so widely discussed in recent years.

Equivalence of Mass and Energy. To understand the source of this energy it is necessary to accept a new idea, the equivalence of mass and energy. In 1905, as part of his special relativity theory, Einstein advanced this hypothesis and supplied the transformation equation

$$E = Mc^2, \qquad\qquad 4-(1)$$

where E is the energy in ergs equivalent to a mass of M grams, c being the velocity of light (2.99776×10^{10} cm per sec). Therefore the mass of a nucleus is a direct measure of its *total* energy content, the energy which would be released if the mass were totally destroyed. Such total destruction is seldom found, but partial mass disappearance can readily be detected.

It is found that the measured mass of a nucleus is always less than the sum of the masses of its constituent nucleons. The difference between the two represents loss of mass in consolidating the nucleons into the nucleus; its energy equivalent is called the *binding energy* of the nucleus.

The energy equivalent of one mass unit (1.6598×10^{-24} gm) is

$$E = 1.6598 \times 10^{-24} \times (2.99776 \times 10^{10})^2$$
$$= 1.492 \times 10^{-3} \text{ erg.}$$

An energy unit more useful in nuclear study is the *electron volt*, the energy acquired by an electron in falling though a potential difference of one volt.

$$1 \text{ ev} = 1.602 \times 10^{-12} \text{ erg}$$
$$\text{or } 1 \text{ erg} = 0.624 \times 10^{12} \text{ ev.}$$

Correspondingly

$$1 \text{ kev (kiloelectron volt)} = 1.602 \times 10^{-9} \text{ erg,}$$
and $$1 \text{ Mev (million electron volts)} = 1.602 \times 10^{-6} \text{ erg.}$$

In these terms,

$$1 \text{ mass unit} = 931.16 \text{ Mev,}$$

and 1 electron mass (0.0005486 mu) = 0.51098 Mev.

The binding energy of the He^4 nuclus may be calculated from the known values of the mass of the helium atom and of its components. The mass of the helium atom is 4.00387 mu. The two orbital electrons account for 0.001098 mu, leaving 4.00278 mu as the nuclear mass. Then

$$\text{Nucleus } He^4 = 2p + 2n.$$

$$4.00278 = 2 \times 1.00759 + 2 \times 1.00898 + Q,$$

$$Q = -0.03036 \text{ mu}$$

Therefore 0.03036 mass units, or 28.26 Mev of energy is used up in binding together the components of the helium nucleus. This is 7.07 Mev per nucleon. The average binding energy per nucleon in general is from 6 to 9 Mev throughout the periodic table. It is a maximum for elements in the region A = 55.

In making calculations for nuclear reactions in which beta particles are emitted, there is sometimes confusion as to what nuclear masses to use. In general, masses of complete neutral *atoms* are tabulated, for the convenience of workers with mass spectrographs. In writing a nuclear reaction for negative beta emission it is only necessary to remember that electrons required to form neutral atoms will always balance out, if they are *all* neglected. This, however, does not hold for positrons. For example, in the reaction

$$_5B^{10} + _1H^2 = _5B^{11} + _1H^1,$$

the equivalence is obvious because there has been no shift in atomic numbers. In the reaction

$$_6C^{14} = {_7}N^{14} + e^-,$$

carbon has six electrons and nitrogen seven. However, a beta particle has been emitted, and if both this and the extra one in the nitrogen atom are neglected, the balance remains. In the case of positron emission, however,

$$_7N^{13} = {_6}C^{13} + e^+,$$

the nitrogen has to lose both the positron and an orbital electron, so that two electron masses have been lost, and these must be included in the reaction equation.

When Einstein proposed his hypothesis, no experimental evidence of the equivalence of mass and energy was available. However, by careful measurement of masses and energies in nuclear reactions, abundant evidence has now been accumulated. For instance, radioactive sodium disintegrates according to the equation

$$_{11}Na^{24} = {_{12}}Mg^{24} + e^- + 2\gamma \ (1.368 \text{ and } 2.754 \text{ Mev}).$$

$$23.9986 = 23.9927 + Q.$$

$$Q = 0.0059 \text{ mu} = 5.5 \text{ Mev}.$$

The two gamma rays account for 4.1 Mev, and the maximum energy of the beta particles is 1.4 Mev, bringing the sum to the calculated value of Q, 5.5 Mev.

Notation for Nuclear Reaction. A nuclear reaction evidently proceeds in two stages. The first is the formation of a very unstable compound nucleus containing all the material of both target and bombarder nuclei; this is followed very promptly by a rearrangement to a more stable state, with the emission of energy, and frequently of particles. To aid in visualizing the two-stage nature of a nuclear reaction, a compact notation has been devised, which can be illustrated by Rutherford's original transmutation. Thus, instead of writing

$$_7N^{14} + {_2}He^4 = {_8}O^{17} + {_1}H^1,$$

the shorter form would be

$$N^{14} \ (\alpha,p) \ O^{17}.$$

The target nucleus is placed before the parentheses, the bombarder just inside, the expelled particle next, and finally, outside the parentheses, the product nucleus. Here the α stands for the alpha particle, p for the ejected proton. The process is referred to as an α-p reaction, indicating that an α particle goes in and a proton comes out.

Corresponding symbols for neutron, deuteron, and photon are n, d, γ. The common forms of reaction are (n,p), (n,α), (p,n), (p,α), (d,p), (d,n), (d,α), (α,p), and (α,n). Simple "capture" of neutrons or protons also occurs; in this case energy is emitted and the reaction is written (n,γ) or (p,γ).

Mechanisms of Nuclear Reaction. The actual mechanisms by which nuclear processes take place are not firmly established, but Bohr, in 1936, developed a concept of nuclear reactions which explains many of these phenomena. He pictures the nucleus as a densely packed but systematic arrangement of protons and neutrons, with distances between the nucleons of the same order of magnitude as the range of the nuclear forces, and inter-action energies between nucleons of the same orders of magnitude as the kinetic energies needed by bombarders in order to penetrate the nucleus, namely a few Mev. A particle comparable in size to the nucleons, coming into the aggregate with a definite kinetic energy, would lose most of this energy in the first few collisions with nucleons, would then become indistin-guishable from them, and would thus be amalgamated into the nucleus, forming a new nucleus whose atomic and mass numbers would depend on the nature of the bombarding particle. This new nucleus contains an extra allot-ment of energy, the kinetic energy which was brought in by the bombarding particle, plus its binding energy. Thus a 5 Mev proton, bringing in a new binding energy of about 7 Mev, gives rise to a new nucleus with atomic and mass numbers each greater by one than the original, and containing about 12 Mev more energy. This happens in a period of the order of 10^{-20} seconds. Now in haphazard motions energy is transferred among nucleons until one by chance finds itself with enough extra energy to escape from the nuclear binding forces. It is not necessary for the escaping nucleon to accumulate *all* the extra energy, but only enough to get away. This takes place in perhaps 10^{-12} seconds, a much longer period than the first step, but still extremely short. Thus there are two distinct steps in the nuclear reaction. The formation and the breaking up of the compound nucleus are independent of each other and may take place in various ways. If the escaping nucleon does not carry all of the extra energy from the nucleus, this is said to be left in an excited condition, and will return to normal with the emission of energy in the form of a gamma ray. (See Chapter 7, p. 93.) This is not radioactivity; the escaping nucleon is simply the second stage in the development of the new nucleus. The ejected unit may be a proton or a neutron, or occasionally a deuteron or an alpha particle. The new nucleus may be stable or radioactive.

In order to initiate the reaction, it is necessary for the bombarder to get into the nucleus. The neutron, having no charge, can enter readily; it is only necessary for it to encounter the nucleus, which occupies a small space. However, the positively charged protons, deuterons, and alpha particles must overcome the electrical repulsion of the positively charged nucleus. This nuclear potential barrier is usually depicted in the form of a potential "well" as in Figure 14. The nucleus is imagined as having its center at point O, and a radius equal to R. The internal potential energy of the nucleus is constant, and equal to $-U_o$ over the distance from $r = 0$ to $r = R$. At this point the potential energy increases suddenly to the value B, here the maximum repulsion will be exerted on an external charged particle. If the nucleus and the bombarder have atomic numbers Z and z respectively, the electrostatic potential energy between the charges at any distance r is $\dfrac{(Ze)\,(ze)}{r}$, e being the magnitude of a unit charge. The nucleus and the particle are considered as spheres, r being the distance between their centers. As r decreases, the potential energy increases, as indicated by the rising curve, to the maximum value at B. If the kinetic energy of the particle is great enough to overcome this potential energy repulsion, it can "get over the barrier" and enter the nucleus. In general,

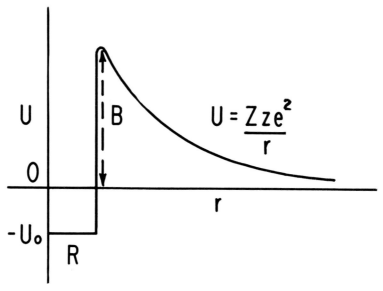

Fig. 14. Assumed form of potential energy curve in neighborhood of nucleus. R, nuclear radius; r, distance between center of nucleus and center of bombarding particle; $-U_o$, internal potential energy of nucleus; U, total potential energy; B, height of potential barrier, $= \dfrac{Z\,z\,e^2}{R}$.

with smaller energy it cannot, although in special cases it may "leak through." (Discussion of this phenomenon is outside the scope of this book.)

The entire region from $r = R$ to $r = \infty$ is called the *coulomb region*, since here only coulomb or electrostatic forces operate between Z and z. The rising curve of U against r is called the *nuclear potential barrier*. The peak of this curve, at the nuclear radius, is the value $B = \dfrac{(Ze)\,(ze)}{R}$. Thus the height of the barrier depends on the charge on the bombarding particle.

It can be shown that the height of any nuclear coulomb barrier is approximately $B = 0.762 \, zZ^{2/3}$ Mev. Thus for an alpha particle to penetrate a sodium nucleus ($Z = 11$), its energy would have to exceed $0.76 \times 2 \times 11^{2/3} = 7.5$ Mev.

Yield of a Nuclear Reaction. The individual nuclear reaction can always be written as outlined on page 50. However, the *yield* in a particular bombardment cannot be predicted without more information. It obviously depends on the number of bombarding particles and the number of nuclei, and further, on some factor having to do with the probability of a collision. In considering a bombardment of relatively large objects such as tennis racquets by smaller objects such as balls, the actual cross-section areas of the target and the bombarder are factors. A similar concept is useful in describing nuclear reactions. A target area, or cross-section, is assigned to each nucleus for each type of reaction. This may be close to the physical area of the nucleus, but this is not necessarily so. Nuclear cross-sections are established by experiments outside the scope of this book, and tabulated in various places.* The unit of cross-section, the *barn*, is 10^{-24} sq cm.

The chance of encounters in bombardment then can be described as follows: The target has an area A sq cm and a thickness x cm. It contains n nuclei per cubic centimeter, so the total number of target nuclei is nAx. If the cross-section for the reaction is σ per nucleus, the total "area" which may be struck is $nAx\sigma$. If the number of bombarding particles is I, the total number of reactions occurring is given by

$$N = I \sigma \, n \, A \, x. \qquad\qquad 4-(2)$$

Thus the total number of radioactive nuclei produced by a particular bombardment can be calculated.

As an example, consider bombardment of Au^{197} by slow neutrons in the pile (page 64) to produce radioactive gold, Au^{198}. Let the target be a gold foil 5 sq cm in area and 0.3 mm thick, a volume of 0.15 cu cm. Since the density of gold is 19.3 gm per cu cm, and its atomic weight is 197.2, the number of gold atoms in the foil is, by Avogadro's hypothesis

$$\frac{6.02 \times 10^{23}}{197.2} \times 19.3 \times 0.15 = 88 \times 10^{20} \text{ atoms, in a mass of 2.9 grams.}$$

The foil is to be exposed to a flux of 10^{12} neutrons per second. For Au^{197} σ is tabulated as 98 barns. Then the number of radioactive atoms produced per second should be given by

$$N = 10^{12} \times 88 \times 10^{20} \times 98 \times 10^{-24} = 86 \times 10^{10}.$$

In one hour the production would be 3×10^{15} atoms of Au^{198}.

The above calculation is based on the assumption that every gold atom has an equal chance of receiving a neutron; this is true only for *very thin*

* See Friedlander, G, and Kennedy, J. W., Nuclear and Radiation Chemistry, Appendix.

targets. Otherwise the effective neutron flux will decrease as the deeper layers of the target are reached, and a correction must be made. The attenuation in I, the neutron flux, in an infinitesimal thickness of the target, is

$$-dI = I n \sigma A dx. \qquad 4—(3)$$

This expression can be integrated in the same manner as that for radioactive decay (see page 33)

$$I_x = I_o e^{-n\sigma Ax}. \qquad 4—(4)$$

I_x is the number of neutrons passing completely through a target of thickness x, hence those absorbed and producing the nuclear reaction are

$$I_o - I_x = I_o (1 - e^{-n\sigma Ax}). \qquad 4—(5)$$

This number should take the place of I in formula 4—(2). For the problem under consideration

$$I_o - I_x = 10^{12} (1 - e^{-88 \times 10^{20} \times 98 \times 10^{-24}}) = 0.58 \times 10^{12}.$$

Accordingly the number of radioactive atoms actually produced in the foil is 58 per cent of the number calculated above, namely 1.74×10^{15} instead of 3×10^{15}, in one hour.

It has been shown (page 38) that 1 mc of any radioactive nuclide contains 4.6×10^{12} T atoms, where T is the half period in days. Therefore 1 mc of Au^{198} contains 12.4×10^{12} atoms, and the above production rate is 140 mc per hour. If there were no decay, this would be 3360 mc in 24 hours. However decay sets immediately as soon as any of the nuclide has been formed, and allowance must be made for this. The appropriate formula will be developed in Chapter 7; at present it will be accepted:—

$$A_t = \frac{R}{\lambda} (1 - e^{-\lambda t}) \qquad 4—(6)$$

where A_t is the net number of atoms after time t, R is the rate of production, and λ the decay constant. For Au^{198} the half period is 64.5 hours, so $\lambda = \frac{0.693}{64.5} = 0.0107$ per hour. R (above) = 140 mc per hour. Then the amount in 24 hours is $A_{24 \text{ hr}} = \frac{140}{0.0107} (1 - e^{-24 \times 0.0107}) = 3000$, instead of the 3360 obtained without considering decay.

In one half period $A_{64.5 \text{ hr}} = 6500$ mc, and for an infinite period $A_\infty = 1300$ mc. Thus one-half of the maximum is produced in an irradiation of one half period, three-fourths in two half periods, and so on.

The specific activity of the Au^{198} in the sample after an irradiation of two half periods is $\frac{9750 \text{ mc}}{2.9 \text{ gm}} = 3360$ mc per gm.

The actual percentage of atoms which have been activated during this period (including those which have already decayed) is

$$\frac{140 \times 2 \times 64.5 \times 12.4 \times 10^{12} \times 100}{88 \times 10^{20}} = 0.0025.$$

In other words, one atom is 40,000 has been transformed.

Reactions in Neutron Bombardment. Historically, as indicated earlier, the first transmutation observed was of the (α,p) type. However, transformations resulting from neutron bombardment appear simpler, and will first be considered.

Only one nuclide is known which will not react with neutrons of moderate energy, this is He^4. The most usual process is the (n,γ) reaction

$$_{z}X^A \ (n,\gamma) \ _{z}X^{A+1}.$$

An atom of mass number A has captured a neutron to form a heavier isotope of the same element, the extra energy being emitted as a gamma ray. This reaction always has a very good yield. Products are frequently radioactive, emitting beta particles. Examples are

$$_{47}Ag^{107} \ (n,\gamma) \ _{47}Ag^{108},$$

$$_{53}I^{127} \ (n,\gamma) \ _{53}I^{128}.$$

Other processes, as mentioned earlier, are (n,p) and (n,α). The (n,p) reaction, $_{z}X^A \ (n,p) \ _{z-1}X^A$, is typified by $_7N^{14} \ (n,p) \ _6C^{14}$ and $_{16}S^{32} \ (n,p) \ _{15}P^{32}$. Examples of the (n,α), $_{z}X^A \ (n,\alpha) \ _{z-2}X^{A-3}$, are $_9F^{19} \ (n,\alpha) \ _7N^{16}$, and $_{13}Al^{27}$ $(n,\alpha) \ _{11}Na^{24}$. There is also a much less common $(n,2n)$ reaction resulting in a positron emitter: $_{z}X^A \ (n, \ 2n) \ _{z}X^{A-1}$. Examples are $_7N^{14}(n, \ 2n) \ _7N^{13}$; $_{15}P^{31} \ (n,2n) \ _{15}P^{30}$.

Neutron Activation Analysis. In most elements introduced into a neutron reactor, radioactive isotopes will be produced. The technique known as neutron activation analysis has been developed for the detection of very small amounts of stable elements in fairly large quantities of extraneous matter. This is applicable to the measurement of so-called "trace" elements* in human tissues. Such elements as zinc, copper, molybdenum and arsenic may exist in extremely minute amounts in certain organs or tissues. They seem to take no part in normal metabolism, but may exert some sort of catalytic action. Changes in these very small amounts may be related to some diseases.

A sample of tissue, thought to contain the trace element, is put in a known neutron flux for a known period, and the resulting radioactivity measured. Of course there may be a number of activities induced in various tissue components, but a chemical separation can be used to isolate the one of interest. (Stable carrier can be added to prevent the loss of the minute quantity of the element in the sample.) Simultaneously with the unknown,

* Not to be confused with "tracer" elements which are usually radioactive.

a small sample of the stable element, of known weight, is irradiated. In this, the expected number of radioactive atoms can be calculated by the method outlined above, and the radioactivity per unit weight of stable element determined. The same degree of activity will be expected in the unknown, hence the initial weight of the stable element in this unknown can be calculated.

For example, to detect the amount of copper present in one gram of tissue, using 1 mg of thin copper foil as control. (Technical details of preparation of samples are omitted.) Normal copper contains 69% Cu^{63} and 31% Cu^{65}. The (n,γ) reactions on these two stable isotopes produce Cu^{64} and Cu^{66} respectively. The half life of Cu^{64} is 12.8 hours; that of Cu^{66} is 5 minutes. Therefore the latter can be ignored, if more than an hour elapses between the end of the irradiation and the measurement. The cross-section for Cu^{63} for slow neutrons is 4.3 barns. The foil is to be exposed to a flux of 10^{12} neutrons per second, for several days (until a convenient time for opening the reactor.) After 3 days, or 6 half lives, essentially the maximum possible amount of Cu^{64} will be present.

The decay constant is $\dfrac{0.693}{12.8} = 0.054$ per hour.

The rate of production per hour is

$$0.69 \times \frac{6.02 \times 10^{23} \times 0.001}{63.54} \times 10^{12} \times 4.3 \times 10^{-24} \times 3600 = 10^{11} \text{ atoms}$$

of Cu^{64}. [formula 4—(2)]

From 4—(6) the maximum production is $\dfrac{10^{11}}{0.054} = 18.5 \times 10^{11}$ atoms.

One millicurie of Cu^{64} contains [formula 2—(10)] 2.5×10^{12} atoms. Therefore the sample at the end of the irradiation contains 0.74 mc. Cu^{64} in 1 mg. copper. The unknown, measured against the standard, shows a content of

10^{-4} μc of Cu^{64} ($= 10^{-7}$ mc.) Then $\dfrac{\text{mg Cu in unknown}}{\text{1 mg Cu in standard}} = \dfrac{10^{-7}}{0.74}$, and the

copper in the tissue sample is 1.35×10^{-7} mg per gram of tissue.

Reactions in Proton Bombardment. The proton was the first bombarder used in experiments with artificially accelerated particles. Simple capture of protons, (p,γ) is a common reaction: $_zX^A$ (p,γ) $_{z+1}X^{A+1}$. An atom of mass number A has captured a proton, to form an isotope of the element with the next higher atomic number. This reaction has a good yield and many of the products are radioactive positron-emitting isotopes. Examples are $_6C^{12}$ (p,γ) $_7N^{13}$, and $_{20}Ca^{46}$ (p,γ) $_{21}Sc^{47}$.

The (p,n) reaction is important; $_zX^A$ $(p,n)_{z+1}X^A$. It will only proceed if the proton has relatively high energy. The product, an isobar of the target and an isotope of the element of the next higher atomic number, is always radioactive and a positron-emitter. This reaction can be used to yield neutrons as bombarders: $_4Be^9$ (p,n) $_5B^9$. It is frequently used in cyclotrons where an intense neutron beam is desired.

The (p,d) reaction, $_zX^A$ (p,d) $_zX^{A-1}$ might be expected, but it is known only in one instance, $_4Be^9$ (p,d) $_4Be^8$, and the product disintegrates in a small fraction of a second into two alpha particles. The (p,α) reaction, $_zX^A$ (p,α) $_{z-1}X^{A-3}$, occurs rather readily, but the products are almost always stable isotopes of the element of the next lower atomic number.

Reactions in Deuteron Bombardment. Since deuterons, being twice as heavy as protons, have twice the kinetic energy for the same velocity, they are now much more generally used for bombarders. Simple deuteron capture apparently does not occur. The deuteron consists of a proton and a neutron not too tightly bound together, and in most deuteron bombardments, one or the other component is rejected. The (d,n) reaction,

$$_zX^A \text{ (d,n) } _{z+1}X^{A+1}$$

gives the same type of products as the (p,γ) reaction. Yields are good if the deuterons are sufficiently energetic. Products are frequently positron-emitting radioisotopes of the next higher element: $_6C^{12}$ (d,n) $_7N^{13}$. A very useful reaction of this type is the bombardment of deuterons by deuterons, $_1H^2$ (d,n) $_2He^3$. This proceeds readily, at relatively low bombarding energies, and supplies a good yield of neutrons; the end product is not radioactive.

In the (d,p) reaction, $_zX^A$ (d,p) $_zX^{A+1}$, a heavier isotope of the target element is formed. This is a beta-emitting radioisosope;

$$_{11}Na^{23} \text{ (d,p) } _{11}Na^{24}$$

The (d,α) reaction, $_zX^A$ (d,α) $_{z-1}X^{A-2}$ occurs, but the products are usually stable, as in the (p,α) reaction.

Reactions with Alpha Particles. Although alpha particles were the first bombarders, they are not used at present to as great an extent as deuterons. Simple alpha capture apparently does not exist. The (α,n) reaction, $_zX^A$ (α,n) $_{z+2}X^{A+3}$, gives rise to positron-emitters. The first artificially radioactive reactions observed by the Curie-Joliots were of this type: $_5B^{10}$ (α,n) $_7N^{13}$, and $_{13}Al^{27}$ (α,n) $_{15}P^{30}$. Not all of these products are radioactive, some give rise to stable isotopes, as in $_4Be^9$ (α,n) $_6C^{12}$. This is the first reaction by which neutrons were produced in a usable quantity, and is still often employed for small sources. A mixture of powdered beryllium and radium or radon produces neutrons at the rate of about 25,000 per second per millicurie of radium or radon. This is very small compared to the output that can be achieved by a cyclotron, but much valuable research has been done with such sources.

The (α,p) reaction, $_zZ^A$ (α,p) $_{z+1}X^{A+3}$ results generally in stable products.

Nuclear Reactions Produced by Photons. Photon induced reactions (γ,n) and γ,p) can be produced with photons of sufficient energy to overcome the nuclear binding energy of the neutron or proton, that is about 9 Mev. The first produces positron emitters, the second electron emitters.

Yields are always low, and the process is not important from the point of view of isotope production.

Energy Considerations. For any of the reactions described above, certain conditions must exist. The mass of the two reacting particles plus the mass equivalent of the kinetic energy of the bombarding particle must exceed the mass of the resulting products. All bombarders must have sufficient energy to surmount or penetrate the potential barrier, which becomes greater the higher the atomic number of the target. There will always be competition among possible reactions, depending on energy conditions. For instance, the bombardment of $_{13}Al^{27}$ by energetic neutrons may result in any of the following:

$$_{13}Al^{27} \ (n,\gamma) \ _{13}Al^{28},$$
$$_{13}Al^{27} \ (n,p) \ _{12}Mg^{27},$$
$$_{13}Al^{27} \ (n,\alpha) \ _{11}Na^{24},$$
$$_{13}Al^{27} \ (n,2n) \ _{13}Al^{26}.$$

In general, the simpler reactions start at lower bombarding energies and produce better yields.

With higher energies even more complicated reactions may occur, such as (p,2n) or (p,p2n), and at energies of 100 or 200 Mev or more complete break-up of the target nucleus (spallation) may occur. However, it is not likely that these processes will be of importance in isotope production.

REFERENCES

EVANS, ROBLEY D.: *The Atomic Nucleus*, New York, McGraw-Hill, 1955.

FRIEDLANDER, G. and KENNEDY, J. W.: *Nuclear and Radiation Chemistry*, Chapters 3 and 4, New York, John Wiley and Sons, 1955, (Revised Version).

LAPP, R. E. and ANDREWS, H. L.: *Nuclear Radiation Physics*, 2nd Ed., Chapter 13, New York, Prentice-Hall, 1954.

POLLARD, E. C., and DAVIDSON, W. L.: *Applied Nuclear Physics*, 2nd Ed., Chapter 5, New York, John Wiley and Sons, 1951.

SEMAT, Henry: *Introduction to Atomic and Nuclear Physics*, 3rd Ed., New York, Rinehart, 1958.

UNITED STATES ATOMIC ENERGY COMMISSION: Catalog and Price List of Radioactive Isotopes, Special Materials, and Services, 1960.

5

Nuclear Fission

In the last chapter the neutron as a bombarder in nuclear reactions was discussed. When sources of neutrons became available by the

$$_4Be^9 \ (\alpha,n) \ _6C^{12}$$

reaction there described, several physicists systematically studied the results of bombarding many elements with these particles. One of these experiments was destined to have extremely far-reaching consequences since it led to the discovery of nuclear fission.

Discovery of Nuclear Fission. Like the discovery of the neutron, this is a complicated story. Fermi, in Italy in 1934 and 1935, exposed practically all the known elements to neutron bombardment and discovered a large number of new radioactive substances. The usual reaction was simple neutron capture, (n,γ) with the production of a heavier isotope of the target element, which is frequently a beta-emitting radioactive isotope. The emission of a beta particle has been shown (p. 31) to result in formation of a new nucleus with atomic number greater by unity than the parent atom. Fermi wondered whether by such bombardment of uranium, with atomic number 92, the highest known in nature, he could produce a new element with atomic number 93. If such an element fell into its proper place in the periodic table, it should be chemically like manganese. Accordingly, a manganese salt was added to a solution of a uranium salt which had been irradiated with neutrons, and then the manganese precipitated as the oxide. A considerable amount of the newly formed radioactive material came down with the manganese. It was demonstrated that neither uranium nor any element between $Z = 86$ and $Z = 92$ could be precipitated in this manner. Other experimenters found radioactivity associated with elements of other chemical families, and assumed that they were producing nuclides of several atomic numbers greater than 93. These were called "transuranic elements"; they were named and their half periods determined. Yet there were many irregularities in the experimental findings, and some of the energy relations were difficult to explain. Three German scientists, Hahn, Meitner, and Strassman, initiated a systematic study to identify these elements and organize the knowledge concerning them.

One method of study which was used was co-precipitation of an unknown with various known substances, to find the chemical family, as in the manganese precipitation just mentioned. In one such precipitation the Curie-

Joliots had brought down a radioactive substance with lanthanum (Z = 57). This might have been actinium (Z = 89), since this is in the same chemical family; it could not well be fitted into the transuranic group, and in fact its discoverers presently abandoned it.

Hahn and Strassmann repeated this work. (By this time Lise Meitner had been obliged to leave Germany and had not yet started more experimental work in Sweden.) They found not only the lanthanum-like precipitate, but one like barium. This, they thought, was radium, since these two elements are chemically much alike. But by differential tests they found that it was not radium but was truly barium. This news reached Meitner in Sweden, and she and Frisch announced the hypothesis that the neutron entering the uranium atom had produced a new kind of instability. Instead of forming a radioactive nucleus which would eventually expel an alpha or a beta particle, it had formed a nucleus so unstable that it instantly split into two nearly equal fragments, or underwent *fission* (adopting a term from biology for the dividing nucleus). This hypothesis was quickly proved experimentally by groups in several countries, including the United States. It was also demonstrated that every fission was accompanied by the release of about 200 Mev of energy—much more than in any previously known nuclear reaction.

Fission Products. There are three isotopes of natural uranium (Z = 92), with mass numbers 234, 235, and 238. It was found that U^{235} was the nucleus involved in the fission phenomenon. If an isotope of barium (Z = 56) is one of the products, then the other must be an isotope of krypton (Z = 36). However, it was soon demonstrated that many different elements were to be found in the fission products. In fact, practically every element from selenium (Z = 34) to lanthanum (Z = 57) was identified. Each individual fission results in two nuclei, one usually definitely heavier than half the uranium atom and one definitely lighter. The two new atomic numbers must add up to 92; the new masses, however, do not quite add up to 235, because two or three neutrons are "spilled out" at each fission. It will be recalled that the neutron-proton ratio constantly increases as higher atomic numbers are reached (Figure 5), so that in one atom of uranium there would be too many neutrons for two atoms of about half its atomic number. Even with the "spilling out" of some of the extra neutrons, the fragments still have too many, and have to return to stability by one or more, probably several, radioactive disintegrations. For instance, one product might be $_{53}I^{139}$ and the other $_{39}Y^{94}$, two extra neutrons having been lost. The iodine disintegration series would be $_{53}I^{139} \rightarrow _{54}Xe^{139} \rightarrow _{55}Cs^{139} \rightarrow _{56}Ba^{139} \rightarrow _{57}La^{139}$, a beta particle being emitted at each step. The lanthanum is stable. At least 75 such series are known.

The Nuclear Chain Reaction. If the fission process is initiated by the entrance of a neutron into a uranium atom, and if in undergoing fission this atom releases two neutrons, it would appear that these might in turn enter other uranium atoms and give rise to further fissions, so that quickly there might be an enormous number of atoms undergoing fission, as indicated in Figure 15.

At first thought it would seem that if such a reaction ever got started in a piece of uranium it would proceed with terrific rapidity until the whole thing had been destroyed. This would be truly the case if all the uranium atoms were fissionable and if no neutrons were lost. And with the enormous energy release of 200 Mev per fission, the reaction would be violently explosive. However in natural uranium it is almost entirely the U^{235} isotope that undergoes fission.* This isotope forms only $\frac{1}{140}$ of natural uranium. The more abundant isotope, U^{238}, usually simply captures the neutron in an (n,γ) reaction which will be discussed later. Thus a single

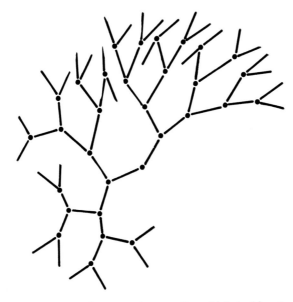

FIG. 15. Chain reaction; five stages in a reaction which doubles at each stage.

fission, or even a considerable number starting in a lump of natural uranium would not be likely to initiate a continuing chain reaction, although there might be several successive fissions before it died out.

It is, however, possible, by various physical procedures, to separate the isotopes, at least partially, so that "enriched" U^{235} may be produced, with a relatively high percentage of fissionable atoms. In this case, the likelihood of a self-sustaining chain reaction becomes greater. Now, the concept of "critical size" enters the picture. In a mass in which a chain reaction is going on, some of the neutrons will be released near the periphery, and may escape. These are then lost, as far as propagation of the chain is concerned. If the volume is small, so many will be lost that the reaction will stop; if

* U^{238} nuclei can be fissioned only by neutrons of a few definite energies, likely to be available only in very small numbers in this haphazard process.

it is sufficiently large, the reaction may just proceed without building up to an explosive level, because just enough neutrons will be kept within the volume to produce one new fission for each one that has occurred. In a still larger volume the chain will spread, at a speed determined by the ratio of neutrons kept in the volume to the number of atoms undergoing fission.

As soon as the possibility of a sustained chain reaction became apparent, physicists saw its potentialities both for power and for wartime explosives. It will be recalled that fission was discovered in 1939. War was sweeping through Europe; the United States was not yet involved, but many people thought her entrance into the fighting was only a matter of rather brief time. Accordingly, a project was set up to study possibilities of exploiting this new source of energy, the "Manhattan Project."

The Atomic Pile or Nuclear Reactor. The first objective was to see whether a self-sustaining chain reaction could be established. Fermi, having earlier left Axis-dominated Italy, was in charge of this phase of the study. Details are fascinating, but would be out of place here. As is well known, he was successful and the first chain-reacting apparatus was put into action on December 2, 1942.

The principle is to capture enough of the neutrons released in fission: if they escape from one lump of uranium without producing a second fission, provision is made for their arrival at other lumps. For this purpose the space between lumps of uranium must be filled with material that will not absorb neutrons, but will slow them down by mechanical collisions, until they have too little energy to interact with the U^{238} in the mass. Even at slowest speeds they will cause fission in the U^{235}. Pure carbon was the first substance used as a "moderator," and the first "reactor" was a pile of blocks of very pure graphite with chunks of natural uranium at regular intervals. Stray neutrons from cosmic rays, or those deliberately introduced, served to start the reaction, and when the "pile" was large enough, it proceeded spontaneously. That is, for every neutron used to produce a fission, more than one was made available. If such a "pile" should be left alone, it would get hotter and hotter until it "blew up," not as a bomb, but simply separating into fragments too small to carry on the reaction. This can be prevented by inserting into the pile a rod of some material such as cadmium, that absorbs neutrons very strongly. If too much of the absorber is introduced, the chain will slow down and finally stop. It is possible to find the point of balance at which the chain will continue at a constant rate. This is the basic principle for all nuclear reactors, the so-called *atomic piles*, although other fuels may be used besides natural uranium, and other moderators besides carbon. A diagram of a working nuclear reactor is shown in Figure 16.

Transuranic Elements. As has been stated, it is possible to separate the isotopes of uranium by various physical processes. Then, instead of natural uranium the fuel elements may contain material rich in U^{235}; in this case, the whole unit can be more compact. The smaller the amount of U^{238}, the less the need for slowing down the neutrons to avoid their capture by this isotope.

However, this very capture leads to the production of a new element, which is also fissionable.

$$_{92}U^{238} \, (n,\gamma) \, _{92}U^{239},$$

$$_{92}U^{239} \rightarrow _{93}Np^{239} + \beta^- \; (T = 23 \text{ minutes}),$$

$$_{93}Np^{239} \rightarrow _{94}Pu^{239} + \beta^- \; (T = 2.3 \text{ days}),$$

$$_{94}Pu^{239} \rightarrow _{92}U^{235} + \alpha \; (T = 24,360 \text{ years}).$$

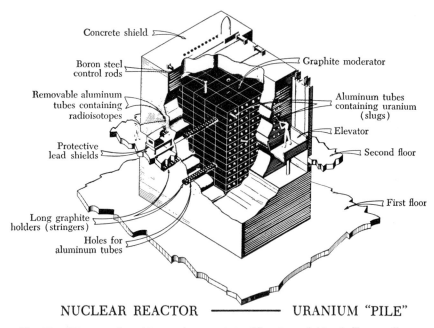

NUCLEAR REACTOR ———— URANIUM "PILE"

Fig. 16. Diagram of working nuclear reactor. (Courtesy of Atomic Energy Commission.)

Here are actually transuranic elements, neptunium and plutonium. Plutonium has a very long half period for natural decay, but it is fissionable with fast or slow neutrons. Since it is a different element, it may be separated chemically from the uranium in which it was created. It can, therefore, be used as "fuel" in a reactor, although its more important use is in weapons, which will be briefly discussed below.

Isotope Production in the Pile. In isotope production the nuclear reactor or pile, has two important roles. First, it supplies a copious source of slow neutrons, of much higher intensity than any cyclotron can produce. Target material to be bombarded by these slow neutrons can be introduced into channels in the pile, in suitable containers, and removed after the

5

required time of bombardment. The most common reaction is simple capture:

$$_{11}Na^{23}(n,\gamma) \; _{11}Na^{24},$$

$$_{27}Co^{59}(n,\gamma) \; _{27}Co^{60}.$$

However, in some important cases the (n,p) reaction also proceeds:

$$_{16}S^{32}(n,p) \; _{15}P^{32},$$

$$_{17}Cl^{35}(n,p) \; _{16}S^{35}.$$

The second isotope source is fission products from spent fuel elements. Within the lump of uranium, the fission products are formed and in general do not escape, but decay there, eventually to stable end products as described above. However, the presence of this extraneous material in the fuel slug results in undue consumption of neutrons in interactions with the fission products. Eventually the uranium is so highly contaminated with these other substances as to become useless. It must then be removed from the reactor and replaced with a fresh fuel element. The uranium in the old one would be reusable if it could be separated from the contaminants; and some of these might also be valuable. The handling of these intensely radioactive chunks of material presents many problems, and a whole new field of "hot" radiochemistry has been developed. Certain isotopes are now regularly separated from these old fuel elements. $_{53}I^{131}$, $_{56}Ba^{140}$, $_{55}Cs^{137}$, $_{38}Sr^{89}$, $_{38}Sr^{90} + _{39}Y^{90}$, and many of the rare earths are supplied by the Atomic Energy Commission as fission products.

Nuclear Weapons. The "atomic bomb" has little to contribute to the isotope program, except for problems concerned with the possible radioactive debris. However it should be discussed briefly.

Nuclear weapons can be made with U^{235}, but the man-made element plutonium is usually employed. Most information about them is secret, and in any case irrelevant here, but certain basic principles may be mentioned.

The first concept is that of "critical size," which has been discussed above. If the volume of fissionable material is smaller than this, the reaction cannot build up. Even in a larger volume, an explosion would not necessarily develop. It will be recalled that 200 Mev of energy is released at each fission, most of this being expended as kinetic energy of the fission fragments. If the material is not constrained in any way, the result of a few generations in the fission chain would be that the mass would "push itself apart" and be reduced to a number of fragments of sub-critical size, in each of which the reaction would cease; a real "atomic explosion" would not occur. For this, a much larger number of fissions would have to occur in a very short time, and the mass would have to be prevented from splitting up prematurely.

This is brought about by confining two or more sub-critical masses of practically pure fissionable material inside a case of heavy material (called a tamper). At the instant of the desired explosion these sub-critical masses are shot into each other to form a greater than critical mass, while the tamper keeps the material from flying apart until a large number of fissions occur and a tremendous energy is released. The unit then blows apart with a terrific detonation, producing a blast wave with tremendous destructive force. During the brief instant of energy build-up the heat is such as to convert the metallic center to gas at a high temperature. When this gas is released it expands to form a "ball of fire" emitting a tremendous flash of heat. Furthermore, the last generation of fission neutrons, released as the bomb flies apart, together with gamma rays released in the process, produce a highly lethal radiation.

If the explosion occurs at or near the earth's surface, a large amount of debris will be carried up with the cloud of fission products; much of this will have been made radioactive by the released neutrons. The larger particles will fall back fairly promptly, but the smaller ones will remain suspended for some time, and eventually be deposited over an appreciable part of the earth's surface. Explosions of low energy yield (so-called kiloton range) result in suspension mainly in the troposphere, to an altitude of possibly 50,000 feet. Most of this will have returned to the earth within a few weeks, in a fairly narrow band encircling the world at the latitude of the detonation.

For explosions of high energy yield (megaton range) most of the bomb debris will be propelled higher, into the stratosphere, from which it dribbles back to earth more slowly, over a period of years, during which some of it will reach all parts of the earth's surface. Of course during this period a great deal of the radioactivity will have decayed away, but there may still be enough to cause concern. This "fall-out" hazard will be considered in a later chapter.

Fusion (Thermonuclear) Reactions. The Hydrogen Bomb. It will be recalled (page 51) that when nucleons unite to form more complex nuclei, mass is lost. Part of this goes into the binding energy of the new nucleus, the rest is emitted as gamma radiation. If many nuclear fusions could be made to take place simultaneously, considerable energy could be released. However it requires a good deal of energy to start such a reaction. This energy can be attained by raising the temperature to very high levels (of the order of a million degrees Centigrade). Under these circumstances the fusion processes are referred to as *thermonuclear reactions*.

Four such reactions apparently can be produced in practical abundance at this temperature level. They are:

$$H^2 + H^2 = He^3 + n + 3.2 \text{ Mev.}$$
$$H^2 + H^2 = He^3 + H^1 + 4 \text{ Mev.}$$
$$H^3 + H^2 = He^4 + n + 17 \text{ Mev.}$$
$$H^3 + H^3 = He^4 + 2n + 11 \text{ Mev.}$$

The most practical way that sufficiently high temperatures can be obtained on earth, to initiate a large amount of such reactions, is by means of a fission explosion. Consequently by combining a quantity of deuterium or tritium or both with a fission bomb, one or more of the above reactions should be initiated, and if the energy can at first be constrained, a thermonuclear explosion may be produced. Since the essential elements are isotopes of hydrogen, these are frequently called hydrogen bombs.

"Dirty Bombs" and "Clean Bombs". Following the explosion of a fission bomb, even though it is so far above ground that there is no incidental dirt, as noted above there will be a large production of radioactive fission products, which will eventually reach the earth as fall-out. If a purely fusion bomb could be achieved, and exploded far enough above ground to prevent the released neutrons from activating the surroundings, this would be a truly "clean" bomb from the point of view of radioactive fall-out contamination. However a small fission bomb is necessary to initiate the fusion reaction, so complete cleanness cannot apparently be achieved. Nevertheless, by adjusting the relative components of the fission-fusion system, some control may be had of the "dirty" radioactive residual.

REFERENCES

FRIEDLANDER, G. and KENNEDY, J. W.: *Nuclear and Radiation Chemistry*, Chapter 3 ' New York, John Wiley and Sons, 1955, (Revised Version).

LAPP, R. E. and ANDREWS, H. L.: *Nuclear Radiation Physics*, 2nd Ed., Chapters 8 and 13, New York, Prentice-Hall, 1954.

POLLARD, E. C. and DAVIDSON, W. L: *Applied Nuclear Physics*, 2nd Ed., Chapters 10 and 11, New York, John Wiley and Sons, 1951.

UNITED STATES ATOMIC ENERGY COMMISSION: *The Effects of Nuclear Weapons*, Washington, D. C., United States Government Printing Office, 1957.

6

Interaction of Radiation and Matter

RADIATION can be detected only by its action on matter. The uses of radiation depend on effects produced in living or non-living material. Any such effect must necessarily be the result of a transfer of energy from the radiation to the matter. This means that a beam of radiation will have its energy diminished as it traverses a material medium. The interactions by which such energy transfer can be brought about, and the results of the interactions on the matter and on the radiation form the subject of this chapter.

Characteristics of the Radiations. The radiations to be considered are charged and uncharged particles, and photons, or electromagnetic rays; all may have considerable energy. The charged particles are alphas, deuterons, protons, and positive and negative electrons; the electromagnetic rays are gamma or x-rays. Alpha particles, $_2\alpha^4$, have a mass number 4 and two positive charges; those from radioactive substances travel at velocities up to about 15,000 miles per second. Protons, $_1H^1$, and deuterons, $_1H^2$, have mass numbers 1 and 2 respectively and a single positive charge. They are not emitted in radioactive disintegrations, but are accelerated in such instruments as the cyclotron, and for the same energies as the alpha particles, have considerably greater velocities. Negative and positive electrons have masses only of the order of $\frac{1}{1800}$ of a mass unit, and single charges of the indicated sign. Both types are emitted in radioactive disintegrations, the negative ones can be accelerated to high velocities artificially; some may travel with speeds up to 99 per cent of that of light. Neutrons, $_0n^1$, have unit mass and no charge. They may have velocities ranging from thermal to many thousands of miles per second. Photons have neither charge nor mass, and travel with the speed of light.

Energies of the Radiations. The energy of *particle radiation* is kinetic;

$$KE = \tfrac{1}{2} m v^2, \qquad\qquad 6-(1)$$

or energy in ergs equals $\frac{1}{2}$ mass in grams multiplied by square of velocity in cm per second. For the alpha particle, m is 6.650×10^{-24} gm, v at 12,000 miles per second is 2×10^9 cm per second.

$$KE = \tfrac{1}{2} \times 6.650 \times 10^{-24} \times (2 \times 10^9)^2 = 1.3 \times 10^{-5} \text{ erg.}$$

Since 1 erg $= 6.24 \times 10^5$ Mev the kinetic energy of the alpha particle travelling with this speed is 8 Mev. Similar calculations can be made for other particles of appreciable mass, namely deuterons, protons, and neutrons.

For beta particles a new phenomenon has to be considered; namely, the increase of mass as velocity attains high values.

Einstein postulated that no particle can travel faster then the speed of light in a vacuum. If the above formula for kinetic energy is applied to a million-volt electron it becomes

$$1 \text{ Mev} = 1.602 \times 10^{-6} \text{ ergs} = 1/2 \times 9.108 \times 10^{-28} \text{ gm} \times v^2 \text{ cm/sec.}$$

Whence $v = 6 \times 10^{10}$ cm/sec. But this is twice the speed of light, and hence inadmissible.

One of the predictions of Einstein's special relativity theory is that the mass of a particle must increase as its velocity increases. If the particle velocity is denoted by v, the speed of light by c, and the ratio v/c by β, the formula for mass at velocity v, in terms of the "rest mass" is

$$m_v = \frac{m_o}{\sqrt{1-\beta^2}}. \qquad 6\text{—}(2)$$

This formula will be accepted without derivation; its validity has been thoroughly demonstrated.

In Chapter 4, the equivalence of mass and energy was discussed, and the energy equivalence of an electron at rest was given as $m_oc^2 = 0.51098$ Mev. Obviously if the electron get heavier by virtue of its motion, its equivalent energy will increase. The total energy will then be m_vc^2. This energy may be considered as having two components, one the rest mass energy, the other the kinetic energy. Then

$$m_vc^2 = m_oc^2 + KE, \text{ or}$$
$$KE = (m_v - m_o)c^2. \qquad 6\text{—}(3)$$

An electron going at 0.9 the speed of light will have mass $m = \dfrac{m_o}{\sqrt{1-0.81}}$

$= 2.3 \text{ m}_o$. The total energy then is 2.3 m_oc^2 or 1.175 Mev. Of this $m_oc^2 = 0.511$ Mev is rest energy, and the remainder, 0.664 Mev. is kinetic. Kinetic energies of electrons or beta particles in general practice range from about 0.1 to 3.0 Mev.

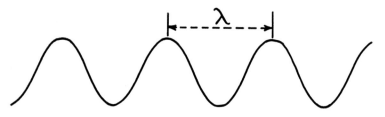

FIG. 17.   Diagram to illustrate wave motion. Wave length, λ, = distance from crest to crest.

The energy of the *photons* is determined in a different manner. These have no associated mass, but are electromagnetic waves travelling with the speed of light.

The wave pattern may be indicated as in Figure 17. The *wave length*, or distance from crest to crest, is usually denoted by the Greek lower case lambda (λ). The velocity, which is the velocity of light, 2.998×10^{10} cm per second, is denoted by c. The frequency, or number of waves passing a given point per second, is indicated by the Greek lower case nu (ν).

$$\nu = \frac{c}{\lambda} \text{ or } \lambda = \frac{c.}{\nu} \qquad\qquad 6-(4)$$

The range of wave lengths to be considered is of the order of 1.0 to 0.01 Angstrom units or 10^{-8} to 10^{-10} cm., which means frequencies of the order of 10^{18} to 10^{20} per second. The shorter the wave length or the higher the frequency, the greater is the energy of the radiation.

However, in describing the interaction of photons with matter, it is difficult to deal with waves, so they are to be considered in a second aspect, as *particles of pure energy*. This is not a contradiction. Neither particle nor wave picture describes the radiation fully, just as neither floor plan nor elevation describes a building completely, but both are true as far as they go. In this sense the energy of the particle is given by

$$E = h\nu \text{ ergs,} \qquad\qquad 6-(5)$$

where h is a number known as Planck's constant, and equal to 6.625×10^{-27} erg-seconds. Thus, for a photon of wave-length 0.1 A, or frequency

$$\frac{3 \times 10^{10*}}{0.1 \times 10^{-8}} = 3 \times 10^{19} \text{ per second, } E = 6.625 \times 10^{-27} \times 3 \times 10^{19} = 2 \times 10^{-7}$$

ergs $= 0.125$ Mev. Photon energies in practice range from a few kev to a few Mev.

There are convenient relations among wave length, voltage and energy:

$$E = h\nu \text{ ergs, } = \frac{hc}{\lambda} \text{ ergs } = \frac{hc}{\lambda} \times 6.24 \times 10^5 \text{ Mev.} \qquad 6-(6)$$

In these formulae λ is expressed in cm. If it is expressed in Angstrom units

$$E(\text{kev}) = \frac{6.625 \times 10^{-27} \times 3 \times 10^{10} \times 6.24 \times 10^8}{\lambda \times 10^{-8}} = \frac{12.40}{\lambda} \text{ Angstrom.}$$
$$6-(7)$$

Possible Types of Interactions of Radiation and Matter. The nature of matter has been discussed in Chapter 1. It is composed of atoms, consisting of nuclei, orbital electrons, and a great deal of empty space. Any of the

---

* This value is used for c, instead of 2.998×10^{10} as given above, for simplification of the computations.

kinds of radiation just discussed, in traversing atoms, may do one of three things:

a. Pass through without encountering any opposition;
b. Interact with an orbital electron;
c. Interact with the nucleus.

That which passes through with no interaction is not detected and is of no interest in this discussion. By far the greatest amount of energy interchange results from interactions with orbital electrons.

Interactions of Alpha Particles with Matter. Consider first an alpha particle, with a velocity of some thousands of miles per second, or an energy of a few million electron volts, a mass about seven thousand times that of the electron and a double positive charge. If it passes close to an orbital electron it will exert a powerful attraction on it, and may pull it entirely out of its orbit and give it a considerable velocity. The atom will then be left lacking an electron, and therefore with a net positive charge; it is a *positive ion*. The electron flying off by itself is a *negative ion*; it may temporarily attach itself to another atom, in which case the whole thing is the negative ion. It will not attach itself to the alpha particle, because this is moving so fast that the electron does not catch it. However, the alpha particle did lose some energy in the encounter, possibly several hundred electron volts, and after hundreds of such interactions it will be slowed down sufficiently so that it can pick up two orbital electrons and become an atom of ordinary helium. Alpha particles, being much heavier than electrons, will not be deflected from their straight paths by these encounters, and since all those from a particular alpha-emitter have the same energy, they will travel the the same distance in a medium, or have a definite *range*. The cloud chamber photograph in Figure 12 (page 45) was made by a mixture of alphas from ThC and ThC', with energies of about 8.8 and 5.6 Mev respectively. The two ranges are clearly shown.

Even the most energetic alpha particles lose their energy fairly rapidly in traversing matter, so that their ranges are not more than a few cm in air or a small fraction of a millimeter in solid substance. The range increases rapidly with the energy, or the velocity of the alpha particle. The 5.3 Mev alphas from $_{84}Po^{210}$ have a range of 3.7 cm in air, while the 7.6 Mev particles from $_{84}RaC'^{214}$ travel 6.6 cm.

A positive ion and a negative ion are always produced simultaneously; it is not possible to have either one alone. The two together constitute an *ion pair*. The *specific ionization* is defined as the number of ion pairs produced per millimeter of path of the ionizing particle in air, and is approximately inversely proportional to the particle velocity. Thus, an alpha particle ionizes more and more strongly as it slows down, until it reaches a maximum just before it is stopped. The 7.6 Mev alphas just mentioned would have an initial specific ionization of about 2000 ion pairs per millimeter of air, and just before the end of the range, of about 7000.

If the alpha particle makes a direct collision with a nucleus the result may be nuclear disintegration, as described in Chapter 4. This is an extremely rare event, and of little importance in the discussion of the interaction of radiation and matter.

The behavior of deuterons and protons is essentially the same as that of alpha particles, and need not be considered separately.

Interactions of Beta Particles with Matter. In the interactions of beta particles of either sign with orbital electrons, mutual attraction of unlike charges and repulsion of like ones is the operative agency, as with alpha particles, and ionization is again the result of the "collision." However, in these cases the interacting particles are of essentially the same mass, and hence the impinging particle may be widely deflected by the encounter, moreover it may lose up to half its energy in a single interaction. Thus the beta particles will pursue very tortuous paths, and even if all started with the same energy they would not have the same range, as do the alphas. The particles are finally slowed down to thermal velocities, the negative ones attach themselves to atoms needing electrons. The positrons disappear by combining with negative electrons to form *annihilation radiation*. This is a process similar to that described in Chapter 4 where the loss of matter resulted in the production of radiation. The same law is followed:

$$E = mc^2.$$

In this case the masses are essentially equal and about 9.1×10^{-28} gm. each. Whence

$$E = 2 \times 9.1 \times 10^{-28} \times (3 \times 10^{10})^2 \text{ ergs} = 2 \times 0.51 \text{ Mev.} \qquad 6-(8)$$

or two photons, each of about one-half million electron volts, are produced. There must usually be two, to comply with the laws of conservation of momentum. Rare specific cases resulting in production of one or three photons may be neglected.

If a beta particle of either sign passes near an atomic nucleus, its path will be bent somewhat toward the nucleus if it is a negative electron, away from if it is positive. This change in direction is considered a negative acceleration of the charged particle, and according to classical electromagnetic theory, in such circumstances electromagnetic energy must be radiated. This is, in fact, the phenomenon leading to the production of the continuous spectrum of x-rays in x-ray tubes, as the electrons from the hot cathode are slowed (negatively accelerated) by the target atoms. This radiation, particularly as it is produced in the passage of beta particles through matter, is called *Bremsstrahlung* (from the German meaning "braking radiation") and represents an energy loss for the electron. This type of interaction becomes more important as the energy of the beta particle is increased, and as the atomic number of the material traversed increases. It can be shown that the *fraction* of the beta energy which appears as external bremsstrahlung is approximately equal to $\dfrac{ZE}{3000}$ where E is the maximum energy of the particle in Mev and Z is the atomic number of the absorber. Thus, for 2 Mev beta particles passing through $_{29}$Cu, the external bremsstrahlung is $\dfrac{29 \times 2}{3000} =$ 2 per cent of the total energy. In $_{82}$Pb it would be $\dfrac{82}{29}$ times as much, or about 6 per cent.

Interaction of Neutrons with Matter. Neutrons, having no charge, do not interact with electrons; their only interaction is with nuclei, in the form of actual collisions. In such an encounter the neutron may be scattered, absorbed with emission of a photon, absorbed with emission of a heavy particle such as a proton, absorbed with production of fission of the target nucleus. A particular case of nuclear scattering interaction occurs when neutrons and hydrogen atoms are involved. Since neutrons and protons (hydrogen nuclei) have essentially the same mass, an energetic neutron striking a hydrogen nucleus can drive it away from its orbital electron, thus making it a positive ion. This can then ionize in the same manner as a positively charged "heavy" particle. (See alpha particle, above.) In absorption processes new stable or radioactive nuclei may be formed. Some of these processes have been described in Chapter 4. Nuclides may thus exhibit very different reactions on collision with neutrons, and the characteristics may change with neutron energy in a complicated way. There are few generalizations which can be made with regard to the variations with atomic number or mass number. Since clinical isotope users are mainly interested in neutron interactions only for the production of isotopes, they will not be further discussed in this chapter.

Interaction of Photons with Matter. The interaction of photons with orbital electrons takes place in different ways depending on whether the electron is essentially free in an outer orbit or tightly bound in an inner one. In the first case the picture may be imagined as similar to the interaction of beta particles with orbital electrons, although the force is not now due to the interaction of electric charges. The photon "collides" with an electron and knocks it from its position, giving up some of its energy and being deflected from its path. Thus it proceeds in a new direction as a photon of less energy or longer wave length. This is called a *Compton collision*; the electron is a Compton or recoil electron. The loss of energy by a photon depends only on the angle of scatter and the initial energy of the photon. Regardless of the initial energy of the photon, the change in wave length is given by

$$\Delta\lambda = 0.024 \ (1-\cos\theta) \ \text{Angstrom}, \qquad\qquad 6\text{—}(9)$$

where θ is the angle of deflection or scatter, as indicated in Figure 18. Thus for a 90° deflection, since cos 90° = 0, any photon has its wave length increased by 0.024 A. For a 100 kev photon, $\lambda = \dfrac{12.40}{100} = 0.124$ A, and the

90° scattered ray has a wave length of 0.124 + 0.024 = 0.148 A, corresponding to 84 kev. However for a 1 Mev photon, with a wave length of 0.0124 A,
90° scattered wave length is 0.036 A, corresponding to 350 kev, a much
more drastic reduction in energy. A photon cannot give up all its energy in
a Compton collision. If it is scattered directly backward θ = 180°, cos θ
= −1 and the wave length is increased by 0.048 A. If the initial wave
length were vanishingly small, the final one would still be equivalent to
260 kev. If the original photon were only 10 kev, with λ = 1.24 A, the
final wave length of 1.288 A would correspond to 9.6 kev.

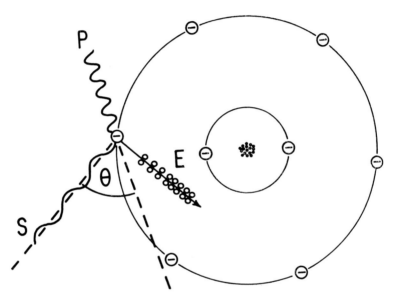

Fig. 18.   Diagram to illustrate Compton collision.
   P, primary photon; S, scattered photon; θ, angle of scatter; E, Compton electron producing ion pairs. (Note the change of scale in the ion track. Each ion pair in E should
be as large as the initial atom. It is not practicable to make the illustration completely
to this scale.)

If the electron is tightly bound in an inner orbit, the photon in removing
it may give up all of its energy and cease to exist. Part of the energy goes
to overcoming the binding energy* of the electron in its orbit, and the rest
to accelerating this electron. This is a *photoelectric collision*, the electron is
a *photoelectron*. In order to be capable of a photoelectric interaction, a
photon must have sufficient energy to overcome the binding energy of the
electron in its orbit, but not so much more that the electron is incapable
of taking all that remains. The binding energies of electrons in the K and
L orbits of certain elements are listed in Table 2. From this it is seen that
the binding energy for a K electron in copper is 8.86 kev. Hence a 10 kev

* This binding energy of orbital electrons must not be confused with nuclear building
energy (p. 51).

photon could eject this electron and have 1.14 kev additional to accelerate it. The ejected electron is then effectively a 1.14 kev beta particle. However, a 10 kev photon could not eject a K electron from silver (K energy = 25.5 kev), but it could remove an L electron from this atom, since this requires only 3.53 kev. A 1 Mev photon would not readily undergo photoelectric interaction with a copper K electron; this would result in production of essentially a 1 Mev secondary beta particle, which is possible but not likely.

Table 2. Binding Energies of Electrons in K and L Orbits

Atomic No.	Element	K-energy (kev)	L-energy (kev)
13	Aluminum	1.56	——
20	Calcium	4.02	——
26	Iron	7.08	0.72
29	Copper	8.86	1.02
38	Strontium	16.15	1.95
42	Molybdenum	20.0	2.52
47	Silver	25.5	3.53
50	Tin	29.2	4.14
55	Cesium	36.0	5.30
74	Tungsten	69.2	11.3
79	Gold	80.5	13.4
82	Lead	87.5	14.8

The ejected electrons in either Compton or photoelectric encounters proceed as ionizing particles in exactly the same manner as primary beta particles.

A photon interacting with a nucleus *may* disintegrate it, but this is highly unlikely except for photons of several Mev of energy. A more probable result of a high energy photon passing close to the field of a nucleus is its complete transformation into a *positron-electron pair*. Again, according to the Einstein equation

$$E = mc^2.$$

For such a pair the mass is $2 \times 9.1 \times 10^{-28}$ gm and the necessary energy to produce it is

$$E = 2 \times 9.1 \times 10^{-28} \times 9 \times 10^{20} \text{ ergs} = 1.02 \text{ Mev.}$$

Photons of less energy than this cannot undergo pair formation. If the energy is greater, the excess goes to accelerating the particles. These then traverse matter in exactly the same manner as primary beta particles, are eventually slowed down to thermal velocities, the positron unites with a free electron to produce two 0.51 Mev photons of annihilation radiation as described above, and the negative electron is annexed by something that needs one.

Recombination and Production of Characteristic Radiation. The net result of the passage of any charged particle or photon through matter is the production of *ions;* for this reason these are called *ionizing radiations.* In producing ionization, the radiation must impart energy to the matter. The ionized state is extremely temporary. In a very small fraction of a second the ionized atom finds another electron, *recombines* with it, and returns to normal. When the vacancy left in a photoelectric interaction is filled, the atom gives up the energy that the photon left with it when it removed the electron. This energy is emitted in the form of one or a few photons, the sum of whose energies is exactly the energy which bound the electron there in the first place. For this reason it is called *characteristic radiation;* its energy is characteristic of the particular orbit in the particular atom from which it arose.

For an atom of any element, the characteristic radiation arising from replacement of an electron in the K orbit (K-characteristic) is more energetic than from the L orbit, and so on, as indicated by the binding energies in Table 2. Characteristic radiation from any orbit increases in energy as the atomic number of the element increases.

The characteristic radiation is not truly mono-energetic, but exhibits a group of slightly different values depending on whether the replacing electron came from the L, M, etc. orbits, or from completely outside the atom. The K_α radiation, resulting from replacement from the L orbit, has slightly less energy than the K_β from the M, and so on.

Recombination after a Compton interaction results in general in the production of much less energetic photons. The radiation is usually in the visible or ultra violet region.

Wilson Cloud Chamber. The paths of ionizing particles in a gas may be made visible by an apparatus called a Wilson Cloud Chamber. An enclosed volume of very clean gas saturated with water vapor is suddenly cooled by expansion, to produce supersaturation. In air containing dust particles, under this condition a fog would be formed, but if the gas is dust-free there is no fog. However, if a beam of radiation is passing through the air in the chamber, the ions will serve as condensation centers for the fog droplets; thus the path of the ionizing particles can be followed. Figure 12, page 45, showed cloud chamber photographs of alpha particles. In Figure 19 are shown tracks of slow and fast beta particles; it will be recalled that specific ionization increases as the particle is slowed down. The cloud tracks due to a beam of photons are actually the tracks of the secondary electrons ejected in Compton and photoelectric interactions. Neutrons, not being themselves ionizing particles, do not leave tracks, but when a neutron interacts with a nucleus, tracks start at the point of interaction and by their characteristics the nature of the interaction may be inferred.

Absorption and Scatter of Radiation. Up to this point in this chapter the discussion has concerned *individual* interactions of specific particles or photons with individual atoms. In general, the interest is in the *gross* effect on the matter which receives energy, and on the radiation beam which loses it.

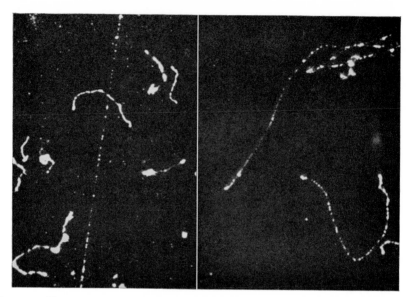

Fig. 19.   Cloud tracks of slow (curved path) and fast (straight path) beta particles.
(Courtesy of C. T. R. Wilson and the Royal Society of London.)

The beam, in traversing matter, tends to become more and more hetero-geneous. This is particularly true with photons, where an initially homo-geneous beam is quickly "contaminated" by Compton and photoelectrons, characteristic x-rays, lower energy scattered x-rays, and (if the original energy was high enough) annihilation radiation. The final result on matter of the absorption of energy is a very slight rise in temperature, although part of the energy may have gone to producing chemical changes, etc.

In addition to absorption of the radiation with utilization of its energy for ionization, part of the rays may be removed from the beam by *scatter*, and so be lost to the detector or to absorbers lying farther along its path. This effect is more marked the larger the beam of radiation impinging on the scattering material, and the smaller the detector. Both absorption and scatter must be considered in studying the interactions of radiation and matter.

Absorption of Beta Radiation.   Absorption is usually studied by measur-ing the radiation transmitted by increasingly thick layers of material, or "filters", and plotting the data as an "absorption curve", as in Figure 20. Semi-logarithmic paper is usually employed, as the decrease is likely to be so rapid at the beginning that a linear plot may be difficult to read. Such curves are usually nearly linear on semi-logarithmic paper. This does not arise from a simple absorption function of mono-energetic particles, but is due to a fortuitous combination of a continuous beta-ray spectrum (see p. 91) and the contribution of scattered radiation to the total activity.

The exact shape of the absorption curve depends on the geometrical arrangements of sample, absorbers, and detector, as well as on the nuclide. The linear part of such an absorption curve as the one in the figure can be represented by the equation

$$A_t = A_o e^{-\mu t}, \qquad 6-(10)$$

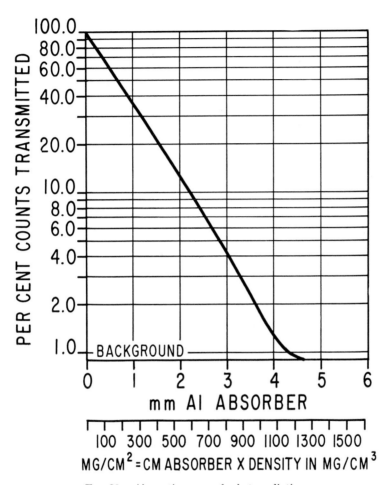

FIG. 20.   Absorption curve for beta radiation.

where A_o is the initial activity and A_t that after passage through a thickness of filter t. μ is the linear absorption coefficient, the rate of absorption per unit thickness of the material.* A half thickness or half value layer bears the same relation to the absorption coefficient as does the half period to the decay constant for a radioactive nuclide;

* The similarity to the isotope decay equation is obvious.

$$t(\tfrac{1}{2}) = \frac{0.693}{\mu}. \qquad\qquad 6\text{—}(11)$$

Frequently, instead of the *linear* absorption coefficient (absorption per unit thickness), the mass absorption coefficient is used (absorption per unit mass). This is μ/ρ, the linear absorption coefficient divided by the density. Filter thickness may be expressed in terms of grams per square centimeter, as shown in the lower legend for abcissa in Figure 20. The gm/cm² is given by multiplying the thickness in cm by the density in gm/cm³. In practice, however, it is often easier to determine it directly by measuring the area of the filter and weighing it; for thin filters of soft and dense metals such as lead, the results are likely to be more accurate. Linear absorption coefficients are usually given in terms of cm⁻¹ (absorption per cm); mass absorption coefficients are specified by cm² gm⁻¹ (cm squared per gram.)*

Table 3a. Ranges of Beta Particles of Various Energies

		Ranges in Various Materials—Mm			
Maximum Energy Mev	*Range mg/cm²*	*Water $\rho = 1$ gm/cm³*	*Lucite $\rho = 1.2$ gm/cm³*	*Aluminum* $\rho = 2.7$ gm/cm³*	*Lead $\rho = 11.3$ gm/cm³*
0.05	4.0	0.04	0.03	0.02	0.004
0.1	13.5	0.14	0.12	0.05	0.012
0.2	40	0.40	0.33	0.15	0.035
0.3	80	0.80	0.67	0.30	0.071
0.5	160	1.6	1.3	0.59	0.14
0.7	210	2.1	1.8	0.78	0.19
1.0	400	4.0	3.3	1.5	0.35
2.5	650	6.5	5.4	2.4	0.58
2.0	950	9.5	7.9	3.5	0.83
2.5	1200	12	10.0	4.4	1.06
3.0	1500	15	12.5	5.5	1.33

* Pyrex glass essentially the same.

It must be remembered that, unlike the curve for radioactive decay, which has no cut-off, these curves come to a definite termination when all the beta particles have been absorbed. Absorption coefficients and half value layers apply only to the region of partial absorption, during which the plot is a straight line on semi-logarithmic paper.

Range of Beta Rays. A value usually desired for beta radiation is the *range*, or the thickness of filter necessary to stop all the particles. In the practical determination of the range, correction must be made for the background (see Chapter 14) and the curve may be complicated by a bremsstrahlung component as in Figure 20. Extrapolation of the linear part of the curve to the background axis gives the range with sufficient accuracy for practical purposes. There is an empiric formula for range of relatively energetic beta rays in mg/cm² of aluminium,

$$R = 0.543 \; E - 0.160, \qquad\qquad 6\text{—}(12)$$

$$* \; \frac{\mu \; \text{cm}^{-1}}{\rho \; \text{gm/cm}^{-3}} = \frac{\mu}{\rho} \; \text{cm}^2\text{gm}^{-1}.$$

where E is maximum beta-particle energy. This is approximately correct for energies greater than 0.5 Mev. On this basis the range of the 1.7 Mev beta particles of P^{32} would be 0.763 gm/cm² or 2.8 mm Al. In the lower energy region there is no good formula. Measurements have been made for various energies. Some published data, especially that of Friedlander and Kennedy, have been used to develop Table 3a.

Scattering of Beta Particles. As a narrow beam of beta particles penetrates matter, some of the particles will be scattered away from the original path. Some of them may undergo very wide angular deflections, so that the path is essentially reversed; this is called *back-scatter*, and introduces

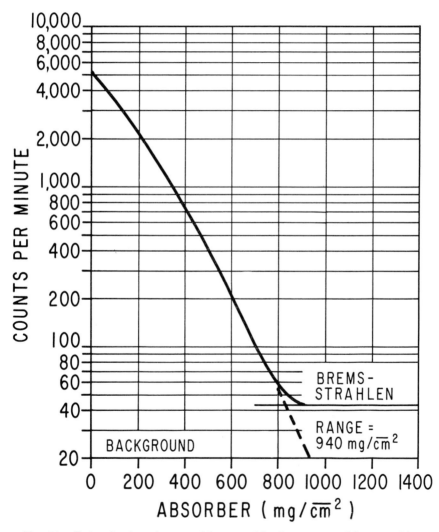

Fig. 21. Determination of range of beta particles in presence of bremsstrahlung component.

6

complications into many isotope measurements. For instance, consider three identical, very thin beta sources, mounted under identical detectors. The first is on a thin film of cellophane, the second on a relatively thin piece of solid material, and the third on a thick piece (Fig. 22). Practically no beta particles will be scattered back from the first source, an appreciable number from the second, and the maximum quantity from the third; thus the three detectors will give different results for the three identical sources.

Back scatter increases with the thickness of the mount, up to about one-third of the maximum range of the particles. After this, most of the scat-

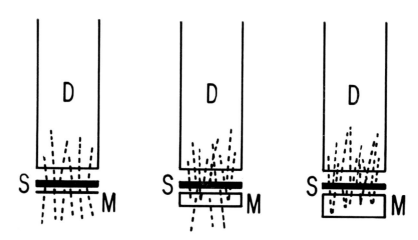

Fig. 22.   Back-scattering of beta particles.   Identical sources and identical detectors;
successively thicker mounts.

tered radiation will be absorbed before it returns to the detector, since the particles seldom travel in straight paths perpendicular to the face of the mount. Back scatter increases relatively rapidly with Z for low atomic numbers, and then more slowly. The effect may be masked by more rapid absorption of the scattered particles within the mount.

Practical aspects of this subject will be discussed in Chapter 15.

Self-Scattering and Self-Absorption of Beta Particles. When a beta-emitting source to be measured has an appreciable thickness, particles emitted from lower layers may be absorbed in upper ones, and particles may be scattered at any level. If sample thicknesses are more than 1 or 2 per cent of the range of the particles, a correction must be made for these effects. Practical methods for carrying this out are also discussed in Chapter 15.

When thicker and thicker samples are prepared from an active material, the counting rate at first increases because of greater total activity, and then becomes constant. This constant or "saturation" value is obviously not a measure of the total activity, but usually is related to that in the upper layer whose thickness is the range of the beta particles in question. It is sometimes easier to prepare all samples of a fixed thickness greater than this range, and make no correction for self-absorption. Thin and thick samples containing the same amounts of radioactive material will of course give different counting rates. Comparison of values for "thin" samples is usually impossible unless each reading is corrected for self-absorption and selfscatter. If "thick" samples are all the same thickness, comparisons based on counting rates are valid.

Absorption (Attenuation)* of Photon Beams. A homogeneous or mono-energetic beam of x- or gamma rays in passing through matter loses energy at a rate which can be described by the exponential equation

$$I_t = I_o e^{-\mu t}, \qquad\qquad 6-(13)$$

where t is the thickness of the sheet of matter and μ the linear absorption coefficient for the particular photon energy in the particular matter. An absorption curve can be obtained in the same manner as for beta rays; it will not exhibit a "range" but will continue indefinitely, as in Figure 23. Half value layer and linear absorption coefficient can be determined from such a curve. As in the case of the beta particle coefficients, the mass

Table 3b. Linear and Mass Absorption Coefficients

Kev	λ	Water, $\rho = 1.0$			Aluminum, $\rho = 2.7$			Lead, $\rho = 11.3$		
	A	μ cm^{-1}	μ/ρ cm^2gm^{-1}	% Trans-mitted by 1 cm	μ cm^{-1}	μ/ρ cm^2gm^{-1}	% Trans-mitted by 1 cm	μ cm^{-1}	μ/ρ cm^2gm^{-1}	% Trans-mitted by 1 cm
20	0.620	0.786	0.786	45	97.8	32.5	—	635	56	--
40	0.310	0.264	0.264	77	12.95	4.80	—	158	14	—
100	0.124	0.168	0.168	84	1.255	0.465	29	63.5	5.62	—
200	0.062	0.137	0.137	87	0.411	0.152	66	11.0	0.97	—
400	0.031	0.106	0.106	90	0.248	0.092	77	2.14	0.19	12
1000	0 012	0.071	0.071	93	0.160	0.059	85	0.68	0.06	51
2000	0.006	0.049	0.049	95	0.113	0.042	88	0.51	0.045	60

absorption coefficient, μ/ρ is frequently employed. In fact, most tabulated data are in terms of mass absorption coefficients, because values for different absorbers for a particular photon energy are more nearly alike. This is demonstrated in Table 3B which gives linear and mass absorption coeffi-cients for a limited number of photon energies for water (or tissue), aluminum and lead. Tabular values are frequently in terms of photon wave length rather than energy; one is readily obtained from the other by the formula

---

* *Attenuation* is generally preferable to *absorption*, because the indicated decrease in the beam includes that due to scatter as well as that due to absorption. However since "absorption" curves and coefficients are more commonly referred to, the custom it followed here.

$\lambda = \dfrac{12.40}{\text{kev}}$, obtained earlier in this chapter. It is also an advantage that

when mass absorption coefficients are used, physical or chemical state, temperature, etc. do not exert important effects.

The absorption coefficient μ/ρ is made up of three parts; the photoelectric (τ/ρ), Compton (σ/ρ), and pair (κ/ρ) (if the energy is sufficiently great).

$$\mu/\rho = \tau/\rho + \sigma/\rho + \kappa/\rho. \qquad\qquad 6-(14)$$

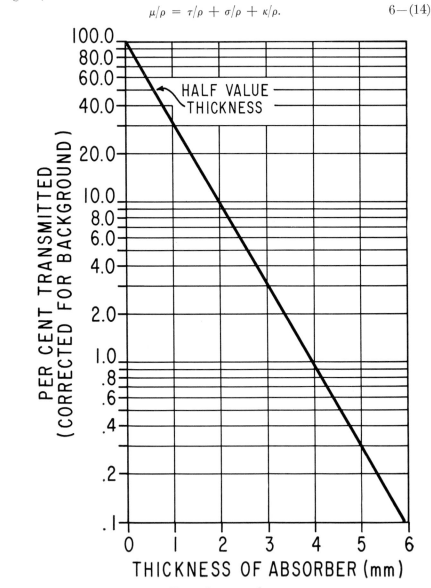

FIG. 23.   Absorption curve for gamma rays.

Photoelectric absorption increases rapidly with increase in atomic number of the absorber, and decreases rapidly with increasing energy of the photon. Approximately $\tau/\rho = k_1 Z^3/E^3$, where k_1 is a constant of proportionality. Compton absorption for any particular energy depends only on the number of electrons present, and therefore is independent of Z since there are essentially the same number of electrons per gram for all substances. It decreases with increasing photon energy. Approximately $\sigma/\rho = k_2/E$. σ/ρ, referring to energy loss by the Compton process, has two components, $(\sigma/\rho)_a$ and $(\sigma/\rho)_s$. The first one is true energy absorption; the second is energy loss from a particular beam by scatter. Only the part defined by $(\sigma/\rho)_a$ is used in producing ionization, although the entire σ/ρ is lost from the beam. Pair formation increases both with increased energy and increased atomic number, so that approximately $\kappa/\rho = k_3 Z E$.

Thus, the total absorption coefficient is an extremely complicated function of the photon energy and the atomic number of the absorber. There are formulae for calculation of the different components, and these or the total coefficients are tabulated in various places.

The curves of Figures 24A and 24B have been constructed from these tabulated coefficients. For water, the photoelectric component vanishes at about 200 kv; pair formation is not significant before 3 Mev. Hence the total attenuation coefficient at any voltage between these two is simply the sum of Compton absorption and Compton scatter coefficients. For lead, on the other hand, photoelectric absorption is appreciable to several Mev; pair formation sets in just about 1 Mev and rapidly becomes important. The total attenuation coefficient is made up of these two plus the two Compton contributions. It is to be noted that μ/ρ goes through a minimum at about 4 Mev and then increases with increasing voltage. This is, of course, due to the large amount of 0.511 Mev annihilation radiation added to the beam as the result of pair production.

The relative importance of the different processes, for various energies and absorbers, is indicated in Table 4.

Table 4. Relative Importance of Different Types of Absorption

Photon Energy	Type of Absorption	
	Water	Lead
Up to 10 kev	τ	τ
10 — 50 kev	$\tau = \sigma$	τ
50 — 100 kev	$\sigma > \tau$	τ
100 — 500 kev	mostly σ	$\tau > \sigma$
500 — 1000 kev	σ	$\sigma > \tau$
1000 — 10,000 kev	$\sigma \gg \kappa$	$\sigma > \kappa$
Higher than 10,000 kev	$\sigma \lessgtr \kappa$	$\kappa \gg \sigma$

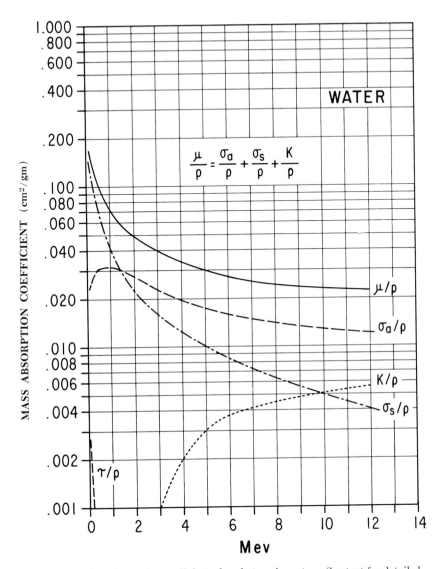

FIG. 24A.   Mass absorption coefficients for photons in water. See text for detailed discussion.

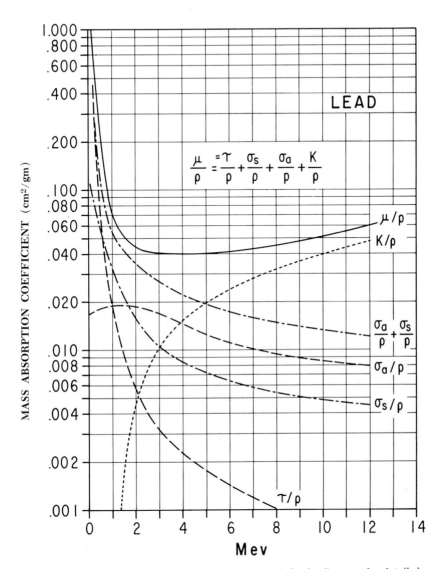

FIG. 24B. Mass absorption coefficients for photons in lead. See text for detailed discussion.

REFERENCES

FRIEDLANDER, G., and KENNEDY, J. W.: *Nuclear and Radiation Chemistry*, Chapters 5, 6 and 7, New York, John Wiley and Sons, 1949 (Revised Version).

GLASSER, O.: *Medical Physics*, Vol. 2. Roentgen Ray Quality (Absorption coefficients, p. 892) Chicago, Year Book Publishers, 1950.

GLASSER, O., QUIMBY, E. H., TAYLOR, L. S., WEATHERWAX, J. L. and MORGAN R. H.: *Physical Foundations of Radiology*, 3rd Ed., Chapter 4, New York, Paul B. 'Hoeber, Inc., 1961.

JOHNS, HAROLD E.: *The Physics of Radiology*, 2nd Ed., Chapters 5 and 6, Springfield, Ill. Charles C Thomas, 1961.

LAPP, R. E. and ANDREWS, H. L.: *Nuclear Radiation Physics*, 2nd Ed., Chapters 8 and 13. New York, Prentice-Hall, 1954.

MORGAN, R. H. and CORRIGAN, K. E.: *Handbook of Radiology*, Sections 2 and 4, Chicago, Yearbook Publishers, Inc., 1955.

RUTHERFORD, E., CHADWICK, J., and ELLIS, C. D.: *Radiations from Radioactive Substances*, Chapter 1, Cambridge, England, University Press, 1951.

7

Sources of the Radiations; Modes of Radioactive Decay

In decay of either naturally or artificially radioactive isotopes, only a very limited number of types of transformation have been observed. The only particles emitted are alphas and negative and positive electrons; any of these may be accompanied by gamma rays, or the gammas may be the only radiation.

Structure of the Nucleus. Much less is known about the actual structure of the nucleus than of the extra-nuclear part of the atom. Bohr, who developed the accepted concept of atomic structure, has proposed a nuclear model. Basing his ideas on assumed characteristics of nuclear forces, and on the fact that only certain ratios of neutrons to protons can exist in stable nuclei, he suggested a "liquid-drop" model. The nucleus may be compared to a small sphere of liquid; as the atoms are uniformly distributed in the drop, so the nucleons are distributed in the nuclear spherical volume. They are in a constant state of motion, but restricted within a very small radius. Thus they make many collisions per second, and all have the same average energy; in a stable nucleus no nucleon will ever accumulate enough energy to escape from the nuclear binding. However, radioactive nuclei have a certain excess of energy, and if a nucleon or group of nucleons can succeed in capturing a sufficent amount of this, it can and will escape. If not all the extra energy is utilized by the escaping particle, the new nucleus may be left in an "excited state," from which it will later recover by emission of a gamma ray, returning to the "ground" or most stable condition of the new nucleus. This may itself, of course, be radioactive.

Alpha Decay. Alpha particles, as has been shown, are helium nuclei, or aggregates of two protons and two neutrons each. Disintegration by alpha emission occurs only among the heavy naturally radioactive nuclides $(Z > 83)$, a few artificially produced ones with either very long or very short periods, of atomic numbers between 60 and 85, and with $_4Be^8$ and $_5B^8$. These two have very short half lives; each atom of the first decays into two alpha particles and of the second into two alphas and a positron. Alpha decay results in a daughter nucleus having atomic number two less and mass number four less than the parent.

Alpha particles from a particular nuclide either all have the same energy

or are emitted in a few mono-energetic groups. In the first case it is assumed that every transition takes place directly to the ground state;
there will then be no accompanying gamma rays. Alpha particles of several
different energies are emitted when the nucleus can be left in different
states of excitation, which will then return to the ground state by gamma
emission. Each gamma ray then represents the difference between the
disintegration energies associated with two alpha particle groups. A cloud
chamber photograph of two groups of alpha particles from Th C and Th C′
was shown in Figure 12, page 45.

Since particular groups of alpha particles are mono-energetic, members
of the group will all travel the same distance, or have the same *range* in
any medium. Alpha particles from different isotopes are emitted at velocities between 8000 and 15,000 miles per second, corresponding to ranges
in air between 2.6 and 8.6 cm. The more rapid the disintegration rate, the
greater is the alpha particle energy, there being an almost linear relation
between the logarithm of the decay constant and the energy in Mev.

Alpha particles have little or no importance in clinical uses of radioactive
isotopes, and will not be studied further at this time.

Beta Decay. Beta decay differs in several basic respects from alpha
decay. The alpha particle is recognized as a group of nucleons, which may
be part of a stable nuclear configuration, but electrons are not tolerated
within the nucleus. Therefore it must be assumed that the electron is
created and ejected. Negative and positive beta particles are believed to
be created by the transformations

$$n \rightarrow p^+ + \beta^-,$$
$$p^+ \rightarrow n + \beta^+.$$

Accordingly, β^- decay would be expected when the neutron-proton ratio
is too high for stability, (see Stability Curve, Figure 5, p. 27) and β^+ decay
when this ratio is too low. Thus β^- emitters would generally be expected
to result from neutron bombardment, and β^+ from proton, although this
is not rigidly adhered to. In general, the farther away from stability, the
more rapid is the disintegration rate. These points may be illustrated by
the radioactive isotopes of iodine, as shown in Table 5.

Positron emission is not as common as negatron; it occurs mainly in
elements of low atomic weight, is not found above atomic number 79, and
only rarely above atomic number 55.

Some nuclei which are close to the stability line may decay in both
ways; in this case the percentage going by each route is constant. For
example, $_{29}Cu^{64}$ lies between the two stable isotopes $_{29}Cu^{63}$ and $_{29}Cu^{65}$.
In 39 per cent of its disintegrations, β^- particles are emitted, in 19 per cent,
β^+. The remaining 42 per cent decay by the process of electron capture
to be described below.

Product nuclei from either β^- or β^+ decay have the same mass numbers as their parents; the β^- daughter has an atomic number one greater, and the β^+ daughter one less than the parent.

Beta particles from a particular isotope are never emitted as a mono-energetic group, as in the case of alphas, nor even in a number of specific energy groups, but always have a continuous energy spectrum, as shown in Figure 25. For each beta-emitting isotope there is a definite *maximum* energy, and all values below this may be observed; the actual shape of the curve varies somewhat from one isotope to another.

Table 5. Isotopes of Iodine

Mass Number	n/p Ratio	Half Period	Radiation
119	66/53	18 min	β^+
120	67/53	30 min	EC*
121	68/53	1.5 hr	β^+, γ
122	69/53	3.5 min	β^+
123	70/53	13.0 hr	EC, γ
124	71/53	4.5 days	EC, β^+, γ
125	72/53	60 days	EC, γ
126	73/53	13 days	β^-, β^+, EC, γ
127	74/53	STABLE	
128	75/53	25 min	EC, β^-, γ
129	76/53	1.72×10^7 years	β^-, γ
130	77/53	12.6 hr	β^-, γ
131	78/53	8.1 days	β^-, γ
132	79/53	2.33 hr	β^-, γ
133	80/53	20.8 hr	β^-, γ
134	81/53	53 min	β^-, γ
135	82/53	6.7 hr	β^-, γ
136	83/53	86 sec	β^-, γ
137	84/53	22 sec	β^-
138	85/53	5.9 sec	β^-
139	86/53	2.7 sec	β^-

* EC—electron capture, see page 92.

The Neutrino. It is not possible to explain this energy distribution on the same sort of decay phenomenon as for the alpha particle, even taking into account the neutron or proton transformation mentioned above. If each beta-decay process releases energy equal to E_{max}, but all values of lower energies are observed, which may be denoted by E_A, there has been a disappearance of energy $E_{max} - E_A$ that is unexplained. Difficulties also arise regarding conservation of momentum. In order to get away from these, Pauli suggested that a new type of particle, the *neutrino*, is involved in beta-decay. This is a fundamental particle of very small mass and electrically neutral. Then the above equation becomes

$$n \rightarrow p^+ + \beta^- + \nu$$
$$p^+ \rightarrow n + \beta^+ + \nu$$

The neutrino carries away the energy indicated by $E_{max} - E_A$, and this may have any value from zero to almost E_{max}. Recent experimental evidence confirms the existence of the neutrino, with rest mass essentially zero.

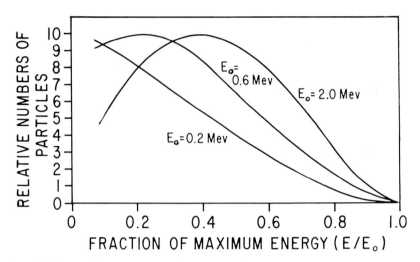

<figure>
FIG. 25. Shapes of beta ray spectra for isotopes of intermediate atomic number. (Courtesy of G. J. Hine, G. L. Brownell, and the Academic Press.)
</figure>

The emission of beta particles may or may not be accompanied by emission of gamma rays. If the electron and the neutrino together utilize all the disintegration energy, there will be no gammas. If the nucleus retains some excess energy, it will be emitted almost immediately as a gamma ray. The interval between beta and gamma emission is usually so short that they appear simultaneous. However the delay is sometimes long enough so that the isomeric state is recognized. (See p. 95.)

Average and Maximum Beta Energy. In dosage calculations it is the average energy of the beta particles that must be used, rather than the maximum, ($\bar{E}_\beta$ rather than E_β max). There is no simple relation between the two.

$\bar{E}_\beta$ can be computed from the β-ray spectrum, but this is a tedious procedure. Figure 26, adapted from Hine and Brownell (Chapter 16) gives the ratio $\bar{E}_\beta/E_\beta(\max)$, for a wide range of values of Z, for β^- emitters. The curve for $Z = -28$ is for positron emitters. A frequently used approximation is that $\bar{E}_\beta$ is about $1/3 E_\beta(\max)$, but from this figure it is seen that the ratio varies from 0.25 to 0.45. Values for $\bar{E}_\beta$ for a number of nuclides are given in the appendix to this book. When accurate data are not available, satisfactory values may be obtained from the figure, interpolating for actual Z's if necessary. For instance, for the 2.25 Mev β of $_{39}Y^{90}$, $\bar{E}_\beta$ would be $0.408 \times 2.25 = 0.92$ Mev, instead of 0.75 Mev as given by the 1/3 rule.

K-electron Capture. An alternative transformation to positron emission is K-electron capture. It will be remembered that the positron results from the transformation of a proton into a neutron, with ejection of a positron and a neutrino. Another way in which a proton can be transformed into a neutron is by nuclear capture of an electron from the inner (K) electron orbit of the atom, and its amalgamation with a nuclear proton; here also the nuclear charge is decreased by unity. Since the atomic number is one less than that of the parent, the new atom will have the correct number of orbital electrons, but there will be one missing in the K-orbit and an extra one in an outer orbit. Readjustment will occur by an outer electron filling the vacancy in the K-orbit, with emission of K-characteristic x-rays of the new atom.

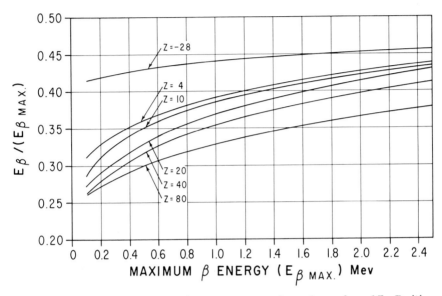

FIG. 26.   Ratio of average to maximum β-ray energy for various values of Z.   Positive values of Z refer to negative β-ray emission, negative values to positron emission. (After Hine and Brownell.)

Gamma Decay.   As already mentioned, radioactive decay involves not only the emission of particles, but sometimes also of energy in the form of radiation.   This results from a decrease in nuclear mass greater than the mass of the ejected particles.   This lost mass is transformed into energy according to the Einstein equation; part of it is used to accelerate the particles.   However, after these have been ejected, there may be residual extra energy in the nucleus, which is then said to be in an excited state.   The nucleus returns to normal by emitting this energy in the form of one or a series of gamma rays.

In general, the emission of gamma rays follows that of the particle in an extremely short time (less than 10^{-9} seconds), so that they appear to be simultaneous.   Gamma ray energies for a specific transformation occur always in the form of one or a few monoenergetic lines, not as a wide spectral range.   In various nuclides, gamma energies have been observed between about 10 kev and 6 Mev.   Typical beta and gamma decay schemes may be indicated as in Figure 27.

Na²⁴ emits a β⁻ particle followed by two γ rays in cascade. There is only one mode of decay; every atom follows the same pattern. Na²² also has a unique pattern, in this case a positron plus one gamma ray. In considering the total positron energy, the annihilation radiation, $2 m_0c^2 = 2 \times 0.511$ Mev must be included. That is, for every 0.575 Mev positron there are two 0.511 Mev new gamma rays to be added.

K⁴² has two types of disintegration. In 75 per cent of the cases, a 3.58 Mev β⁻ particle is released. In the other 25 per cent the β⁻ has only 2.04 Mev and is followed by a 1.53 Mev γ ray, for the same total energy per atom disintegrating.

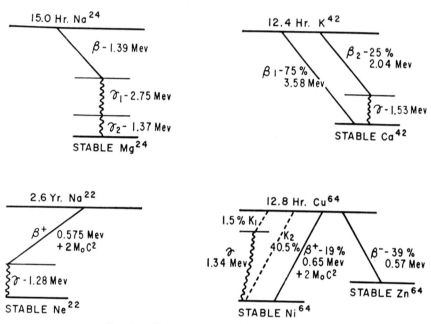

Fig. 27.   Some radioactive decay schemes.

Cu⁶⁴ has a very complicated pattern. It lies almost on the stability line· and can become a stable isobar by either β⁻ or β⁺ decay. Thirty-nine per cent of the atoms go to stable Zn⁶⁴ by β⁻ decay, 19 per cent to Ni⁶⁴ by β⁺ decay, and 42 per cent to Ni⁶⁴ by K-electron capture (which will be recalled as an alternative to β⁺ decay.) In 40.5 per cent of these last disintegrations, the entire disintegration energy (or essentially all) must be carried out by the ejected neutrino. However in 1.5 per cent, the nucleus is left in an excited state and must emit a 1.34 Mev gamma ray to come to stability.

Internal Conversion. When gamma ray energies are relatively low, this type of decay may be accompanied or replaced by internal conversion. This is a sort of intra-atomic photoelectric reaction, where the emitted gamma ray ejects a photoelectron from an orbit of its own atom. The photoelectron is ejected with an energy which is the difference between the gamma ray energy and the binding energy of the electron. For a given disintegration, these will be monoenergetic electrons. If there is also beta-particle emission, the continuous beta spectrum will have superimposed on it the lines of the conversion electrons. There will also of course, be emission of the characteristic radiation of the parent atom when the ejected photo-electron is replaced.

Nuclear Isomers. Sometimes the excited state of a nucleus persists for an appreciable time; it is then said to be *metastable*. The atom in this condition is an *isomer* of the final product nucleus, having the same atomic and mass numbers and only a difference in internal energy. Since in this case the gamma radiation is emitted some time later than the particle, the isomer may appear as a pure gamma-ray emitting isotope. Such atoms are known with half periods from a fraction of a second to several months. The energy may all appear as gamma rays, or part of it may undergo internal conversion, with emission of conversion electrons.

A few such isomers are useful in experimental work, although none is at present employed in clinical practice. It is of interest, however, that the gamma radiation attributed to cesium^{137} (half life 33 years, used in tele-therapy sources) is actually due to a daughter, barium^{137m}, with a 2.6 minute half life, which emits a 0.662 Mev gamma ray and reverts to stable barium^{137}.

Other Modes of Decay. Proton emission has never been observed, al-though it has been carefully looked for. There appear to be strong theoreti-cal reasons for its non-existence.

Neutron emission with appreciable lifetimes has not been observed and is not expected. "Delayed" neutrons are emitted from some highly excited fission products following beta-decay. Half lives are from a fraction of a second to about one minute; they are usually the same as that of the pre-ceeding beta-decay. The phenomenom is of no clinical importance, and is only mentioned for completeness of the picture.

Spontaneous fission sometimes occurs in some of the heaviest natural and artificial nuclides; it is very much less common than the normal alpha or beta reaction. For instance, U^{235} emits alpha particles and has a half life of 7.1×10^8 years. It also occasionally undergoes spontaneous fission, but at such a rate that if this were the only mode of decay, the half life would be 1.9×10^{17} years.

Isotope Charts. Various charts have been developed for giving informa-tion about stable and radioactive isotopes of the elements. A popular type is in a sense an amplification of the stability curve shown in Figure 5. A sketch of a portion of such a chart is given in Figure 28. Z, the number of protons, is plotted along the vertical axis, and N, the number of neutrons, along the horizontal.* Stable nuclei are indicated as open squares, bearing

---

* The coordinates are reversed for those of Figure 5 because available commercial charts use the scheme of Figure 28. These commercial charts carry in each square decay data, abundances, etc., for the particular nuclide.

the chemical symbol of the element; radioactive nuclei are indicated by dots. Isotopes (nuclides with the same Z) obviously must appear along horizontal lines, and isobars (same $Z + N$) will be found on the diagonals. In general nuclides to the left of stable ones decay with β^+ emission or electron capture, since they have too few neutrons and must make one out of a proton. Those to the right of stable ones decay with β^- emission, since they have too few protons, and must make one out of a neutron.

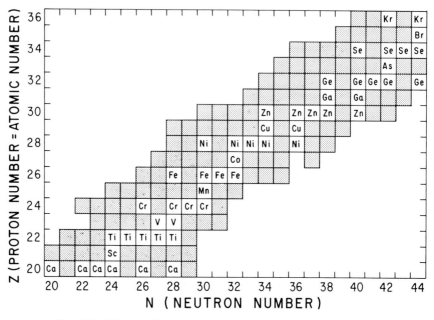

Fig. 28.   Diagram illustrating part of one type of isotope chart.

Radioactive Series.   All the alpha-emitting heavy nuclides occurring in nature, and those which have been artificially produced, fall into four decay series, headed respectively by uranium, thorium, actinium, and neptunium. The uranium series is shown in Figure 29, with the beta and gamma transformations and half periods indicated. The final product, indicated as Ra G, is an isotope of lead, $_{81}Pb^{206}$. The parent element of each series must have a very long half life, otherwise there would be none remaining on earth; it would all have decayed since its creation, and its shorter-lived descendants would have also. It is probably because neptunium has a half life of only two million years that it is not found in nature. (The age of the earth is at least 1000 times this, so that if there had originally been any created, the amount left now would be undetectable.) Any members later than a long-lived first ancestor will always exist, no matter how short their half lives, because the supply will be continually replenished.

With the discovery of nuclear fission a large number of beta-decay series were observed among the fission products, as mentioned in Chapter 5. Since here the half periods of the parents are very short, continued existence of the daughters is not assured.

Radioactive Equilibrium. In Chapter 2, disintegration rules for radioactive nuclei were outlined. There the only radioactivity corresponded to the transformation of a single isotope. However, the daughter substance may in turn be radioactive, and so on. Relations among quantities present of different members of the series depend on the various decay constants.

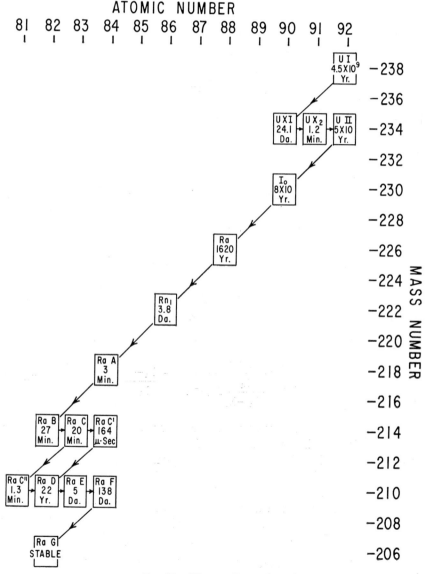

FIG. 29. The uranium series.

According to the simple law of radioactive decay for a single isotope, if there are present N_1 atoms of a particular nuclide, whose decay constant is λ_1,

$$- \frac{dN_1}{dt} = \lambda_1 N_1, \qquad\qquad 7-(1)$$

and

$$N_1 = N_1^o e^{-\lambda_1 t}, \qquad\qquad 7-(2)$$

where N_1^o represents the original number of atoms of this element at time $t = 0$. The number of atoms of the daughter substance is represented by N_2, and if this is radioactive, its decay constant is λ_2. Every atom of N_1 which decays becomes an atom of N_2, and this in turn decays with its own rate. Therefore

$$\frac{dN_2}{dt} = \lambda_1 N_1 - \lambda_2 N_2, \qquad\qquad 7-(3)$$

the first term representing the growth from the parent and the second the decay of the daughter. Mathematical development of this equation leads to*

$$N_2 = \frac{\lambda_1}{\lambda_2 - \lambda_1} N_1^o (e^{-\lambda_1 t} - e^{-\lambda_2 t}) + N_2^o e^{-\lambda_2 t}. \qquad 7-(4)$$

Here again the first term shows net growth of the daughter from parent atoms, and the second the contribution from any daughter atoms initially present. For products resulting from an initally pure parent fraction, the second term is zero.

In considering special parent-daughter relationships, two cases are evident, depending on whether the parent or the daughter is longer-lived. In the first case λ_1 is less than λ_2, and after a sufficiently long time $e^{-\lambda_1 t}$ is so much larger than $e^{-\lambda_2 t}$ that the latter can be neglected. Then

$$\frac{N_1}{N_2} = \frac{N_1^o e^{-\lambda_1 t}}{\dfrac{\lambda_1}{\lambda_2 - \lambda_1} N_1^o e^{-\lambda_1 t}} = \frac{\lambda_2 - \lambda_1}{\lambda_1}, \qquad 7-(5)$$

or the ratio of the amounts of the two elements becomes constant. They are then said to be in a state of *equilibrium*.

Consider a radioactive parent with half period 10 days, and a daughter with half period 1 day. Then the decay constant for the parent, λ_1, $= 0.0693$ per day, and that for the daughter, $\lambda_2 = 0.693$. The numbers of atoms of the two nuclides present at any time, N_1 and N_2, may be calculated from formulae 7—(2) and 7—(4). If the parent is initially free from any of the daughter then $N_2 = 0$, and the second term of 7—(4) disappears. Figure

---

* Steps in the development are omitted here. They may be found in various texts. Vide Friedlander and Kennedy, pp. 129–130.

$30A$ shows the relative quantities of the two over a period of a month. After an initial increase, N_2 reaches a maximum, and then decreases at the same rate as N_1.

The ratio of the two [(formula 7—(5)], $\dfrac{N_1}{N_2} = \dfrac{\lambda_2-\lambda_1}{\lambda_1} = 7.55.$ Here both parent and daughter have relatively short lives, and the equilibrium is said to be *transient*.

Equilibrium curves are frequently plotted to show the *activities*, or numbers of atoms disintegrating, rather than the total number present. The activity is in each case, of course, the number of atoms present multiplied by the decay constant, so $A_1 = N_1\lambda_1$ and $A_2 = N_2\lambda_2$. If the data of Figure $30A$ are treated in this way, the curves of Figure $30B$ are obtained. For every 1000 atoms of the parent initially present, the curves show the numbers of each nuclide decaying at any instant, and the total number of disintegrations at that time. Decrease in total quantity of each nuclide is at the rate of λ_1, characteristic of the parent.

Since the number of millicuries present is determined by the number of atoms disintegrating rather than by the number present, it appears from Figure $30B$ that at transient equilibrium the number of millicuries of the daughter is greater than that of the parent. It is seen from formulae 7—(1) and 7—(5) that this should be so.

$$A_1 = \lambda_1 N_1 \text{ and}$$

$$A_2 = \lambda_2 N_2 = \lambda_2 \frac{\lambda_1}{\lambda_2-\lambda_1} N_1 = \frac{\lambda_2}{\lambda_2-\lambda_1} \lambda_1 N_1.$$

Since $\dfrac{\lambda_2}{\lambda_2-\lambda_1}$ is greater than unity for transient equilibrium, A_2 is always greater than A_1, or the daughter millicuries are greater than those of the parent.

If the half life of the parent is very much longer than that of the daughter so that it does not decay appreciably over the period of study, the situation is shown in Figure 31, the equilibrium being called *secular*. In this case λ_2 is very much greater than λ_1, so that $\lambda_2-\lambda_1$ is essentially equal to λ_2. Then

$$A_1 = \lambda_1 N_1 \text{ and } A_2 = \lambda_2 N_2 = \frac{\lambda_2\lambda_1}{\lambda_2-\lambda_1} N_1 = \lambda_1 N_1. \text{ Thus the two activities}$$

are equal; the same numbers of atoms of both are present after equilibrium has been attained. This may be illustrated by the growth of radon ($T_2 = 3.8$ days) in an initially pure preparation of radium ($T_1 = 1620$ years, $= 267000$ days.

$\lambda_1 = 2.6 \times 10^{-6}$, $\lambda_2 = 0.18$. $\lambda_2-\lambda_1$ is essentially $= \lambda_2$ whence $\dfrac{\lambda_2-\lambda_1}{\lambda_2} = 1$ and $A_2 = A_1$.

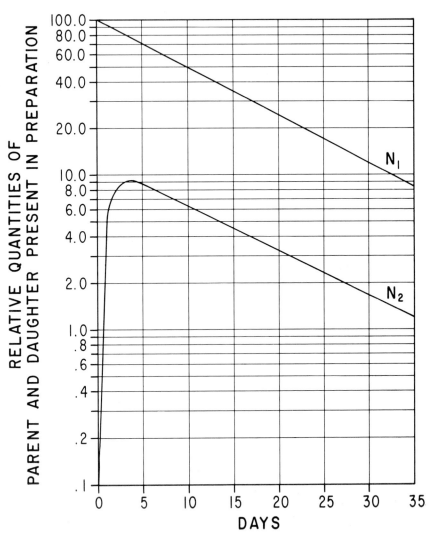

Fɪɢ. 30A.   Transient radioactive equilibrium, N_1, decay of parent, initially pure; N_2, growth and decay of daughter.

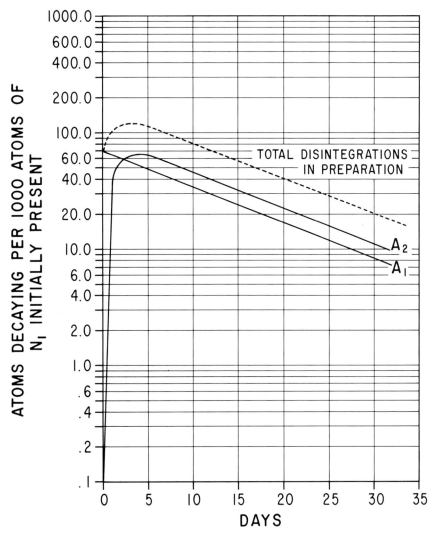

Fig. 30*B*.   Transient radioactive equilibrium.   A₁, activity of partent, A₂, activity of
daughter, dotted line, combined activities (total activity of preparation.)

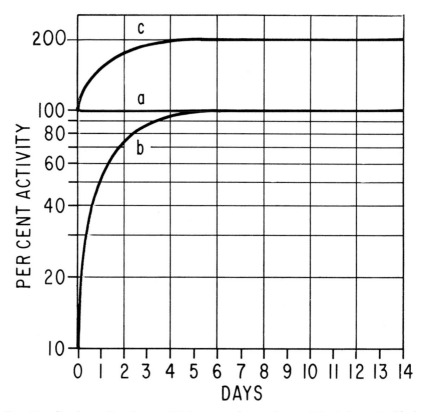

Fɪɢ. 31. Secular radioactive equilibrium. *a*, decay of parent (not demonstrable in period of observation); *b*, growth and decay of daughter; *c*, total activity in preparation of initially pure parent.

Of course, if the life of the daughter is longer than that of the parent, there is no equilibrium.

Growth of Radionuclide in Neutron Flux. The production of a radioactive substance by any steady bombardment source may be considered analogous to the growth of a short-lived daughter in an infinitely long-lived parent. Thus, the time necessary for a target to be bombarded in a pile or cyclotron, to produce a desired activity, can be determined. In this case $-\lambda_1 N_o$, the rate of destruction of the parent is the rate of production of the radioactive daughter, and may therefore be replaced by R. Since $\lambda_1 N_o$ is an extremely small fraction of the stable atoms of the target, $e^{-\lambda_1 t}$ is essentially unity. Furthermore λ_1 is very much smaller than λ_2, the decay rate of the product, whence $\lambda_2 - \lambda_1$ is essentially $= \lambda_2$. Then equation 7—(4) becomes

$$N_2 = \frac{R}{\lambda_2} (1 - e^{-\lambda_2 t}).$$ 7—(6)

If t becomes very long, $e^{-\lambda_2 t}$ becomes very small, and N_2 approaches $\dfrac{R}{\lambda_2}$ as a limiting value, the maximum amount of the daughter isotope that could ever be produced. The ratio of N_2 at any time to N_2 at maximum is

$$\frac{N_2}{N_{2(max)}} = \frac{\dfrac{R}{\lambda_2}(1-e^{-\lambda_2 t})}{\dfrac{R}{\lambda_2}} = 1-e^{-\lambda_2 t} \qquad\qquad 7-(7)$$

Thus, if t is one half period, $1-e^{-\lambda_2 t} = 0.5$, or half the maximum amount can be produced in a bombardment of one half period. Similarly three fourths of the maximum are produced in two half periods, and so on. In practice it is seldom economical to irradiate for more than two half lives of the product.

In Chapter 4, page 55, an example was given of the production of Au^{198} by slow neutron bombardment of Au^{197}. The above formulae were used in the calculation of the quantity of Au^{198} produced. Of course the process may be complicated by neutron bombardment of the first radioactive nuclide to form a second. Details of calculations in such cases are outside the scope of this book.

REFERENCES

HINE, G. J. and BROWNELL, G. L.: *Radiation Dosimetry*, Chapter 2, and 16, New York Academic Press, 1956.

FRIEDLANDER, G. and Kennedy, J. W.: *Nuclear and Radiochemistry*, Chapter 7, New York, John Wiley and Sons, 1949, (Revised Version).

GLASSER, O., QUIMBY, E. H., TAYLOR, L. S., WEATHERWAX, J. L. and MORGAN, R. H.: *Physical Foundations of Radiology*, 3rd Ed., Chapter 4, New York, Paul B. Hoeber, Inc., 1961.

General Electric Chart of the Nuclides, Knolls Atomic Power Laboratory, Schenectady, New York, 1956.

MORGAN, R. H. and CORRIGAN, K. E.: *Handbook of Radiology*, Section 4, Chicago, Yearbook Publishers, Inc., 1955.

Nuclear Research Center, Karlsruhe, Chart of the Nuclides, revised to 1961. Gersbach und Sohn Verlag, Munich, Germany.

POLLARD, E. C. and DAVIDSON, W. L.: *Applied Nuclear Physics*, 2nd Ed., Chapters 5 and 6, New York, John Wiley and Sons, 1951.

RUTHERFORD, E., CHADWICK, J. and ELLIS, C. D.: *Radiations from Radioactive Substances.* Chapters 3, 7, 8, 9, 14, 15, Cambridge, England. University Press, 1951.

SULLIVAN, WM. H.: *Trilinear Chart of Nuclides.* Oak Ridge, National Laboratory, 1957. (Obtained from Superintendent of Documents, United States Government Printing Office, Washington, D. C.)

8

Dosage Calculations for Radioactive
Isotopes

RADIOACTIVE isotopes may be employed as sources for external irradiation, in which case they are encapsulated or in some way controlled as to position, or they may be administered to an individual for internal irradiation, when, in general, control is lost; the material is distributed more or less uniformly throughout the organism. Sources may be used primarily for beta or for gamma irradiation. It must be remembered that every positron emitter has also two 0.51 Mev photons per disintegration, which must be considered in any dosage problem.

External (Controlled) Sources. External sources may be employed for α-, β-, or γ-irradiation. In these cases the radioactive material is confined either on a plaque or in a volume, in a known distribution.

For particle radiation the dose unit is the *rad*, which is 100 ergs absorbed per gram of the absorbing material. It is equivalent to the absorption of 6.24×10^7 Mev per gram. For photon radiation the exposure dose unit is the roentgen, which is related to ionization in air. These units and the relation between them will be discussed in detail in following sections. Dose rates from radioactive sources can be measured with suitable instruments, or can be calculated, when certain basic data about the nuclides are available.

External Alpha-Particle Sources. Since α particles have ranges in tissue of the order of 0.1 mm or less, such sources would have very limited biological or chemical applications. Loevinger (1) has measured surface emission from polonium plaques with an ionization chamber, and has studied the effects of these radiations on human skin. His source, a 1-cm disc of nickle on which 15 mc of polonium had been deposited, was covered with a gold plating approximately 1 micron thick, to reduce "creeping" of polonium from the nickle, and was further covered with a Mylar film of 0.9 mg/cm². The dose rate at the surface of the Mylar, measured with a suitable ionization chamber, was approximately 20,000 rads per minute per mc. The range of the polonium α particles was about 3.5 mg/cm², or about 35 microns. The more penetrating α particles of thorium X have a range about twice as great, but they are always contaminated by the β and γ radiation from later members of the thorium series. Alpha irradiation from external sources is of little clinical importance and dosage considerations will not be carried further.

External Beta Particle Sources. Controlled beta sources are usually either flat plaques for surface irradiation, or tiny seeds or grains for implantation. In the case of the flat applicator, its face is placed in contact either with the lesion itself, or with the tissues immediately over it. The dose delivered at a particular level below the source depends on the nuclide, the thickness of the source, and the thickness of the tissue layer.

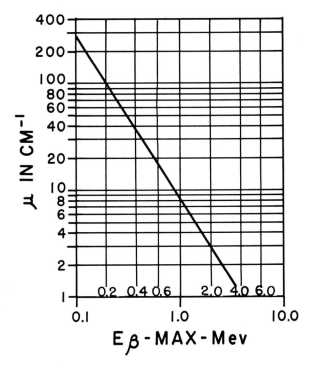

Fig. 32. Average absorption coefficient for beta rays in tissue, as a function of maximum beta energy. (Courtesy of H. H. Rossi, R. H. Ellis, Jr., and the American Roentgen Ray Society.)*

There is no simple and general method of calculating beta ray dose from such external applicators. Rossi and Ellis[2] have developed some charts which can be used without the necessity of extensive mathematical calculation, and these will be presented here. Their basic assumption is that the average absorption coefficient for beta rays in tissue is a function of the *maximum* beta energy; the relation is given in Figure 32. From this the absorption coefficient may be read for any beta energy. Now for flat sources, a general set of curves is prepared, shown in Figure 33, in which

*This curve does not agree with Figure 7, Chapter 16, of Radiation Dosimetry, by Hine and Brownell, since this is based on infinite plane sources and theirs on point sources. Using Hine and Brownell figures and formulæ, the same results will be obtained as using Rossi's, but it is not possible to use charts or formulæ interchangeably.

one coordinate is the distance in tissue from the beta source, multiplied by the absorption coefficient, and the other is the rads* per minute divided by the product of the *average* energy of the radiation, $\bar{E}_\beta$, and the concentration of the isotope in millicuries per cubic centimeter of applicator. The parameter of the set of curves is the thickness of the source multiplied

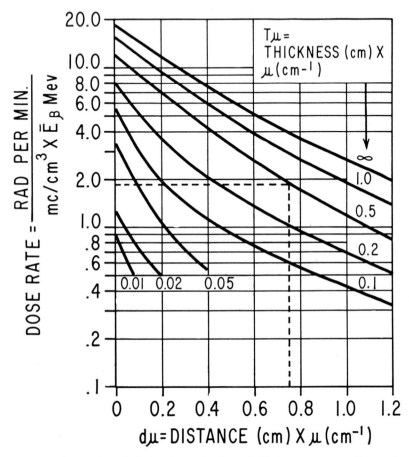

Fig. 33.   Curves for calculating dose rates from flat beta ray sources. For explanation, see text. (Courtesy of H. H. Rossi, R. H. Ellis, Jr., and the American Roentgen Ray Society.)

by the absorption coefficient. This complicated-sounding chart makes dosage determination relatively simple, once the relevant constants have been established.

For example, consider a flat applicator of 1.25 mm thickness which contains P[32] at a concentration of 2 mc per cu cm in a plastic medium of approximately unit density. It is desired to find the dose rate at a depth

* Rossi's published curves are based on dosage in "equivalent roentgens." This unit is now obsolete, and his data have been re-calculated to give doses in rads in accordance with present conventions as used throughout this chapter.

of 2 mm in tissue. For P^{32}, $E_\beta(max)$ is 1.7 Mev, and $\overline{E}_\beta$ is 0.70 Mev (See Appendix, p. 325). From Figure 32, for energy 1.7 Mev, μ is 3.8* per cm. The thickness, t, of the applicator is 0.125 cm and the depth d is 0.2 cm. Therefore $t\mu = 0.5$ and $d\mu = 0.76$. The curve for $t\mu = 0.5$ will therefore give the dose rate. For an abcissa of 0.75, the ordinate for this curve is 1.85. This number, multiplied by the concentration and by $\overline{E}_\beta$ gives $1.85 \times 2 \times 0.70 = 2.6$ rads per minute at this depth. One millimeter closer to the surface the value is 6.1 rads per minute, and at the surface it is 17. These curves are adequate for determining dose rate in tissue beneath radioactive slabs, as long as the diameter of the slab is a few times the tissue depth under consideration.

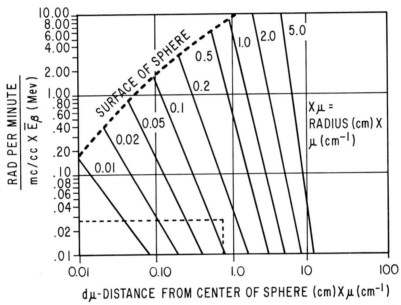

FIG. 34. Curves for calculating beta dose rates from small spheres. For explanation, see text. (Courtesy of H. H. Rossi, R. H. Ellis, Jr., and the American Roentgen Ray Society.)

For small implants, an approximation may be made on the basis of spheres. The curves of Figure 34, plotted in the same coordinates as Figure 33, give the dose rates. For example, find the dose rate 3 mm. from the center of an yttrium-90 pellet 1 mm. in diameter and containing 250 μc of the isotope The volume of the pellet is 5.25×10^{-4} cubic centimeters, and the concentration is $\dfrac{250 \times 10^{-3}}{525 \times 10^{-6}} = 475$ mc per cu cm. For Y^{90},

$E_\beta(max)$ is 2.24 Mev and $\overline{E}_\beta$ is 0.93 Mev. From Figure 32, $\mu = 2.4$ cm^{-1}. The radius of the pellet is 0.05 cm and the distance d is 0.3 cm. Therefore

*From the curve it is not possible to read μ so accurately; $\mu = 4$ would be obtained. The value 3.8 is used because this is the value used for Figure 33.

$x\mu = 0.12$ and $d\mu = 0.72$. The dose rate will be found for the abcissa 0.72, one-fifth of the way between the $x\mu$ curves 0.1 and 0.2. The reading for the 0.1 curve is 0.012, and for the 0.2 curve, 0.084. Therefore for 0.12 it would be 0.026. This, multiplied by the concentration and by $\overline{E}_\beta$ gives $0.026 \times 475 \times 0.93 = 11.5$ rads per minute. The rads delivered at this distance in the total life of the pellet will be 11.5 times the average life of the isotope in minutes. The half life of Y^{90} is 65 hours. Therefore the total D_β at the distance in question is $11.5 \times 65 \times 60 \times 1.443 = 65000$ rads. One millimeter farther out the dose would be 8 rads per minute.

The dosage problem for external beta ray sources is not a very important one in practice, and more detailed consideration does not seem warranted here.

External Gamma Ray Sources.   Gamma ray exposure doses are specified in roentgens at the present time. One roentgen is defined as "that quantity of x-or gamma radiation such that the associated corpuscular emission per 0.001293 grams of air, produces, in air, ions carrying 1 esu of quantity of electricity of either sign." The associated corpuscular emission consists of the Compton and photoelectrons liberated by the photons in their passage through matter. The passage of one roentgen of radiation will result in the production of 2.083×10^9 ion pairs per cubic centimeter of air under standard conditions. The energy absorption in tissue for one roentgen of fairly high energy photons is essentially equivalent to one rad. This relation will be discussed later in connection with addition of beta and gamma ray doses.

The basic value for calculation of gamma ray dosage from any encapsulated source is the dose rate in roentgens per hour at a distance of one centimeter in air from a point source of one millicurie. This is variously designated by I_γ, Γ, and K. However, I_γ might be expected to have a connotation of intensity, and K is already used for other purposes in physics. Accordingly the symbol Γ (capital Greek gamma) is becoming generally accepted, and will be used here. The value of this constant may be determined experimentally if the disintegration *rate* is known. If the disintegration *scheme* is known, Γ may be calculated from known physical constants.[3,4]

Consider a nuclide which emits one gamma ray of energy E_γ Mev per disintegration. In one hour the energy emitted by 1 mc is $3.7 \times 10^7 \times 3600 \times E_\gamma$ Mev, and the flux per sq cm at a distance of 1 cm from the point source of 1 mc is

$$F = \frac{3.7 \times 10^7 \times 3600 \times E_\gamma \times 10^6}{4\pi} \text{ ev per sq cm per hr} \qquad 8\text{—}(1)$$

This energy will be absorbed in air according to the true linear absorption coefficient μ_a. That absorbed in a unit area of a thin shell (thickness dr) at 1 cm from the point is $F\mu_a$ dr. This absorbed energy produces ions. W, the energy required to produce an ion pair, is approximately 34 electron volts, and N, the number of ion pairs per roentgen is 2.083×10^9 per cubic centimeter of air.   Whence

$$\Gamma = \frac{F\ \mu_a dr}{NW \times 4\pi dr} = \frac{3.7 \times 10^7 \times 3600 \times E_\gamma \times 10^6 \times \mu_a \times dr}{4 \times 3.1416 \times 34 \times 2.083 \times 10^9 \times dr}$$

$$= 1.5 \times 10^5\ E_\gamma \mu_a \text{ roentgens per mc-hr at 1 cm.}$$

$$8\text{—}(2)$$

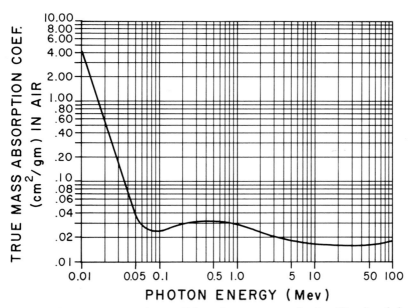

FIG. 35.   True mass absorption coefficients for gamma rays in air.   (Density of air = 0.001293 gm per cu cm).   (Courtesy of G. J. Hine, G. L. Brownell, and the Academic Press.)

For the calculation of Γ it is necessary to know the *true* absorption coefficient.   Coefficients usually tabulated are for $\mu = \tau + \sigma_a + \sigma_s + \kappa$; for these calculations σ_s must be eliminated.   Radiation corresponding to this factor is removed from the beam by scatter but is not utilized for the production of ions.   Values for the true mass absorption coefficients for photons of various energies in air are shown in Figure 35.   The true linear absorption coefficient can be obtained by multiplying values from this curve by the density of air, 0.001293 gm per cu cm.

If a nuclide emits more than one gamma ray, a similar calculation can be made for each one, and the sum taken.   If gamma rays are emitted only in a fraction of the disintegrations, this can be allowed for.   For example, Co^{60} emits two gamma rays per disintegration, of energies 1.173 and 1.332 Mev.   The values of μ are essentially the same for the two, 0.34×10^{-4} per cm.   Then $\Gamma = 1.5 \times 10^5 \times (1.173 + 1.333) \times 0.34 \times 10^{-4} = 12.8\ r^*$ per

*The value 12.9 given in Appendix C, results from using three significant figures in the value for μ; 12.8 however is generally used at present.

mc-hr at 1 cm. Values of Γ are tabulated in the appendix for most nuclides used in medicine. A curve to facilitate calculation of other Γ's is given in Figure 36.[3] Here are plotted values of Γ for one gamma ray of the indicated energy per disintegration. If several gammas are emitted, the partial values can be obtained here and added. Thus for the two gamma rays of Co^{60}, the contributions are 6.1 and 6.7 or a total of 12.8 r per mc-hr at 1 cm.

The dose rate at any practical distance from a gamma ray emitting point source in air can be obtained by means of the inverse square law. For a source of N mc at a distance of d cm the dose rate is $\dfrac{N\Gamma}{d^2}$ r per hour.

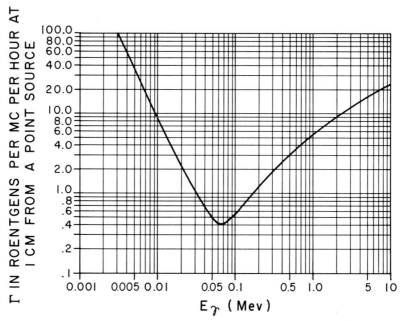

Fig. 36.   Gamma ray dose rate in roentgens per millicurie-hour at one centimeter from a point source.

For extended sources the inverse square law will not be followed. Furthermore, if the source contains a considerable quantity of radioactive material, such as the large Co^{60} units used in therapy, there will be appreciable self-absorption and each individual installation must be studied by means of ionization chambers. For smaller sources (tubes or plaques) dose rates at various places can be found by considering the source as a close array of point sources of small activity, and integrating to obtain the total dose at the point in question. Due allowance must be made for filtration by container walls, which varies with the obliquity of the path of the rays through them. This procedure has been carried out for a wide range of radium sources and the results are available in various texts. It does not seem desirable to reproduce them here.

Besides radium, at the present time radioactive cobalt, gold, and iridium are being employed in small sources used in body cavities or implanted directly into tissues. The radiations from Co^{60} have nearly enough the same average energy as radium so that the same dosage tables can be used, with the correction factor in the ratio of the Γ's, $\dfrac{12.8}{8.4}$, for the dose delivered per mc-hr. Radiations from Au^{198} and Ir^{192} are less penetrating, but still within the energy range in which this type of approximation should be satisfactory.

Radioactive Nuclides Administered Internally (Out of Control). Nuclides may be ingested or injected intravenously in soluble form; they may also be instilled into cavities in the form of colloidal suspensions. These colloidal suspensions may also be injected directly into solid tissues, with the hope that they will not diffuse away, and into vascular or lymphatic systems in the hope that they will drain into a particular organ or region. In any of these cases, they will be deposited with a degree of non-uniformity; measurements by means of external instruments are usually impracticable or unsatisfactory and calculations of the types used for fixed sources are not applicable. However when the physical factors of half life and radiation energy, and some physiological factors of uptake and excretion are known, it is frequently possible to make satisfactory estimates of tissue dosage. The approach is different for particle and photon emitters.

Alpha-Emitting Nuclides in the Body. Since the range of the α particles from available nuclides does not exceed about 70 microns in tissue, for uniform irradiation within a mass the radioactive atoms would have to be distributed uniformly with spacings of this magnitude. All of the energy carried by the α-particles will be absorbed almost exactly where it is emitted.

One μc emits 3.7×10^4 particles per second. For a concentration of C μc per gram, of an α-emitter whose particles have an energy of E Mev, the total energy released and absorbed per second per gram is $3.7 \times 10^4 \times$ E $\times$ C Mev, and since 1 rad is equal to 6.24×10^7 Mev absorbed

$$d_\alpha/\text{sec} = \frac{3.7 \times 10^4 \text{ E C}}{6.24 \times 10^7} = 5.92 \times 10^{-4} \text{ E C rad.} \qquad 8\text{---}(3)$$

For doses in longer periods the same line of reasoning will be followed as for β-doses in the next section.

However in the case of α-doses another factor must be taken into account, the relative biological effect. It has been found that the biological effectiveness of a particular radiation may depend not only on the energy absorbed from it, but on the distribution of the ions in the material. For many biological reactions, heavy charged particles are more efficient than electrons or photons. In order to take this into account, a dose unit has been developed, the *rem*, the quantity of any ionizing radiation which has the same biological effect as 1 rad of medium voltage x-rays. The dose in rems is the dose in rads multiplied by the relative biological effectiveness (RBE). For certain reactions α particles are about four times as effective as β's, whence the dose in rems, *for these reactions*, would be four times the dose in rads. The whole concept of RBE is rather inexact, and doses in rems are accordingly approximate. (Further discussion of this subject will be found in Chapter 9.)

The greatest interest in internal α-dosimetry lies not in masses of appreciable size, but rather in the fact that most α-emitters (radium, plutonium) are bone-seekers, and that soft tissue immediately adjacent to, or enclosed in the bone may receive a considerable dose. The problem has been considered in some detail by Hoecker (5) and by Spiers (6). Spiers bases his calculations on the experimental observation that when radium is deposited in the bone, about half the radon escapes via the blood. He can then determine the number of α particles per cubic micron deposited by the radium and its decay products, and hence the dosage in bone, based on uniform distribution of the radioactive material in the bone. He extends his calculations to very small cavities of various sizes in the bone, and develops the formula

$$\text{Dose rate} = 34 \times 10^3 \text{ N } \overline{\text{F}} \text{ rads/day*} \qquad\qquad 8\text{---}(4)$$

where N is the number of α particles per cubic micron per day, and $\overline{\text{F}}$ is a factor depending on cavity size, which he tabulates.

When it is possible to obtain a bone section and make autoradiographs, as in the work of Hoecker and Roofe, the actual distribution of the α-tracks in the medium can be studied. They found numerous microscopic localizatons of about the same radium density, but the frequency of the localizations varied greatly from one bone to another. Obviously the assumption of uniform distribution of the radioactive material is useful only as a first approximation.

Beta-Emitting Nuclide in the Bodys. When a radioisotope emits only beta rays, the dose is essentially confined to the region containing the material, at least in most human organs. The range of these particles in tissue is generally only a few millimeters, and most human organs are large in comparison. This, however, is not true for organs in small animals used in experiments with nuclides emitting high energy beta particles. Proper estimate of correction factors in these cases is difficult, but some discussion of the problem will be given later.

Consider a beta-emitting nuclide uniformly distributed throughout a volume large in relation to the range of the beta particles, with a concentration of C μc per gram. Then, since 1 μc produces 3.7×10^4 disintegrations per second, except for a rim close to the boundary, the energy released and absorbed per gram of tissue per second is $3.7 \times 10^4 \, \overline{\text{E}}_\beta$ C Mev, where $\overline{\text{E}}_\beta$ is the *average* beta ray energy per disintegration in

---

*In the published paper dose rates are given in "reps," one rep being 83×10^{-12} ergs per cubic micron. A rad is 100×10^{-12} ergs per cubic micron of unit density material.

Mev. Now it will be remembered that one rad is equivalent to 6.24×10^7 Mev absorbed per gram, whence

$$d_\beta \text{ (sec)} = \frac{3.7 \times 10^4 \times \overline{E}_\beta \, C}{6.24 \times 10^7} = 5.92 \times 10^{-4} \, C \, \overline{E}_\beta \text{ rad.} \qquad 8-(5)$$

and
$$d_\beta \text{ (min)} = 3.55 \times 10^{-2} \, C \, \overline{E}_\beta \text{ rad.} \qquad 8-(6)$$

For half lives longer than about 20 hours, decay is slow enough so that

$$d_\beta \text{ (hr)} = 60 \times d_\beta \text{ (min)} = 2.13 \, C \, \overline{E}_\beta \text{ rads,} \qquad 8-(7)$$

and for half lives longer than about 20 days

$$d_\beta \text{ (day)} = 51.2 \, C \, \overline{E}_\beta \text{ rads.} \qquad 8-(8)$$

For complete decay of the nuclide, the total dose is given by the dose per minute multiplied by the average life in minutes. The average life is 1.443 times the half life; the latter is usually tabulated in days. Therefore

$$D_\beta = d_\beta \text{ (min)} \times T \text{ (days)} \times 1440 \text{ (min per day)} \times 1.443$$
$$= 73.8 \, C \, \overline{E}_\beta \, T* \text{ rads.} \qquad 8-(9)$$

The part of the dose delivered in any time can be found by use of the decay equations of Chapter 2. If the amount of the nuclide remaining at any time t is $Q_t = Q_o e^{-\lambda t}$, the amount used up is $Q_o - Q_t = Q_o(1 - e^{-\lambda t})$, and the part of the dose delivered in time t is

$$D_\beta \text{ (t)} = D_\beta \, (1 - e^{-\lambda t}), \qquad 8-(10)$$

or, using the substitute notation of equation 2—(9)

$$D_\beta \text{ (t)} = D_\beta \left(1 - \frac{1}{2^{t/T}} \right). \qquad 8-(11)$$

Thus one-half the total dose will have been delivered by the end of one half period, three-quarters by the end of the second half-period, and so on.

As an example of dosage from an internal beta-emitter, consider a patient who has received 5 mc of P^{32} as treatment for polycythemia vera. Assuming uniform distribution and no excretion of phosphorus, the concentration in a 70-kg man is $\frac{5000}{70,000} = 0.07 \, \mu c$ per gram. $\overline{E}_\beta = 0.70$ Mev and T 14.3 days. $D_\beta = 73.8 \times 0.07 \times 0.70 \times 14.3 = 51$ rad. Half of this will be delivered during the first two weeks.

In practice, elimination and non-uniform concentration will make the dose somewhat different from that calculated by these formulae; these topics will be discussed later in this chapter.

---

* Some earlier publications give the value of the constant in this equation as 88 instead of 73.8. This is due to the use of the old "equivalent roentgen" instead of the currently employed rad.

8

Dose in Regions Small in Comparison to Range of Beta Particles. The general solution of dosage problems for organs small in comparison to the range of the beta particles has not been developed. Rossi and Ellis have given data for spheres, which may be used as an approximation for other shapes. Their curves are shown in Figure 37, the coordinates being in terms of the same units as Figure 34. For example, consider one lobe of a thyroid of a two-day-old chick to be represented as a sphere 1.5 mm in diameter. Assume that 20 μc of I^{131} have been deposited in this lobe,*

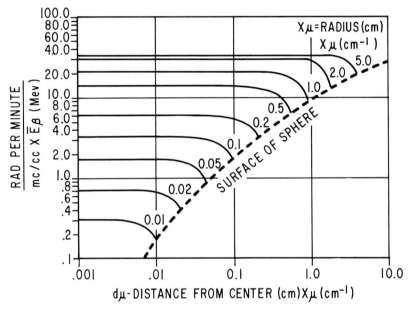

FIG. 37. Curves for calculating dose rate from beta-emitters deposited inside spheres small in relation to range of beta particles. (Courtesy of H. H. Rossi, R. H. Ellis, Jr., and the American Roentgen Ray Society.)

and it is desired to find the dose rate at its center and at its surface. For I^{131} there are several beta rays; the most important is 0.608 Mev, and this may be used as E_β(max), whence $\mu = 18$ cm^{-1}. $\overline{E}_\beta = 0.188$ Mev. The radius is 0.075 cm so for the surface $\mu x = 1.35$. The distance for the center may be considered 0.01 cm, since the curve is flat at that point and the reading will not increase toward the center. The concentration is 11.4 mc per cu cm. Data will be obtained by interpolation between the $x\mu$ curves for 1.0 and 2.0. For the center the reading is $\frac{1}{3}$ of the way between 21 and 30, or 24; this multiplied by 0.188 $\times$ 11.4 gives 51.5 rads per minute. For the surface $x\mu = d\mu = 1.35$, and the dose rate is 10.3 $\times$ 0.188 $\times$ 11.4 = 22 rads per minute. The dose rate in an extended medium with the same

---

* The separation of the two lobes in such that each may be considered independently of the other.

concentration would be [from formula 8—(4)] $3.55 \times 10^{-2} \times 11.4 \times 1000 \times 0.188 = 75.7$ rads per minute.

Application to Treatment of Very Small Masses. According to the above section, the dose in a spherical mass, from a given concentration of radioactive material deposited uniformly within it, decreases with the radius of the mass. Since there is a limit to the amount of radionuclide which can be administered to a human being, there is a limit to the concentration which can be obtained. Thus, in practice, doses to very small isolated masses are strictly limited. The problem must be considered particularly with regard to the desire to treat small metastatic deposits of thyroid cancer with radioactive iodine. By following the above procedure, the doses at the center and the surface of spheres of various radii are found, relative to the dose in an extended mass containing radioactive material in the same concentration. From these can be found the relative concentrations in small masses necessary to give the same dose as unit concentration in the large one. Data for iodine and for phosphorus are presented in Table 6.

Table 6. Doses in Small Spheres, Relative to Doses in an Extended Volume, for the Same Concentration of Iodine or Phosphorus

				Sphere Diameter—Mm					
	0.1	0.3	0.5	0.7	1.0	2.0	3.0	5.0	10.0
				Iodine–131					
Ratio Average D in Sphere to $D\beta$	0.077	0.27	0.33	0.42	0.50	0.67	0.77	0.9	0.9
$\mu c/gm$ in Sphere to give dose $= D\beta/\mu c/gm$	13	3.7	3	2.4	2	1.5	1.3	1.1	1.1
				Phosphorus-32					
Ratio as above	0.012	0.033	0.06	0.084	0.11	0.25	0.33	0.50	0.72
$\mu c/gm$ as above	81	30	17	12	9	4	3	2	1.4

Dose in Objects Floating in Radioactive Solutions. The same curves of Figure 37 can be used to find the dose in a small spherical organism immersed in a solution of radioactive material. If the sphere contained radioactivity at the same concentration as the medium, the entire system would receive radiation at the same rate, which would be that of the large volume with uniform distribution of isotope. But if the organism contains no activity, the dose at its center would be that in an extended medium, minus that at the center due to the sphere itself.

Consider a frog's egg, stripped of its jelly, floating in a medium containing P^{32} in a concentration of 1 mc per cu cm, with none permeating the egg. The diameter of the egg is 3 mm; the dose rate at a point 0.5 mm inside the surface is to be determined. For P^{32}, $E_\beta(max)$ is 1.7 Mev and $\bar{E}_\beta$ is 0.70

Mev; μ is 4 cm^{-1}. The distance from the center, d, is 0.1 cm (radius is 1.5 mm). Therefore μd = 0.4 and μx = 0.6. The reading at μd = 0.4 for μx = 0.6 is 12, hence the dose rate at this point due to the sphere itself is 12 × 1 × 0.695 = 8.35 rads per minute. The dose rate in the extended medium is $3.55 \times 10^{-2} \times 1 \times 1000 \times 0.695 = 24.6$ rads per minute. Hence the dose rate at the point in question, with no radioactive material in the egg, is 24.6—8.4 = 16.2 rads per minute.

Gamma Ray Emitting Nuclides in the Body. In the case of gamma rays emitted within an organ or anywhere within the body, absorption is rarely complete within the tissue of interest. The approach to the dosage problem must therefore be different from that for beta rays.

When the nuclide is distributed throughout a volume of tissue such as V (Figure 38), with a concentration of C μc per gram, the dose rate per hour at any point P due to the quantity of radionuclide CdV present in a small volume at a distance r from P will be

$$d(d\gamma) = \frac{10^{-3} \; \Gamma \; C \; e^{-\mu r}}{r^2} \; \text{roentgens per hour}, \qquad 8\text{---}(12)$$

where μ is the *effective* absorption coefficient of the radiation per centimeter of tissue. The value of this absorption coefficient depends on the fraction of the scattered radiation which is absorbed within the tissue. Its evaluation is very complicated, but fortunately, for absorption in unit density material it is essentially constant, and less than 0.03 cm^{-1} for gamma ray energies in the range from 0.1 to 2.0 Mev. (The dose rate for 1 μc at 1 cm is $10^{-3} \; \Gamma$.)

The total dose rate at point P then is

$$d_\gamma/(\text{hr}) = 10^{-3} \; \Gamma \; C \int_v \frac{e^{-\mu r}}{r^2} dV \; \text{roentgens per hour}. \qquad 8\text{---}(13)$$

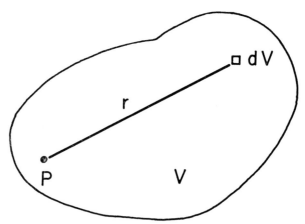

FIG. 38.   Basis for calculation of dose rate from gamma-emitter distributed through large volume of tissue.

This expression is not readily integrated except when the volume is a sphere, but it can be evaluated for some other shapes. It may be called the *geometrical factor* and represented by g. In any volume the value of g will depend on the position of the point of reference, being a maximum at the center and a minimum at the surface. Usually what is desired is an *average*

Table 7. Average Values of Geometrical Factor for Gamma Ray Dosage Calculations

(Courtesy of G. J. Hine, G. L. Brownell, and Academic Press)

Gamma Ray Emitter Uniformly Distributed in Average Human Body

Weight of Individual	Height of Individual—Cm						
	200	190	180	170	160	150	140
Kg	Values of $\bar{g}$						
100	138	139	142	145	147	150	154
90	134	136	138	140	143	146	148
80	129	130	131	134	136	139	141
70	123	124	125	126	129	131	135
60	117	118	119	120	122	125	128
50	112	113	114	116	117	119	122
40	102	104	105	106	108	109	110

Gamma Ray Emitter Uniformly Distributed in Cylinder

Height of Cylinder	Radius of Cylinder—Cm							
	3	5	10	15	20	25	30	35
Cm	Value of $\bar{g}$							
2	17.5	22.1	30.3	34.0	36.2	37.5	38.6	39.3
5	22.3	31.8	47.7	56.4	61.6	65.2	67.9	70.5
10	25.1	38.1	61.3	76.1	86.5	93.4	98.4	103
20	25.7	40.5	68.9	89.8	105	117	126	133
30	25.9	41.0	71.3	94.6	112	126	137	146
40	25.9	41.3	72.4	96.5	116	131	143	153
60	26.0	41.6	73.0	97.8	118	134	148	159
80	26.0	41.6	73.3	98.4	119	135	150	161
100	26.0	41.6	73.3	98.5	119	136	150	162

gamma dose rate, and for this purpose it is desirable to define an *average* geometrical factor, $\bar{g}$. For a sphere of unit density material, of radius R,

$$\bar{g} = 3\pi R, \text{ for radii up to 10 cm.} \qquad 8—(14)$$

For the average human body, Hine and Brownell have developed values for $\bar{g}$, based on data published by Bush.[4] These are given in Table 7, where values for $\bar{g}$ for cylinders are also listed.

The total gamma ray dose, D_γ, is of course $d_\gamma/(hr)$ multiplied by the average life in hours:

$$D_\gamma = 10^{-3} \, \Gamma \, C \, \bar{g} \times 1.443 \times 24 \, T = 0.0346 \, \Gamma \, C \, T \, \bar{g} \text{ roentgen,} \quad 8{-}(15)$$

where T is the half life in days.

For partial decay, the formula is analogous to that for partial beta dosage;

$$D_\gamma(t) = D_\gamma \left(1 - \frac{1}{2^{t/T}} \right).$$

These formulæ of course hold only for the region in which μ is essentially constant, namely from 0.1 to 2.0 Mev.

Very Low Energy Gamma Rays. When a nuclide decays by electron capture, radiation is emitted in the form of characteristic x-rays, which are often of such low energy that they will be absorbed in a centimeter or less of tissue. They should, therefore, be considered as behaving like beta radiation, and their dosage calculated in that manner. For instance, Cu^{64} decays with 39% β^-, $\bar{E}_\beta = 0.187$ Mev; 19% β^+, $\bar{E}_\beta$ 0.285 Mev, and 42% electron capture. The characteristic radiation of the daughter, $_{28}Ni^{64}$ is 7.5 kev or 0.008 Mev. The net $\bar{E}_\beta$ then is $0.39 \times 0.187 + 0.19 \times 0.285 + 0.42 \times 0.008 = 0.130$ Mev. In this case the electron capture radiation constitutes a negligible factor. It must not be overlooked that the 19% β^+ disintegrations contribute 0.38 annihilation photons per disintegration, which produces most of the Γ value of 1.1 r/mc-hr.

A different situation arises with such a nuclide as $_{24}Cr^{51}$. Here 100% of the decay is by electron capture, with emission of the K-characteristic radiation of vanadium, 0.0049 Mev. $\bar{E}_\beta$ is then 0.0049 Mev. In addition, in 9% of the disintegrations a 0.323 Mev γ ray is emitted, whence Γ is 0.18 r/mc-hr. In this case the "β" contribution to the dose cannot be ignored. It should be noted that these characteristic x-rays are mono-chromatic, therefore their actual energy is used as $\bar{E}_\beta$.

For x-rays or gamma rays of energies less than about 0.015 Mev the above procedure is satisfactory. For the few which fall between 0.015 and 0.1 Mev (where the gamma ray formula becomes applicable) special procedures are necessary. (See Radiation Dosimetry, Hine and Brownell, page 842).

Effective and Biological Half Life. In the formulæ developed above, the physical half life of the isotope has been employed. However frequently physiological elimination removes some of the material, so that the de-crease in quantity in any organ is due to both elimination and physical decay. In many cases elimination follows an exponential law, with a different rate from the physical decay. Then

$$Q_t = Q_o \, e^{-\lambda_p t} \, e^{-\lambda_b t} = Q_o \, e^{-(\lambda_p t + \lambda_b t)} \quad\quad 8{-}(16)$$

where λ_p and λ_b are the physical and biological decay coefficients respectively. These are equal to $\dfrac{0.693}{T_p}$ and $\dfrac{0.693,}{T_b}$ where T_p and T_b are physical and biological half lives. The net result is

$$Q_t = Q_0\, e^{-\lambda_e t} \qquad\qquad 8\text{—}(17)$$

where $\lambda_e = \lambda_p + \lambda_b$, and is the "effective" decay constant.

$$\text{Whence}\quad \frac{0.693}{T_e} = \frac{0.693}{T_p} + \frac{0.693}{T_b}$$

$$\text{or}\quad \frac{1}{T_e} = \frac{1}{T_p} + \frac{1}{T_b} \qquad\qquad 8\text{—}(18)$$

This expression is sometimes presented in the form

$$T_b = \frac{T_p \times T_e}{T_p - T_e} \qquad\qquad 8\text{—}(19)$$

In all these expressions, T_p is the tabulated physical half life, T_e the experimentally determined effective half life. T_b, the biological half life, can be obtained by calculation from these two.

For example, a patient has been given a tracer dose of I^{131}. Daily measurements over the thyroid gland reveal that the quantity therein is decreasing at such a rate that the effective half life is 6 days instead of the physically accepted value of 8.1 days. This effective half life is of course the value which should be used in dosage calculations when it is known. Use of the physical half life will give maximum dose, the actual one will be somewhat less. The effective half life is not always available. Average values for many nuclides are given in National Bureau of Standards Handbook 52, but in the individual case there may be considerable variation from the average. In the case of the I^{131} patient just mentioned, if a therapeutic dose were administered, the substitution of 6 for 8.1 in the dosage formulae would result in an actual dose only 74 per cent of the maximum.

The biological half life represents the actual turnover of the *element*, not only of the radioactive isotope, in the tissues. For the iodine case just

mentioned $T_b = \dfrac{8.1 \times 6}{8.1 - 6} = 23.1$ days.

Addition of Beta and Gamma Ray Doses. In considering the total dose from any nuclide, the beta and gamma contributions must be added. The beta doses were calculated above in rads, and the gamma doses in roentgens. The number of ergs absorbed per gram per roentgen varies with the quality of the radiation and with the atomic number of the absorbing material. For muscle tissue, and for photons from 200 kev to 3 Mev the rads per roentgen vary between 0.95 and 0.98. Obviously no appreciable error will be introduced within this range by using rads instead of roentgens to specify gamma dose, with no change in numerical value. It is then correct to add the two, and the dosage formulæ become

$$d_{(\beta+\gamma)}/\text{hour} = C\,(2.13\,\overline{E}_\beta + 10^{-3}\,\Gamma\,g)\text{ rads, } T > 20 \text{ hours.} \qquad 8-(20)$$

$$d_{(\beta+\gamma)}/\text{day} = C\,(51.2\,\overline{E}_\beta + 0.024\,\Gamma\,g)\text{ rads, } T > 20 \text{ days} \qquad 8-(21)$$

$$D_{(\beta+\gamma)} = C\,T\,(73.8\,\overline{E}_\beta + 0.0346\,\Gamma\,g)\text{ rads,} \qquad 8-(22)$$

Integral Dose. It is generally assumed that the radiation effect in a particular tissue, or in the whole body, is due to the total energy absorbed therein. If the rads delivered in the significant tissue are represented by the dose D, then in m grams of that tissue, D m gram-rads will have been absorbed. This is called the *integral dose* or *volume dose*. However it is often true that the entire effect on the organism is due not only to the integral dose in the organ, but also to that in the whole body. This will depend not only on the total amount of nuclide administered, but also on its distribution, and on the effective half lives of the nuclide in the different physiological compartments. In practice this may mean variable distributions and effective half lives to an extent which may be extremely complicated. However some simplifications serve to bring out certain points.

The maximum permissible dose to a normal individual in 3 months is 3 rads of radiation to the whole body. (See Chapter 10). For a 70 kg man this would be an integral dose of 210,000 gram-rads or 0.21 megagram-rad. If, however, this individual has cancer, and is to be treated with a radioactive nuclide in the hope that the lesion will take up enough radioactive material to destroy itself, it would be legitimate to give a much larger whole body dose. It is believed that about 450 rads to the whole body would be lethal in half the cases; certainly a dose of this magnitude would not be permissible in therapy. It may be assumed that, at a maximum, 200 rads to the whole body, or 14 megagram-rads could be used. The dose in the tumor should be no less than 6000 rads, or for a 200 gm mass, 1.2 megagram-rads. If m_1 and m_2 are tumor and body masses respectively, and D_1 and D_2 the doses in rads, the ratio of the integral doses is

$$\frac{D_1\,m_1}{D_2\,m_2} = \frac{1.2}{14} \qquad\qquad 8-(23)$$

But $D_1 = C_1\,T_1\,(73.8\,\overline{E}_\beta)$ and
$D_2 = C_2\,T_2\,(73.8\,\overline{E}_\beta)$ (considering for the present only the beta radiation) whence the above ratio becomes

$$\frac{C_1\,T_1\,m_1}{C_2\,T_2\,m_2} = \frac{1.2}{14} \qquad\qquad 8-(24)$$

If T_1 and T_2, the effective half periods, are equal, as may well be the case, then, for the doses assumed as desirable,

$$\frac{C_1}{C_2} = \frac{1.2 \ m_2}{14 \ m_1} = \frac{1.2 \times 70{,}000}{14 \times 200} = 30 \qquad\qquad 8\text{---}(25)$$

In words, this states that for successful cancer therapy the concentrations in the tumor masses must be of the order of 30 times the average in the rest of the body. Such a differential is seldom attained except by iodine isotopes in functioning thyroid tissue, or by direct injection of the radioactive material into the tumor in such a form that it will stay there.

If the radioactive nuclide emits γ rays as well as β, the formula for the dose includes a geometrical factor which is different for the small mass and the large body. For the particular case of I^{131}, putting g for the small mass as 65 and for the large body as 125, the relative values become approximately $D_1 = C_1 \, T_1 \times 19$, $D_2 = C_2 \, T_2 \times 23$,

and $\dfrac{C_1}{C_2} = 36.$

A larger ratio is to be expected, since the γ radiation in general increases the whole body dose faster than it does the organ dose. But the order of magnitude of the ratio remains the same.

Examples of Dosage Problems.   In any particular case the relative importance of beta and gamma dosage depends on the radiation energies and on the size and shape of the mass containing the radioactive material. Widely different cases may be illustrated by the dose to the thyroid gland from I^{131} deposited therein, and dose to the entire body from Na^{24} administered intravenously.

For the first case, consider a 40-gram thyroid gland containing 3 mc of I^{131}. Essentially all of the isotope not deposited in the gland by 24 hours after administration has been excreted and may be neglected. The following are the constants of the irradiation:

T_{eff} (measured) $= 5.5$ days,
$\overline{E}_\beta = 0.188$ Mev,
$\Gamma = 2.20$ r per mc-hr at 1 cm,
$\overline{g}$ for 40 gm sphere $= 19.$

Whence $\qquad D_\beta = 73.8 \times 0.188 \times 5.5 \times \dfrac{3000}{40} = 5700$ rads,

$$D_\gamma = 0.0346 \times 2.20 \times 5.5 \times 19 \times \frac{3000}{40} = 600 \text{ rads*}$$

$D_{\beta+\gamma} = 6300$ rads, of which 90 per cent is due to the beta rays. The part of this dose delivered in the first week is $(1 - \dfrac{1}{2^{7/5.5}}) = (1 - \dfrac{1}{2^{1.3}}) = $ about $(1 - \frac{1}{3}) = \frac{2}{3}$. Half would have been delivered in 5.5 days, and three fourths in 11 days.

* Gamma ray doses will now be stated in terms of rads instead of roentgens, in accordance with the discussion of the previous page.

In contrast, consider the dose to the entire body of a 60 kg man receiving an intravenous dose of 500 μc of Na^{24}.

$$T_{eff} = T_{phys} = 0.625 \text{ day,}$$

$$\bar{E}_\beta = 0.56 \text{ Mev,}$$

$$\Gamma = 18.7 \text{ r per mc-hr at 1 cm,}$$

$\bar{g}$ for a 60 kg man 170 cm tall is 120.

$$D_\beta = 73.8 \times 0.56 \times 0.625 \times \frac{500}{60,000} = 0.215 \text{ rad.}$$

$$D_\gamma = 0.0346 \times 18.7 \times 120 \times 0.625 \times \frac{500}{60,000} = 0.407 \text{ rad.}$$

$D_{\beta+\gamma} = 0.62$ rad, of which 66 per cent is due to the gamma rays.
Essentially all of this dose will be delivered in 4 days, which is 7 half lives.

On page 113 a calculation was done for dosage from P^{32} uniformly distributed throughout the body. It was pointed out there that this did not represent the true situation; after an early uniform distribution, the nuclide becomes more concentrated in some tissues than in others. Accurate information on this is difficult to obtain, but John Lawrence[7] has presented data based on his extensive observation of patients undergoing therapy with this nuclide. For the 5 mc dose in a 70 kg patient discussed on page 99, the dose for uniform distribution and no elimination was 51 rads to the whole body. According to Lawrence, this situation may be considered as prevailing for the first 3 days, during which 14% of the nuclide has decayed. Therefore, up to this point, 3 days, the whole body dose is 51 × 0.14 = 7 rads.

From here on, concentration in a compartment consisting of bone, marrow, liver, and spleen (the "bone compartment" of Lawrence) is 10 times that in the rest of the body, and the effective half life is 11 days. The "bone compartment" weighs about 12,000 grams and the "soft tissue compartment" about 58,000 grams. Since 14% of the material has decayed, there remain 0.86 × 5000 = 4300 mc. Since the relative concentrations are 10 to 1,

$$\text{Concentration (bone)} = \frac{\mu c \text{ bone}}{12000}$$

$$\text{Concentration (soft tissue)} = \frac{\mu c \text{ soft tissue}}{58,000}$$

and $\dfrac{\mu c \text{ bone}}{12000} = 10 \times \dfrac{\mu c \text{ soft tissue}}{58,000}$

whence $\dfrac{\mu c \text{ bone}}{\mu c \text{ soft tissue}} = \dfrac{10 \times 12000}{58,000} = 2 \text{ (approximately)}$

Therefore $\frac{2}{3}$ of the 4300 mc are in the bone, and $\frac{1}{3}$ in the soft tissue, or approximately 2850 mc in bone and 1450 mc in soft tissue.
The bone dose after the third day is then

$$\frac{2850}{12,000} \times 0.7 \times 11 \times 73.8 = 136 \text{ rads,}$$

and the soft tissue dose is 14 rads.

To each of these must be added the original 7 rads for the first 3 days, therefore the total bone dose is $136 + 7 = 143$ rads, and the total dose to the soft tissue compartment is 21 rads, from the 5 mc of P^{32} administered intravenously.

This analysis does not allow for early excretion of P^{32}, which may be important especially if the material is given by mouth.

Dosage with Iodine Isotopes Other than I^{131}. Both longer-lived and shorter-lived iodine isotopes have been used for diagnostic purposes. I^{132}, with half life 2.26 hours, and I^{130}, half life 12.6 hours, have been advocated for therapy, particularly in the very toxic hyperthyroids, where iodine turnover is very rapid. The thyroid dose resulting from 1 μc per gram of each, deposited in a 30 gm gland, is shown in Table 8. It is assumed that T_{eff} with I^{131} has been determined to be 6 days, whence T_{biol} is 23.1 days, and T_{eff} for the other isotopes can be calculated. g is taken as 16.

Table 8. Dosage to Thyroid Gland Using Various Iodine Isotopes

Isotope	T_{phys} days	T_{eff} days	$E\beta$ Mev	Γ	$D\beta+\gamma$ per μc per gm rads
I-125	60	16.7	0.027	0.6	37.5
I-130	0.52	0.51	0.285	12.1	14.1
I-131	8.1	6	0.188	2.20	90.5
I-132	0.097	0.097	0.483	12.3	4.1

It is immediately apparent that the dose from I^{125} is almost 40 per cent of that from I^{131}, in spite of its very much lower energy. Accordingly it would not be desirable to use several times as much of the longer-lived nuclide as of the shorter.

Approximate Formula for Thyroid Dose with I^{131}. If an average effective half life of 6 days is assumed, and an average $\bar{g}$ for the thyroid gland of 15, a formula may be developed for rapid calculation of thyroid dose, when the radioiodine content of the gland is known and the gland weight can be estimated. In formula 8—(22), C becomes $\dfrac{\text{I in gland}}{\text{gland weight}}$, and

$$D\beta+\gamma = \frac{\text{I in gland}}{\text{gland weight}} \times 6 \,(73.8 \times 0.188 + 0.0346 \times 15 \times 2.20)$$

$$= 90 \times \frac{\text{I in gland}}{\text{gland weight}}.$$

In using this formula it should be kept in mind that if the effective half life is appreciably greater or less than 6, the dose will be proportionately greater or less. Gland size will not make a significant difference unless the gland is really enormous, more than 100 grams.

Calculation of Quantity of Radio-Nuclide to Administer to Deliver a Specified Dose. Formula 8-(22) can be used to plan administration of a specified dose; it is only necessary to put in the known constants and the desired dose, and solve for C, the concentration per gram of the tissue in which the material will be deposited. If all of the material remains in the tissues there will be no correction for elimination, but if there is excretion, this must be allowed for.

For example, it is desired to administer 8000 rads to a thyroid gland estimated to weight 60 grams. On a tracer study the gland took up 65 per cent of the dose in 24 hours; this decreased with an effective half life of 5 days.

$\overline{E}_\beta = 0.188$ Mev; $\overline{g}$ (60 gm sphere) $= 23$; $\Gamma = 2.20$; $T = 5$; $D_{\beta+\gamma} = 8000$ rads; $C = $ concentration to be found.

$$8000 = 5 \, C \, (73.8 \times 0.187 + 0.0346 \times 23 \times 2.18).$$

Solving this equation for C, the result is 103 μc per gm.

This is the concentration to be *retained* in the gland; according to the uptake study this would be 65 per cent of that *administered*. Therefore the amount to be administered would be $\dfrac{100}{65} \times 103$ or 158 μc per estimated gram of gland weight. $158 \times 60 = 9500$ μc or 9.5 mc to be administered to deliver the desired dose in the gland specified.

Calculations for Administered Dose for a Short-Lived Iodine Isotope. In the above calculation the dose delivered during the first 24 hours, the period of accumulation of the radioactive isotope in the gland, was neglected; it would be very small compared to the total. This, however, cannot be the case for the short-lived isotopes, nor can their decay during the first hours be omitted.

Consider a very toxic patient, who has been studied with I^{131}. Her thyroid content at 4 hours was 90% of the administered dose, and at 24 hours, 80%. The effective half life was 2.5 days, whence the biological half life was 3.6 days. The gland was estimated to weigh 60 gm, so $g = 23$. It was decided to treat her with I^{130} to a dose of 6000 rads.

By the use of the above formula it is found that there must be 27 mc of this isotope in the gland at 4 hours, to give 6000 rads thereafter. Since the 4-hour uptake is 90%, 30 mc would have been the necessary initial dose. But in 4 hours the decay is to 80%, whence to have 30 mc available at 4 hours, $\dfrac{30}{0.80}$ or 37 mc must have been injected. Now in the first 4 hours some of this will have been irradiating the gland. Uptakes were not determined for earlier periods, but as an approximation it may be assumed to have been linear. Then it was 22.5% at one hour, 45% at 2 hours, and 67.5% at 3 hours. If 45% be assumed as the average content of the gland for those first four hours, this would mean a gland content of $0.45 \times 37 = 16.6$ mc. But the 2-hour decay must also be considered; it provides a reduction to $90 \times 16.6 = 15$ mc. The dose delivered to the gland by this average 15-mc content in 4 hours is 4 times the dose per hour.

$$4 \times \frac{15000}{60} (2.13 \ \overline{E}_\beta + 0.0346 \ \Gamma \ g) = 880 \text{ rads.}$$ Then the total dose given by the 37 mc administered would be 6880 rads. For a dose of 6000 rads, the administered quantity of I^{132} should be $\dfrac{6000}{6880} \times 37 = 33$ mc.

Non-uniformity of Irradiation. In reality the isotope distribution is never actually uniform, and sometimes it is decidedly patchy within such an organ as the thyroid gland. In these cases the calculated dose is an average, but local maxima and minima may vary widely from this dose. On a basis of radioautographs, Sinclair[8] estimates that in toxic diffuse goiter the maximum dose averages three times the mean and in non-toxic nodular goiter ten times the mean. No data are given for the minimum doses. There is little that can be done about these variations at the present time.

However, there may be also a broader variation, a difference in uptake of the nuclide by different organs, as has already been noted in the case of the thyroid gland and radioiodine. In no other instance is the differential between uptake in a particular organ and the rest of the body as great, but significant variations do exist. Uptake, deposition, and elimination for a particular isotope may vary with its chemical form, solubility, presence of carrier, and so on. The Report of Committee II of the International Commission on Radiological Protection, on Permissible Dose for Internal Radiation, lists critical organ, effective half life, fraction in critical organ of that in body, and so on, for a large number of isotopes. These values furnish useful starting points for some dosage studies, but reservations as to the applicability of the table to the particular chemical compound under consideration must always be kept in mind.

An illustration of the use of this table can be made with a study of the behavior of sulfur[35] which is used as a tracer in studying various topics related to the skin. According to the handbook, the skin is the critical organ, containing 17 per cent of the total sulfur in the body, and weighing 2 kilograms. The physical half life of the isotope is 87.1 days, but the effective half life is given as about 18 days. The only radiation is beta, with $\overline{E}_\beta = 0.049$ Mev. If a tracer dose of 1 mc were administered to a 50 kg individual, 17 per cent, or 170 μc would be concentrated in 2 kg of skin. The total dose to the skin then would be

$$D_\beta \text{ (skin)} = 73.8 \times 18 \times 0.049 \times \frac{170}{2000} = 5.6 \text{ rads.}$$

The average dose to the rest of the body would be of the order of

$$D_\beta \text{ (average body)} = 73.8 \times 18 \times 0.049 \times \frac{830}{48,000} = 1.12 \text{ rads.}$$

If, however, either the part deposited in the skin, or the effective half life were different, both doses would be different.

Special Dosage Problems. 1. *Dose to blood and to entire body from* I^{131} *for treatment of thyroid cancer.* A problem which is important in the treatment of thyroid cancer with radioiodine is the determination of the dose to the blood and to the entire body, from a therapeutic dose of radioactive

Table 9.   Calculation of Blood Dose in a Thyroid Cancer Patient

Hours after Administration	C_b μc per gm Blood	Hours for this Average Concentration	Average C_b during Interval	$0.53\,C_b \times Hr.$ Rads
4	1.8	4	1.9	4.0
8	1.3	4	1.55	3.3
12	0.9	4	1.10	2.3
24	0.65	12	0.78	5.0
48	0.60	24	0.62	7.8
96	0.4	48	0.5	12.8
192	0.2	96	0.3	15.2
288	0.1	192	0.15	15.2
at 24 days	0.025			15.4*
			Total D_{blood}	81.0 rads

$$\text{and total } D_{tissue} = \frac{0.33}{0.53} \times 81 = 50 \text{ rads}$$

*The dose from 24 days on is the dose per hour at that time multiplied by the average life in hours.

iodine most of which either concentrates in thyroid tissue or is excreted. There have been several studies of this problem.[9,10,11] The treatment developed by Seidlin, Yalow, and Siegel will be reviewed here, with adjustment of their constants to conform with the use of rads instead of reps as the dose unit.

The dose in any tissue has been shown to be proportional to the concentration of the isotope within that tissue. For a concentration of C μc per gm, the beta dose rate is $2.12\ \bar{E}_\beta\, C$ rads per hour. Hence for a concentration of I^{131} in the blood denoted by C_b, the dose rate to the blood, due to beta radiation is $2.12 \times 0.188 \times C_b = 0.4\, C_b$ rads per hour. The gamma dose rate will depend not on the concentration in the blood, but on that in the whole body, since gamma rays released outside the blood vessels will still irradiate the entire organism. This will depend on a concentration C_t, the average for the whole body, which the authors assume to be roughly equivalent to half the blood concentration; $C_t = \frac{1}{2}C_b$. The gamma ray dose rate is $10^{-3}\ \Gamma\, C_t\, \bar{g}$ rads per hour. For a 60 kg man this is $10^{-3} \times$

$2.20 \times 120 \times \frac{1}{2} \times C_b = 0.13 \, C_b$ rads per hour. Then the total dose rate to the blood is $0.53 \, C_b$ rads per hour.

The beta dose rate to the whole body would be half that to the blood if $C_t = \frac{1}{2} C_b$, but the gamma dose rate would be the same throughout. Hence the total dose rate to the body outside the blood vessels is $0.33 \, C_b$ rads per hour. The gamma dose to the rest of the body from the iodine concentrated in the thyroid gland can be shown to be negligible for calculations of the degree of accuracy possible here.

It now becomes a question of evaluating C_b, which of course changes constantly as the iodine is eliminated. This has to be done for the individual patient, by taking repeated blood samples and determining the average concentration during the period represented by each sample. Details for one patient are given in Table 9. This patient received 100 mc of I^{131}. Blood samples were taken at the indicated intervals; the average concentration during an interval was assumed to be the mean of the values at the start and the end of that interval.

The elimination pattern varies greatly among thyroid cancer patients. In the 82 cases reported by the authors of the above-mentioned report, the *average* blood dose per 100 mc administered was 55 rads, but the extremes were from 18 to 200 rads per 100 mc administered, depending on elimination and retention of the isotope.

2. *Dose to bladder mucosa from Br^{82} in a rubber balloon.* For treatment of widespread but superficial cancer of the bladder mucosa, treatment may be administered by radioactive material introduced into a balloon in the bladder. Various radionuclides have been employed; Br^{82} seems to be one of the most satisfactory. The balloon is introduced into the bladder and then filled with 100 cc of a solution of calcium bromide. Various techniques are used for introducing the material and maintaining it in place; description of these would be out of place here.[12]

For the calculation it will be assumed that 250 mc of the nuclide are introduced and that the bag will be tolerated for 4 hours. $T = 35.7$ hours; $\bar{E}_\beta = 0.142$ Mev; $\Gamma = 14.6$ r per mc-hr at 1 cm; $g = 31$. The attenuation of the beta radiation by the stretched rubber balloon has been experimentally determined; about 30% is transmitted. The dose per hour at the inner surface of the balloon is $\frac{1}{2}$ that at the center of the sphere, for both beta and gamma components; the beta component is further reduced by the bag before it gets to the bladder mucosa. Then

$$d(\text{mucosa}) \text{ per hour} = 0.5 \times \frac{250000}{100} (2.13 \times 0.142 \times 0.3 + 14.6 \times 31 \times 10^{-3}) \text{ rads per hour.}$$

In four hours the total dose at the surface of the mucosa is 2700 rads. The beta radiation would be mostly absorbed by any urine seeping between the bag and the mucosa, but the gamma radiation would not be affected. At a depth of 2 mm the beta radiation would be completely gone, but the gamma radiation would be very little less than that at the surface.

REFERENCES

HINE, G. J. and BROWNELL, G. L.: *Radiation Dosimetry*, Chapters 16, 18, and Appendices, New York, Academic Press, 1956.

GLASSER, O., QUIMBY, E. H. TAYLOR, L. S., WEATHERWAX, J. L. and MORGAN, R. H.: Physical Foundations of Radiology 3rd Ed., Chapter 13, New York, Paul B. Hoeber, Inc., 1961.

International Commission on Radiological Protection; Report of Subcommittee II: Permissible Dose for Internal Radiation, Pergamom Press, New York, 1959

VENNART, J. and MINSKI, M. Radiation doses from administered radio-nuclides. Brit. Jour. Radiology XXXV, 372, 1962.

BIBLIOGRAPHY

1. WITTEN, V. H., WOOD, W. S., and LOEVINGER, R.: The Erythema Effects of a Polonium Plaque (an Alpha Emitter) on Human Skin. Jour. Investigative Dermatology, *28*, 199–210, 1957.

2. ROSSI, H. H., and ELLIS, R. H.: Calculations for Distributed Sources of Beta Radiation. Am. Jour. Roentgenol., Radium Therapy, and Nuclear Med. LXVII, 980–988, 1952.

3. MARINELLI, L. D., QUIMBY, E. H., and HINE, G. J.: Dosage Determination with Radioactive Isotopes. II Practical Considerations in Therapy and Protection. Am. Jour. Roentgenol. and Radium Therapy, LIX, 260–280, 1948.

4. HINE, G. J. and BROWNELL, G. L.: *Radiation Dosimetry*, pp 850–859. New York, Academic Press, 1956.

5. HOECKER, F. E. and ROOFE, P. G.: Studies of Radium in Human Bone. Radiology, *56*, 89–99, 1951.

6. SPIERS, F. W.: Alpha-ray Dosage in Bone Containing Radium. Brit. Jour. Radiology, XXVI, 296–301, 1953.

7. LAWRENCE, J. H.: *Polycythemia, Physiology, Diagnosis and Treatment*. New York, Grune and Stratton, 1955.

8. SINCLAIR, W. K., ABBATT, J. D., FERRAN, H. E. A., HARRISS, E. B., and LAMERTON, L. F.: A Quantitative Autoradiographic Study of Radioiodine Distribution and Dosage in Human Thyroid Glands, Brit. Jour. Radiology XXIX, 34–61, 1956.

9. MARINELLI, L. D. and HILL, R. F.: Radiation Dosimetry in the Treatment of Functional Thyroid Carcinoma with I-131. Radiology, *55*, 494–502, 1950.

10. ROBERTSON, JAMES, and GODWIN, J. T.: Calculation of Radioactive Iodine Beta Radiation Dose to Bone Marrow. Brit. Jour. Radiology XXVII, 241–242, 1954.

11. SEIDLIN, S. M., YALOW. A. A., and SIEGEL, E.: Blood Radiation Dose During Radioiodine Therapy of Metastatic Thyroid Carcinoma. Radiology, *63*, 797–813, 1954.

12. DYCHE, G. M. and MACKAY, N. R.: Techniques for the Intracavitary Treatment of Bladder Neoplasms with Radioactive Solutions Contained in a Rubber Balloon. Brit. Jour. Radiology XXXII, 752–756, 1959.

9

Biological Effects of Ionizing Radiations

General Phenomena. When radiation falls upon living matter it produces changes which may be more or less profound, depending on the radiosensitivity of the system and the quantity of radiation. Grossly, four broad stages may be noted:

(*a*) For a small dose of radiation there will be no visible effect. It is true that some changes of at least a temporary nature have been induced in some of the cells, but there is nothing detectable by present means.

(*b*) For somewhat larger doses of radiation there will be observable phenomena, very slight, or fairly obvious, but from which there will apparently be complete recovery. In cells there will be increased permeability of the membranes, with swelling, increased acidity and granularity of the protoplasm, clumping of chromosomes, and halting of cell division. In the entire organism, especially of mammals, there may appear the syndrome called radiation sickness—nausea, vomiting, malaise, possibly accompanied by changes in the blood picture, decreased white count usually being the first thing observed. Such localized phenomena as erythema or epilation also may be produced. However, none of the changes is permanent, and after a time it is again impossible to observe anything to indicate that radiation has been administered.

(*c*) With still larger doses, all these effects are increased, and now complete recovery is impossible, although the worst symptoms may be alleviated. At the cellular level, reproduction or cell division is permanently altered. At the organism level, general debility may be accompanied by profound changes in the blood picture, with depression of all the elements—red and white cells, platelets and hemoglobin. Intractable anemia may develop, and if the gonads have been heavily irradiated, sterility may result. Heavy irradiation to the eyes may lead to cataract formation. Epilation will be permanent instead of temporary, possible skin changes are many and varied. Occasionally there may be malignant degeneration of some cells, with cancer formation.

(*d*) At a still higher dose level, all the results mentioned are increased beyond the point where the organism can combat them. Death results.

These various effects will be discussed in some detail in the following sections.

It is interesting that, except for fantastically high doses, no *immediate* result of irradiation is observable. There is always a longer or shorter

9

latent period, whose duration depends on the effect to be observed, the quality of the radiation, the magnitude of the dose, and its rate of administration. With moderately large doses delivered at a single exposure, radiation sickness may appear in a few hours, a skin erythema in one day, blood changes in a few days, epilation in a week or two. Even with really large doses, radiation death may not occur for a month or more. Such delayed effects as leukemia or cancer formation may not be evident for years. Yet the *immediate* effect of irradiation, the production of ion pairs, occurs only while the irradiation is going on. The ionization results in the production of abnormal atomic or molecular fragments; this condition is, however, very transient; positive and negative ions quickly recombine to form neutral atoms or molecules. Yet during the brief instant of ionization, physicochemical changes can be initiated in living matter which may ultimately lead to detectable radiation changes. Once initiated, this chain of biological events is apparently irreversible except under very special conditions. The search for antidotes, or means to reverse the effects of radiation doses after their delivery, is one of the fascinating fields of current radiobiological research.

Units of Radiation Dose. Radiation dose has been discussed in Chapter 8. The dose unit, the rad, represents an energy absorption of 100 ergs per gram of absorber, and results in the ionization of something like one tissue atom in 20 billion. This is a very small amount of energy; it would raise the temperature of soft tissue by only about two-millionths of a degree centigrade. A really large therapeutic dose would be less than ten thousand times this; that is, it would result in a temperature rise of less than two one-hundredths of a degree. Nevertheless, this would result in profound and irreversible changes in the living organism.

Classes of Biologic Effects. The most obvious effects are, of course, those arising in the irradiated individual. These are called *somatic*. However it is also true that certain changes can be transmitted to future generations, if they arise in the germ plasm. Such effects are called *genetic*.

Factors Influencing Somatic Radiation Effects. Some somatic radiation effects are observable after a relatively small dose of radiation, say 50 rads, while others require some hundreds of times as much. A number of other factors besides the actual dose enter into the degree of the final reaction produced.

1. *The rate at which the dose is administered:* Living tissues are not inert; as soon as any degree of damage has been produced, a corresponding repair process sets in. If a particular dose is spread out over a long time, it is possible that repair may keep up with damage, and no visible change ever be observed; whereas if it had been given all at once a violent reaction might have been provoked. Even within relatively short periods the effect of a given dose is less, the longer the irradiation time. Or, conversely, to produce a specified effect, more radiation is required for a long irradiation period (days or weeks) than for a short one. Irradiation need not be

continuous during this time. The fact that it is given in small daily incre-
ments is sufficient. However, there are some forms of biological damage,
notably gene mutation, in which this time factor apparently does not
operate.

2. *The extent of the body irradiated.* If the whole body receives a large
or moderate dose of radiation, a severe and possibly fatal illness will ensue.
Smaller doses to the whole body may not produce any prompt effects, nor
some of the late ones due to larger doses. On the other hand, if only a
small fraction of the body is irradiated, as in x-ray therapy, systemic effects
are very mild, even for very large doses. Local effects may be quite severe
in these cases, and there may be some degree of permanent local change
in the tissues.

3. *The part of the body irradiated.* General reactions are much more
severe if the dose of radiation is delivered to the upper abdomen, or possibly
to the spine, than if a field of similar size elsewhere is exposed to the same
dose.

4. *The age of the individual.* In general, physically immature individuals
are more sensitive to the effects of radiation than are adults.

5. *The biological variation among individuals.* While experience makes
it possible to set an *average* dose for the production of a certain effect,
individuals may vary greatly in their response. For instance, it requires
600 rads in a single dose to result in death within 30 days of half of a group
of a certain strain of rats (MLD 30 days). However, some of the same rats
will die after 400 rads and some will survive after 800.

Sources of Information Regarding Radiation Effects. Sources of information regarding radiation effects are varied. Of course, it is not possible
deliberately to experiment with human beings. Animal experiments are
fruitful; all radiation effects produced in man can be produced in animals.
However, dose-effect relations are not necessarily the same, so the data
thus obtained need such checks as are possible with human experience.
This is of three types:

1. *Occupational.* Early radiological workers received small doses of
x- or gamma rays at fairly constant rates over long periods. In many
instances it has been possible to evaluate these fairly accurately and cor-
relate them with observed changes, if any. Painters of luminous dials
ingested paint containing radioactive material, much of which was retained
in the skeleton; many of these developed serious damage years later.
Some miners in uranium mines worked in an atmosphere containing high
concentrations of radioactive gas and subsequently developed lung cancer.
In atomic energy plants a very few accidents have occurred in which
individuals were exposed to a flash of nuclear radiation.

2. *Medical.* X-rays and radium rays have been used for over 60 years
in diagnosis and in treatment of cancer and other diseases. For nearly
20 years, radioactive isotopes have been administered internally for diagno-

sis and treatment of disease. Observations on these patients have provided data.

3. *Atomic Bomb.* Although fire and blast caused most of the damage in the Hiroshima and Nagasaki bombings, about 15 to 20 per cent was caused by gamma and neutron radiations emitted during the explosions. Since 1946 the United States has had an Atomic Bomb Casualty Commission, studying the immediate and long-term effects on the population of those cities. In 1954 during atom bomb tests in Bikini, a heavy fall-out of bomb debris was experienced by dwellers in neighboring islands. Here doses could be quite accurately evaluated; they were much less, of course, than those in Japan. All exposed individuals are being carefully followed and studied.

Radiation Doses to Produce Particular Effects. Radiation effects are usually classified as early or immediate, and late. As has been pointed out, even the early reactions have a certain latent period, but if this is only days or weeks, the response is called immediate. These are the effects usually observed in animal research and in treatment of human beings.

For human beings, a dose of 500 rads given in a short time to the whole body would be very drastic; many individuals would die from its effects. Within a few hours after such an exposure, the individual would probably be violently sick, with nausea and diarrhea. Exhaustion, fever and delirium might follow, and death ensue. On the other hand, there might be a fair degree of recovery for a week or two, followed by a second cycle of sickness, with loss of hair, hemorrhages from skin and mucous membranes, profound anemia and low white blood count, loss of ability to combat infection, and again, possibly death. Both these cycles of illness would be classed as immediate effects. Those who survived would have a long slow convalescence, and probably never be really well. Years later there might be the development of leukemia, or of tumors or cataract. These last would be the late effects.

Half of those exposed to 500 rads would be expected to die. With smaller doses, fewer people would develop severe symptoms and the illness would be less severe. For 100 rads probably not more than 15 per cent of the population would be really sick, and few would die. For 25 rads it is probably that no one would observe any serious symptoms.

If only a small part of the body is exposed, very much larger doses are tolerated, and it is rare that death ensues, even after several thousand rads in a small region, unless this involves very sensitive vital organs. Such doses are regularly given in the treatment of cancer, not in a single exposure, but within a few weeks.

Delayed effects may appear years after the exposure, and may follow a period in which no radiation effect was observable. These effects include local tissue breakdown, sometimes leading to cancer, development of leukemia and possibly anemia, cataract formation, and possibly shortening of life.

The knowledge that such delayed effects may be produced by radiation indicates a need for a statistical study. It must be found out, from mortality data, how often any one of these conditions appears in the absence of exposure to radiation in addition to that from unavoidable internal sources and cosmic rays. This figure is to be compared with the incidence of the same condition following radiation exposure. If an increase is demonstrated, the frequency with which the condition develops at different levels of radiation dose must be determined, and the relationship between dose and incidence of the disease must be evaluated. Only in this manner will it be possible to assess the hazards, if any, associated with different uses of radiation. Some of these effects will be reviewed briefly.

Effects on Skin. This information is mostly obtained by following patients treated with x-rays. Doses up to 1000 rads or so, given within a few days, leave little or no permanent mark of any kind. For two or three times this, there may be permanent tanning and some superficial blood vessel damage. Hair loss may be permanent and sweat glands destroyed. Above 3000 or 4000 rads the skin may remain somewhat thin, covered with dilated blood vessels, sensitive, and subject to infection. Cancer may develop following this type of single large dose, but this is extremely rare. More often (though still not really frequently) it follows a long series of much smaller doses, repeated over months or years.

Effects on Blood. Anemia is a very rare late sequel of large doses to the bone marrow. This may be so damaged as not to be able to produce red cells in sufficient numbers. A much more common effect is the depression of white blood cell production, resulting in a leukopenia which may be transient or protracted. Platelet count may also be depressed. The final result of serious damage to the blood-forming organs may be the development of some form of leukemia. This is a disease in which uncontrolled over-production of the white blood cells occurs. It is apparently always fatal, although some forms may run chronic courses over many years, and long remissions may be produced by various types of therapy. The disease may follow a single large exposure or several smaller ones. In Nagasaki and Hiroshima up to 1955 there had been 93 proven and 15 suspected cases among those present at the time of the explosion and still living in one of those cities at the time of the diagnosis. Vital statistics would predict about 25 deaths from leukemia in a comparable unexposed population. This is too big a difference to be merely statistical. Furthermore, the distribution of the 93 cases within the radiation zone is instructive. For persons within 1000 meters of the center of the explosion, the incidence is at a rate of 128 per 10,000 population; at greater distances the numbers decrease fairly rapidly, until at more than 2000 meters the incidence is 2 per 10,000, which is not statistically different from the unirradiated group. Here the dose was probably of the order of 10 to 50 rads to the whole body. For those close to the center it is impossible to make even approximate estimates of dosage, for shielding of buildings, etc, is in all cases an unknown factor. Such shielding certainly existed; the unprotected individual close to the center of the blast did not survive. The first cases appeared within two years after the bomb exploded; from that time until 1951–53 the annual incidence increased; it then maintained a plateau for about three years, but now since 1957 appears to be definitely on the decline.

Repeated smaller whole body exposures have been given in the treatment of certain non-cancerous diseases. A careful study in England of a group of such patients showed a steadily increasing incidence of leukemia with dosage to spinal marrow from 2 per 10,000 with a dose less than 500 rads to 17.6 per 10,000 with a dose exceeding 2750 rads. The expected rate in an unirradiated population would be $\frac{1}{2}$ per 10,000. The average time between first x-ray treatment and diagnosis of leukemia was six years, but some patients had had several series of treatments.

Long-continued chronic exposure of the type received by some early radiologists might also be expected to lead to leukemia. There is some evidence that the death rate among American radiologists from leukemia is considerably higher than among the general population, but accurate statistics are not available. It would be expected that this difference would disappear with current knowledge and adequate planning for protection for the radiologist.

Induction of Cancer. Occasionally long after a single large dose of radiation or a long-continued series of small ones, there will be malignant degeneration of some cell system, with cancer formation. This may have been preceded by serious local effects, but in many cases the immediate local effects were very mild. The malignant transformation may arise in the blood-forming organs, with leukemia development, as just described, or it may be local in skin and other regions. Such changes leading to cancer formation occur only rarely in human beings, although in certain strains of inbred animals they can be produced regularly. Very little is known regarding the special trigger that sets off this type of transformation; it is regarded as being probably some form of cell mutation.

Lung cancer has been reported among Austrian uranium miners, a very high incidence arising among those who had continued to do this work for a very long time. The average interval between beginning of work and cancer development was 17 years, and in this time the average dose to the lungs was about 1000 rads. However, the possibility of inhalation and lodgement of highly active particles, resulting in very high local doses, cannot be ignored. No other record of production of lung cancer in man is found. Occasionally lesions can be produced in laboratory animals under special conditions.

This is also true for the assimilation of bone-seeking radioactive isotopes such as radium, strontium, or plutonium. Bone cancer can be produced in animals at will by these materials. In man, such cancers have arisen in individuals who had painted luminous dials with radioactive materials. It was their custom to point the brushes between their lips, thus ingesting some of the material. The latent period was of the order of 15 years, and the individuals developing cancer apparently all had retained at least 3.6 μc of radium or its equivalent. A few similar effects have been observed in individuals long ago given radium compounds internally for treatment of disease, and in people who have consumed large amounts of radioactive water, containing small amounts of radium salts in solution. The radium concentrates in the bones, and there continues to give off its radiations all through the lifetime of the individual.

A number of cases of cancer of the thyroid gland have been reported in children who had some years previously received x-ray treatment for enlargement of the thymus gland, infected tonsils, and other disorders. These treatments frequently were given in early infancy. Some years ago this was very popular; it has now been practically discontinued except in real emergencies,—which are *very* rare. The dose of radiation was always much smaller than that mentioned earlier as causing skin cancer, sometimes only 300 or 400 rads. The possibility of an additional hormonal factor cannot be over looked, but it has not been demonstrated.

Induction of Cataract. X-rays can produce cataract, but the necessary dose is at least some hundreds of rads. Of 98 cases of cataract among survivors of the Hiroshima explosion, 85 occurred in persons within 1000 meters of the center. Here the neutrons accompanying the explosion probably were mainly responsible; it is well known that they are several times as effective as x-rays in producing cataract. Of the cases mentioned, two later developed leukemia.

Effects of Exposure During Pregnancy. After a large dose of radiation, probably more than 1000 rads to the pelvic region, a pregnant women may have a miscarriage or a still-birth, although several cases are on record of women receiving more than this for treatment of cancer and producing normal children. Of 98 pregnant women in Nagasaki who were within 1000 meters of the center, about 23 per cent of those who had severe radiation sickness miscarried, compared to 4 per cent of those who were not sick, and 3 per cent of those 3000 or 4000 meters away.

Children irradiated *in utero* may be abnormal. The stage of pregnancy during which irradiation occurs is significant. There are few data on the effects of small doses of radiation on human pregnancy, but careful studies on mice by various workers are very suggestive. In these animals the fetus is much more radiosensitive during the period of development of organ primordia by differentiation from primitive cell types. This, in the human, is from the 18th to the 38th day. During this period it appears that a dose of the order of 50 r might produce serious abnormality. Later in pregnancy much larger doses would probably be necessary to produce the same defects. Relatively large doses, such as those employed in radiotherapy, would be expected, if the fetus survived, to result in overt damage. It is true that from time to time cases are reported of the birth of apparently normal children after intensive radiotherapy. There are also, however, many reports of various abnormalities, especially microcephaly. There are not enough of such reports for statistical evaluation. The Japanese records show an abnormally high percentage of mentally retarded children, and of microcephaly among those exposed before birth at distances of the order of 1000 meters from the center. In the group exposed at 5000 meters, no variation was found from the unexposed population.

Sterility. Permanent sterility may be produced in either man or woman by doses of the order of 500 r to the reproductive organs. This dose is close to the lethal one for the whole body, and would produce serious radiation sickness. Sterility is sometimes deliberately induced for medical reasons; in this case the radiation is closely confined to the critical organs. Under modern conditions of occupational exposure, for instance among radiologists and atomic energy plant workers, there is no evidence of any impairment of fertility. It should be pointed out that impotence is not produced by even large doses of radiation.

Shortening of Life Span. A number of reports based on observations made on animals suggest that exposure to ionizing radiations may lead to a reduction in the expectancy of life. In animals this can be demonstrated with chronic exposure at low doses. In man, definite statistical evidence is lacking. A widely quoted statement that in radiologists the average age at death is less than for the general population has been shown to be based on unsatisfactory evidence. A careful analysis of all available data leads to the conclusion that, at even the earlier permissible dose rates for occupational exposure, there is no evidence of life shortening. For larger chronic exposures, this would doubtless occur, but factual information has not been accumulated.

Genetic Effects of Radiation. Recently, the subject of genetic damage— harm to future generations—has assumed an important place. Unlike the systemic or somatic damage just discussed, there seems to be no lower level to the amount of radiation which can produce at least some order of gene mutations. It is not possible in such a discussion as this to go into much detail in the matter of genetic damage. However, there are certain points to be brought out.

It is hardly necessary to review the fact that in man, and all higher animals, every individual arises from a single cell formed by the fusion of two germ cells from the two parents. Each cell contains a nucleus, which in turn contains a number of microscopic, thread-like structures called chromosomes. Each chromosome is an aggregate of sub-microscopic structures, the genes, which determine the hereditary nature of the individual. The germ cell receives half its genes from each parent, and these determine the family likenesses.

However, occasionally a sudden change occurs in a gene; this is called a mutation, and the characteristic which it governs may be passed on in a new form to subsequent generations. Some mutations are *dominant*; that is, they can change the characteristic in the next generation, if either parent develops the mutation. Others are *recessive;* in this case the characteristic must be passed on by both parents for it to appear. This is an over-simplification of course; there are various possible combinations of which these might be considered the two extremes.

The hereditary variation found among human beings is the result of mutations which have occurred in past generations. As far as is known, all genes are subject to mutation, and over the population as a whole, mutation is constantly occurring at a definite but very low rate. Natural selection tends to eliminate harmful genes from the population, but they are again replenished by new mutations, so that in general a state of equilibrium exists. Evolution has occurred slowly by successions of small variations from the average. The cause of these natural mutations is not completely known; some are doubtless produced by cosmic rays and other unavoidable radiations, but these are apparently not responsible for all.

In animals the production of gene mutations by radiation has been studied; the mutation rate is proportional to the radiation exposure; there seems to be no lower threshhold and little or no recovery. There is no valid information about genetic effects of ionizing radiations in man, but it is reasonable to suppose that they follow the same general pattern.

The genetically effective dose to a population and to future generations depends on the ages of the exposed individuals as well as on the dose. If they are past the reproductive age, there is of course no effect. It is apparently the *frequency* of gene mutations that is increased by radiation; there is no evidence and little likelihood that radiation produces any new kinds of change. Damage to genetic material is cumulative and essentially irreparable, and is carried on from generation to generation. Long continued exposure to radiation of low intensity apparently induces as much gene mutation as a single exposure to an equal dose of higher intensity. This is unlike the recovery previously described for damage to the individual or to his organs,—the so-called *somatic* damage.

Genetic mutation is spoken of as damage; it is considered to be generally undesirable. True, the human race has arrived at its present state as a result of mutations, but in the generations during which these developments have taken place natural selection has also acted to get rid of many other, probably less desirable, mutations.

The increase in damage to be expected from radiation is usually discussed in terms of a "doubling dose". This is the dose that would eventually cause a complete doubling of gene mutations. The total effect in the population would, of course, depend on the kinds of mutations, and the interdependence of the various characteristics. It is impossible to assess this with any degree of accuracy, but certain general lines can be followed.

In any analysis of genetic changes in human beings it must be remembered that accurate data are completely lacking. There is a good deal of information on fruit flies and mice, both as to natural and radiation-induced mutations, but extrapolation to man must be done with caution. Such differences as total number of genes, total length of reproductive period during which mutations can be collected, and so on, complicate the picture. Accordingly, at the present time numerical data must be taken as probably of correct order of magnitude and broadly illustrative, not as rigidly factual.

The Doubling Dose. There are two effects to be considered if all individuals in the reproductive age receive a "doubling dose" of radiation; first, the effect on their immediate off-spring; and second, that on their later descendants and on the population as a whole.

The effect on various types of inheritance of doubling the mutation rate can be analyzed in some detail. Here, however, only the extremes of dominant and recessive mutations will be considered briefly. For a dominant trait, doubling the number of mutations in one generation would almost double the number of cases in the next. In successive generations the excess would be eliminated, and return to equilibrium established. However, if the doubling rate persisted generation after generation, equilibrium would eventually be established at double the original rate. In case of a recessive trait, a single doubling dose would produce an extremely small increase in the first generation; at a permanently doubled rate it would take more than 50 generations to increase the incidence by 50 per cent. Of course there are various intermediate sorts of inheritance, such as those requiring specific combinations of genes; the whole problem is very complex.

From one point of view the simplest way to discuss genetic effects due to radiation is to consider the total number of tangible serious genetic damages in presently living individuals,—damages such as epilepsy, idiocy, congenital malformation, defects in vision or in endocrine organs, etc,—and then see how the population would be expected to be affected by radiation. Roughly 2 per cent of all live births in the United States have genetic defects of this sort. If every member of the population were subjected once to a doubling dose of radiation, this level would rise in the first generation, but would eventually return to equilibrium. If the doubling dose were continued generation after generation, the figure would, after many generations, rise to the double level. Numerically, in the United States at present there are about 100 million children born in a generation; of these about 2 million will have genetic defects as a result of "spontaneous" unavoidable genetic changes which have occurred during the generations of their ancestry. If a doubling dose of radiation were applied to the total population for many generations, this would eventually rise to 4 million defectives. This would take a very long time; perhaps 10 per cent of the increase, or 200,000 new defectives would be found in the first generation. If the added dose were $\frac{1}{5}$ of the doubling dose for each generation, the first generation casualties would be 40,000 in the total 100 million, and the ultimate additional load 400,000 in the 100 million.

Dominant damaging mutations are much rarer than recessives,—perhaps only 1 per cent as common. The risk of one of these occurring spontaneously in any individual parent in almost negligible,—possibly 1 in 2000,—and even after a doubling dose of radiation it is still very small. For the more frequent recessive traits, *if* a parent carries the mutated gene the chance is 1 in 2 that a child receives it, 1 in 4 for a grandchild, and so on. Furthermore, every human being carries his natural load of harmful recessive genes received from his own ancestors; the addition of a few more by a doubled rate during his lifetime will be only a "drop-in-the-bucket" of the whole story. Therefore, any particular individual need not fear that just because he has received such a dose of radiation, he will run an appreciable risk of starting a bad line of descendants.

If a relatively small group of prospective parents receives the doubling dose of radiation, no noticeable effects will be produced in the sum total of the first generation or of any subsequent one. *For levels of radiation up to the doubling dose and even definitely beyond it, the genetic effects of radiation are only appreciable when reckoned over the population as a whole.*

For determining the doubling dose for human beings there are really no data which have any quantitative significance. Man is not a pure species, like a pure strain of fruit flies or white mice. The Japanese bomb cases are being studied carefully, to be sure, but little accurate information is available about the dosage, the regular incidence of mutations in the un-irradiated population, and so forth. Furthermore, so far, in a single generation of a few individuals, only a very few types of mutations can be observed.

Various lines of argument lead to estimates of from 25 rads to 150 rads for the doubling dose, with the probability that it lies between 30 and 80 rads. This dose can be delivered all at once or in many small portions during the reproductive period.

REFERENCES

British Medical Research Council: *The Hazards to Man of Nuclear and Allied Radiations*, London, Her Majesty's Stationery Office, 1956. Second Report, 1960.

HOLLAENDER, A. (Editor): *Radiation Biology*, McGraw Hill, New York, 1954.

STERN, CURT: *Principles of Human Genetics*, 2nd. Ed., W. H. Freeman, San Francisco, 1960.

United States National Academy of Science: *The Biological Effects of Atomic Radiations; Summary Reports*. Washington, D. C., National Research Council, 1956. Second Report, 1960.

United States National Academy of Science: *The Biological Effects of Atomic Radiations; A Report to the Public*, Washington, D. C., National Research Council, 1956. Second Report, 1960.

National Bureau of Standards Handbook 59, *Permissible Dose from External Sources of Ionizing Radiations*.

10

Radiation Hazards and Their Avoidance

Historical Introduction. Within a short time after the discovery of x-rays and of radioactive substances, it was recognized that the radiations were potential health hazards. Skin areas repeatedly exposed to them became dry, scaly, ulcerated, and as years went by cancer developed in some of these ulcers. Experiments with animals showed that other types of lesions could be produced, that life could be shortened, and even that the progeny of the irradiated creatures could show defects. A relationship was demonstrated between quantity of radiation received and degree of damage, and there were radiation levels below which no effects could be detected. These effects have been discussed in some detail in the preceding chapter.

The idea of setting up levels of "safe" exposure for radiation workers began to be developed in the 1920's, but it was not until after 1930 that radiation measurements were adequate to put "radiation-safety" standards on a workable basis. The first approach to a numerical value was based on surveys of existing installations, where individuals had been working for considerable periods under conditions such that their exposures could be evaluated, at least approximately. Based on the observation that no detectable radiation effects had been produced in a group of individuals who had been receiving radiation at rates definitely higher than 1 roentgen per week, this limit was adopted in 1934 by the International Commission on Radiological Protection. In the United States in 1936 this was lowered to 0.1 roentgen per day, partly as a result of the belief that there was not an adequate factor of safety in the 1934 recommendation.

In 1946 the National Committee on Radiation Protection, of the United States, undertook a review of the whole problem of permissible exposures. Up to that time, the level set earlier had been described as a "tolerance dose", namely a dose which could be tolerated by anyone without expectation of harm. As more information became available about radiation effects, it became a question whether there was such a thing as a tolerance dose; it appeared more likely that *any* amount of radiation might produce some damage, and that it would be necessary to balance this possible damage against the known benefits. Therefore the term *tolerance dose* was rejected, and in its stead came the expression *maximum permissible dose* (MPD). The Committee then undertook to set up such permissible limits, with the understanding that these might be subject to revision as more information became available.

During the decade between the 1936 recommendations and the time of the study, new and more powerful sources of x-rays had been developed, artificially radioactive nuclides had become available, the conditions under which persons might be exposed to radiation became more numerous and varied, and more was known about biological effects of radiations. At this time the permissible whole-body exposure to gamma rays and x-rays in the usual energy range was set at 0.3 roentgen per week. This reduction was made in spite of the fact that, so far as was known, there was not a single case on record where an individual whose exposure did not exceed the previously established maximum had developed any detectable injury that could reasonably be attributed to that radiation exposure. National Bureau of Standards Handbook 59, *Permissible Dose from External Sources of Ionizing Radiation,* contains a detailed treatment of these recommendations.

Present Recommendations. Nevertheless a further reduction in maximum permissible dose was agreed upon by national and international organizations in 1956. This is still not based on any positive evidence of damage at the earlier levels, but is rather in accordance with trends of scientific opinion. It is recognized that there are many uncertainties in the available data, and it is believed that there will be a large future increase in radiation uses.

Until the current recommendations, no overt attention was paid to the genetic problem. It was recognized that genetic damage could be produced, but it was felt that the great mass of the population received so little radiation that the contribution to the genetic *average* by the dose received by radiation workers would be negligible. However with the greatly increasing use of medical x-rays and the wide-spread applications of atomic energy, this may no longer be the case. Accordingly the entire populace has been divided into two groups, a small one consisting of those who work with radiation or radioactive substances under the supervision of a radiation safety officer, and a very large one consisting of everyone else. The recommendations for radiation workers (occupational exposure) apply to all medical users of radioactive nuclides and to their patients except when these are receiving treatments or tests deigned to benefit them; they apply to personnel in departments where radiation use is adequately controlled, but not to the general hospital or office staff nor to casual visitors.

Present Sources of Radiation to Which Human Beings are Exposed. Sources of radiation may be divided into *natural,* over which little or no control can be exerted, and *man-made,* which could be subject to modification.

Natural sources are cosmic rays, radiations from earth and building materials, and radioactive substances regularly found as constituents of the body. Cosmic rays increase in intensity with altitude, being about twice as great in places a mile or so high as at sea level. Environmental radiation depends on the type of soil or rock upon which the individual lives, and on the material (stone, brick, or wood) of which his buildings are constructed.

Inside a stone house on a granite base radiation may be more than twice as great as in a wooden house on deep soil. The radioactive content of the average human adult is about $\frac{1}{7}$ μc of potassium-40, $\frac{1}{17}$ μc of carbon-14, and a trace of radium. The total radiation to the average individual from all these natural sources, external and internal, is about from 100 to 200 millirads per year, and this dose is received by everyone.

Of man-made sources, for those who are not actually radiation workers, by far the most important is medical and dental x-rays, and here, of course, the variation among individuals is tremendous. In addition there are small contributions from various luminous devices and other equipment containing radioactive material, from nuclear power plants and related activities, and from fall-out from nuclear weapons. This last is often greatly exaggerated. For individuals in the United States, now and in the foreseeable future (unless there is nuclear war) it amounts to something like $\frac{1}{5}$ of the dose received from cosmic rays.

In the preceding chapter it was pointed out that genetic changes were the only ones of real concern for the general population, and that these depended on the *average* exposure to all prospective parents throughout their reproductive lifetimes. If the medical, dental, and occupational exposures of part of the population are averaged for everybody, and the fall-out contribution included, the result is approximately the same as the exposure from natural sources.

If any individual is engaged in an occupation involving use of x-rays, radioactive substances, or nuclear reactors, the somatic rather than the genetic hazard is to be considered; it is now a question of individual welfare rather than that of the race. Since radiation workers are only a fraction of one per cent of the total population, they may be considered as a very special class. Users of radioactive nuclides, of course, fall into this class, and the control of their exposures will be considered at some length.

Maximum Permissible Dose Recommendations for Occupational Conditions (MPD's in Controlled Areas). The basis of the present recommendations is the *total* accumulated dose in an individual's lifetime, rather than a daily or weekly allotment. The unit is the *rem;* this is the quantity of any ionizing radiation which has the same biological effectiveness as 1 rad of x-rays in the usual energy range. Various radiations have various *relative biological effectiveness (RBE)*, which differ according to the specific ionization; the dose in rems is equal to the dose in rads multiplied by the RBE for the radiation in question. Since for all beta and gamma radiations from radioactive nuclides considered in this book, the RBE is unity, it is satisfactory to use rads in thinking of the recommendations, although they will be quoted below in rems.

The maximum permissible accumulated dose to the whole body, in rems, at any age, is equal to five times the number of years beyond 18, provided no annual increment exceeds 15 rems. Thus the accumulated MPD = 5(N-18) rems, where N is the age and greater than 18. (Occupational exposure may not start before age 18). This implies an *average* weekly dose of 0.1 rem if the exposure is a regular part of the occupation. However, there are provisions for fluctuations as long as the annual total is kept at about 5 rems. A permissible weekly whole body dose of 0.3 rems may be maintained for an appreciable period, provided that in another period the dose is enough less to keep the total for the year within the set limit. Even the 0.3 rems in a week may be exceeded for short periods, but in this case the total accumulation in 13 consecutive weeks must not exceed 3 rems. Again, such a period of high exposure must be compensated for by an adequate period of low.

In radiation work the hands and forearms are often exposed to more radiation than any other part of the body. Since hands and forearms do not constitute a critical region involving either gonads or vital organs, it is permissible for them to receive considerably more radiation. Their annual maximum permissible dose has been set at 75 rem; fluctuations may be treated in the same manner as for whole body doses.

Maximum Permissible Dose Recommendations for the Whole Population. (MPD's for the General Public.) The maximum permissible dose *to the gonads* for the population of the United States as a whole, from all sources of ionizing radiation, including medical and other man-made sources and natural background, shall not exceed an average of 14 rems per individual over the period from conception to age 30, and one-third that for each decade thereafter during the reproductive period. This means an average of about 0.5 rem per year for the first 30 years. It must be kept in mind that in the genetic picture it is the *average* that counts, and that there may be very wide variations among individuals.

At present it is estimated that the average dose per person per generation of 30 years due to natural background is about 4 rems, and that due to medical x-rays and other "appurtenances of civilization" about 5. Therefore it appears that currently the average exposure is well below that accepted as permissible.

Dosage Due to Internal Emitters. Radiation levels for radio-nuclides deposited within the body must conform to the same general principles as for external irradiation. Whole body irradiation to individuals in controlled areas should be limited to 0.3 rem for the first week after administration of a short-lived isotope. For a long-lived one this may be too high a dose level, the 3 rem in 13 weeks must also be adhered to, with correspondingly less during the remainder of the year.

Methods for determining dose from isotopes within the body have been discussed in Chapter 8, and their application to protection problems will be discussed later in this chapter.

All medical uses are considered as coming more or less under controlled area regulations. However, when it is a question of isotope therapy, or of diagnostic procedures from which the patient is expected to receive some advantage, it is evident that these limits cannot be imposed, any more than they can in diagnostic and therapeutic applications of x-rays. Here the matter of the benefit to be obtained from the radiation must be weighed against the possible harm, and the patient's doctor must make the final decision. On the other hand, in research, where normal (or even diseased) individuals are to be used in isotope studies, every effort must be made to keep the dose at the lowest practicable level.

For individuals outside controlled areas, dose levels should in general be not more than $\frac{1}{10}$ those inside. Internal isotope exposure outside controlled areas can only come from drinking contaminated water or inhaling contaminated air, and is therefore related to radioactive waste disposal. This subject will be considered in the next chapter.

The Radio-Isotope Laboratory. The laboratory must be designed to provide all necessary safety. Some specific suggestions will be presented in Chapter 21; various books and AEC publications supply more details. A few points sometimes given insufficient emphasis may be mentioned.

All surfaces should be smooth, non-porous, and waterproof. Floor covering should be asphalt, rubber, or vinyl tile, or linoleum; concrete and wood are highly undesirable. Walls, especially around sinks and other critical areas, should be covered with high-gloss enamel paint. Bench tops should be stainless steel, especially where radioactive solutions are to be handled. In any case, operations should be carried out in easily cleanable plastic or metal trays.

In most isotope laboratories a fume hood is installed, although this is not necessary for handling solutions at room temperature. The hood must be of such design that eddy currents cannot return contaminated air to laboratory space. It is necessary for the hood to be mounted on a base sturdy enough to support considerable shielding, if appreciable quantities of gamma emitters are to be handled. It must not discharge into a general institutional duct system, but must have its own exhaust high enough above the roof of the building to ensure that contaminated gases cannot re-enter through windows.

Sinks should be of stainless steel or alberene stone, with separate drainboards for clean and dirty glassware. Water valves should be controlled by foot or knee levers.

For manipulating moderate amounts of beta emitters, a "gloved box" is convenient. This is rarely necessary in the medical isotope laboratory, but is frequently useful in radiochemical and radiobiological procedures. It is simply a closed container with a suitable ventilation and exhaust system, into which shoulder-length gloves have been built. The operator, outside the box, inserts his hands and arms into the gloves, and can then carry out procedures inside the box without danger of contamination.

Safety Procedures with External Beta-Particle Emitters. Beta rays *per se* never constitute a whole-body external radiation hazard; their range in tissue seldom exceeds a few millimeters. Ranges in water and in glass, in relation to maximum beta energy are given in Figure 39. Thus it is

seen that P³² betas (E_max = 1.7 Mev) cannot traverse more than 9 mm of
water or tissue; a glass bottle with 3 mm walls will stop most of them.

However, it must be remembered that in traversing matter these beta
rays give rise to bremsstrahlung. It was stated in Chapter 6 that the
fraction of the beta energy appearing as external bremsstrahlung is approximately equal to $\dfrac{ZE}{3000}$, where E is the maximum beta energy and Z the atomic
number of the absorber. Thus the 3 mm glass which stops the beta
particles serves as a source for penetrating x-rays whose maximum energy
is over a million volts. Only about 1 per cent of the total energy will

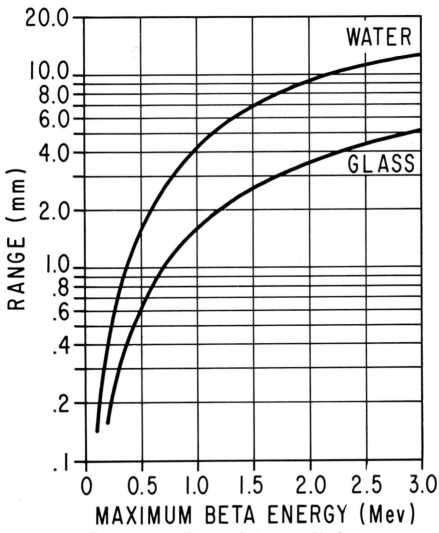

Fig. 39.   Ranges of beta particles in water and in glass.

10

emerge in this way, but for a large quantity of the nuclide this would not be negligible. Therefore appreciable quantities of radioactive nuclides emitting penetrating beta particles should be stored in shielded containers.

A gamma emitter may have low energy gammas but higher energy betas, so that the bremsstrahlung is more penetrating than the gamma rays. In this case the heavy shield against the gamma rays (see below) should have a lining of low atomic number material to reduce the quantity of bremsstrahlung. For instance K^{42} has 3.58 Mev betas and 1.5 Mev gammas. An aluminum lining in the lead shield stops the betas and greatly reduces the bremsstrahlung.

One of the greatest hazards with beta-emitters is the handling of uncovered vessels containing the material. In Chapter 8 a method is given for calculating dose due to beta-emitting flat sources. In an open solution of P^{32} with a concentration of 1 mc per cu cm the dose rate at the surface is about 13 rads per minute. This will not be appreciably reduced by attenuation in a few centimeters of air, nor will there be much reduction by inverse square law from a source of this kind. Obviously a hand or face over such an open container may receive a considerable dose of radiation in a short time.

Safety Procedures with External Gamma Ray Emitters. Gamma rays are in general much more penetrating than beta rays, and accordingly require more precautions in handling. Two methods are available for reducing radiation intensity, increasing the distance between the radiation source and the recipient, and interposing a barrier to absorb the radiation.

The decrease in intensity due to increased distance results from the geometrical phenomenon known as the *inverse square law*. Consider a point source of radiation at the center of a sphere of radius r. The surface of this sphere is $4\pi r^2$ sq cm, hence 1 sq cm will receive $\dfrac{1}{4\pi r^2}$ times the total energy emitted. On the surface of a larger sphere, of radius R, 1 sq cm will receive $\dfrac{1}{4\pi R^2}$ times the total.

Hence

$$\frac{\text{radiation per unit area at distance r}}{\text{radiation per unit area at distance R}} = \frac{\dfrac{1}{4\pi r^2}}{\dfrac{1}{4\pi R^2}} = \frac{R^2}{r^2},$$

or, the intensity of the radiation is inversely proportional to the square of the distance from a point source. For sources which are not points, the actual falling off of intensity with distance is slower.

In general it is not feasible to carry out all operations at considerable distances from radiation sources, and so shields or barriers are interposed. In the case of radioactive nuclides these barriers usually take the form of containers of lead or other heavy material in which the radioactive substances are placed. The thickness of lead necessary depends on the quantity of the nuclide, the distance to the person, the duration of the expected exposure, and the gamma ray dose rate Γ.

For any number of millicuries, N, the dose rate at 1 cm from a point source is $N\Gamma$ roentgens per hour, and at any other distance d it is $\dfrac{N\Gamma}{d^2}$ r per hr. For example, at 50 cm from 20 mc of I^{131} the dose rate would be $\dfrac{20 \times 2.20}{(50)^2} = 0.017$ r per hr or 17 milliroentgens per hour.

Working conditions should be based on the MPD of 0.1 rem per week for constant exposure. For a 40-hour week this corresponds to 2.5 mr (millirem) per hour. To reduce 17 mr per hr to 2.5 mr per hr would require a barrier cutting down the intensity by a factor of 7 times. In calculating barrier thicknesses it must be remembered that one half value layer of the barrier material reduces the radiation to one-half, two half value layers to one-fourth, three to one-eighth, and so on.

Lead is usually employed in the construction of barriers and shielded containers, since for a given reduction in radiation its bulk will be less than that of any other practicable material. In Table 10 are listed half value layers in lead for radioactive materials likely to be employed in hospitals, together with the gamma dose rate constants.

Table 10. Lead Half Value Layers and Gamma Ray Dose Factors for Various Radioactive Nuclides

Isotope	Half Value Layer Cm Lead	Γ r per mc-hr at 1 cm
Bromine^{82}	1.0	14.6
Cesium^{137}	0.5	3.0
Chromium^{51}	0.2	0.18
Cobalt^{60}	1.2	12.9
Copper^{64}	0.4	1.1
Gold^{198}	0.3	2.27
Iodine^{130}	0.7	12.1
Iodine^{131}	0.3	2.20
Iodine^{132}	1.0	12.3
Iron^{59}	1.1	6.8
Manganese^{52}	1.0	18.5
Potassium^{42}	1.2	1.40
Sodium^{22}	1.0	13.2
Sodium^{24}	1.5	18.7
Tin^{113}	0.3	3.5
Zinc^{65}	1.0	2.9

For any particular situation, with a specified amount of any isotope, the r per hr at the position is calculated as just indicated:

$$r \text{ per hr} = \frac{N\Gamma}{d^2}. \qquad\qquad 10-(1)$$

The attenuation which must be supplied by the barrier (attenuation factor) is then found by dividing this value of r per hour by the permissible r per hour for the situation in question.

$$\text{Att. Fact} = \frac{\dfrac{N}{d^2}}{\text{Permissible dose rate per hour}} \qquad 10{-}(2)$$

From this factor the necessary number of half value layers is immediately obtained. Table 11 is useful for this purpose.

Table 11.   *Relation between Attenuation Factor and Number of Half Value Layers*

Att Fact	1	2	3	5	7	10	15	20	30	50	75	100
No HVL		0	1	1.6	2.3	2.8	3.3	3.9	4.3	4.9	5.6	6.2	6.6

In deciding barriers for any particular set of conditions, a *work factor* may be employed. For instance, the technician will not spend an entire 40-hour week 50 cm from strong radiation sources. If the entire isotope laboratory is to be maintained at 2.5 mr per hour or less, this factor must be used for all barrier calculations. In this case the dose level at the worst location will be 2.5 mr per hr and much less throughout most of the area. If, on the other hand, she spends a maximum of 10 hours a week close to sources, and the rest of the time in rooms with radiation levels less than 1 mr per hr, the activity at the working position may be about 10 mr per hr.

The barrier to be employed will usually be selected according to the total isotope load. Because some nuclides emit much more penetrating radiations than others, it may not be the greatest number of millicuries that sets the limit. As an example, consider a laboratory where on different days the working space will have to accommodate in one week

200 mc of I^{131},
150 mc of Au^{198},
20 mc of Na^{24},
15 mc of P^{32}.

The average distance for the period of actual manipulation is about 50 cm; less than half an hour will be spent in this position with each nuclide. However, two hours may be spent at an average distance of 1.5 meters with the sodium and the iodine. In addition it should be expected that 10 hours will be spent in a region of possibly 2.5 mr per hr. Out of a 40-hour week, then, about half is at set levels of activity and the 100 mr may be divided among them. The phosphorus may, of course, be neglected in planning gamma ray barriers.

If the 50-cm dose rate is maintained at 15 mr per hr, three half-hour exposures add to 22.5 mr. The 1.5 meter distance dose rate automatically drops to $\frac{1}{9}$ that at 50 cm, or 1.7 mr per hr. Four hours at this level total 6.8 mr. Ten hours in a general 2.5 mr per hour field total 25 mr. Thus all the exposures mentioned add to just about half the weekly permissible dose, leaving a good margin of safety. The necessary barrier is set by the manipulation at the work table with 50 cm distance for one-half hour.

For 200 mc I^{131} $\dfrac{200 \times 2.20}{2500} = 0.176$ r per hr.

150 mc Au^{198} $\dfrac{150 \times 2.27}{2500} = 0.136$ r per hr.

20 mc Na^{24} $\dfrac{20 \times 18.7}{2500} = 0.150$ r per hr.

To bring these to 15 mr per hr the attenuation factors are

For the I^{131} $\dfrac{176}{15} = 11.7$, requiring 3.5 hvl or 1 cm Pb.

Au^{198} $\dfrac{136}{15} = 9.1$ 3.2 hvl or 1 cm Pb.

Na^{24} $\dfrac{150}{15} = 10$ 3.3 hvl or 5 cm Pb.

Obviously the sodium barrier is the important one, and if 5 cm of lead are used the radiations from all the other isotopes will be reduced much below the necessary level. It might then be inquired what the result would be of using only 3 cm of lead as a barrier. This is only two half value layers for the sodium, so that during the half hour of exposure to this isotope the dose would be 18.5 mr. However, the dose rates for the iodine and the gold would still be reduced to very low levels, so that this reduction would be justified if there were a reason for reducing barrier weight or thickness.

It is obviously unreasonable to insist on providing such a barrier that the radiation everywhere is reduced to 2.5 mr per hr or less. If an analysis of the expected work load is carried out as indicated, with a reasonable factor of safety for occasional exposure, there will be adequate protection.

It should be pointed out that mere interposition of a barrier between the source and the operator may not be sufficient. If the source is close to a wall, and there is no barrier between source and wall, a considerable amount of radiation may be scattered back into the room. Similarly, if the source is on a table, the bottom of the container should be shielded to prevent scatter from the floor. Of course protection must always be provided for occupants of rooms beyond walls or under floors.

Although the body of the operator is protected by shields, his hands and face may not be, as manipulations are carried out. Care must be taken to keep containers closed and adequately covered with lead except during actual pipetting or diluting. Pipetting by mouth should *never* be done, and pipettes or other instruments should be tilted so that the hand does not come over the open container. Forceps and other tools should have adequately long handles, but not so long as to cause awkwardness. There are many special tools available on the market; this is not the place to describe them.

The Accidental Radioactive "Spill". It is inevitable that, in a busy laboratory or hospital, radioactive material will some time be spilled on floor, furniture, or personnel. If a container has been upset, it should immediately be righted, care being taken not to touch wet parts with bare hands. Paper towels should immediately be dropped on spilled liquid to keep it from spreading, but further operations usually need not be done in a hurry. The first thing is to make sure that no person has become contaminated. If he has, he must immediately get rid of contaminated clothing and scrub contaminated skin. (Detailed instructions for these and other procedures will be found in National Bureau of Standards Handbook 48, Control and Removal of Radioactive Contamination in Laboratories, which should be in the hands of every user of appreciable quantities of radioactive nuclides.)

The procedure in cleaning up the spill is to prevent its spread. As much as possible of the spilled material should be taken up with damp papers, which must be handled with forceps and deposited immediately into a container for contaminated waste. After as much as possible has been removed in this way, the surface should be washed with damp—not wet— rags, always working toward the center rather than out from it. Monitoring should be carried out throughout the procedure. Reduction of counting rate over 1 or 2 square feet to 5 times background, or over a few square inches to 10 times background is usually satisfactory, especially for short-lived nuclides.

Transportation of Radioactive Material within the Institution, and Administration of Doses to Patients. When radioactive material is to be transported from one part of the hospital to another, the thickness of the portable lead container will depend on the amount and kind of nuclide and the time in transit. Very heavy containers for large doses of radioactive gold or iodine should be mounted on wheeled carts or tables.

In administering radioactive material to patients by mouth, different procedures may be used depending on the quantity of isotope. Tracer and small therapy doses are available from commercial suppliers in capsule form; in this case the patient handles the capsule and swallows it with an adequate amount of water. When the tracer dose is in solution, it is usually poured into a paper cup, the bottle rinsed two or three times, the rinsings added to the liquid in the cup, and the whole given to the patient to drink, followed by more water poured into the same cup. For a therapy dose the bottle is not taken out of its shield. The patient drinks the active solution through a beverage straw; water is then poured into the bottle and drunk through the same straw, and the process repeated to be sure that no radioactive residue remains. All used cups, straws, and wipes of any kind are taken back to the isotope laboratory for proper disposal.

For intracavitary colloidal gold, the infusion apparatus is usually transported on the same cart with the isotope, and after the procedure all the contaminated equipment is returned to the laboratory.

The Radioactive Patient. The patient who receives radioactive material now becomes a potential source of radiation and must be treated accordingly. No tracer or test dose will make a patient active enough to demand any precautions, and this is also true for therapy doses up to a few millicuries, *as long as the material remains in the patient.* Radioactive vomitus or excreta can cause contamination; in a hospital personnel should be instructed as to precautions to be taken in disposing of the material. Some details will be given in the next chapter. At home, a single treatment would never lead to a hazardous situation.

For larger doses more definite precautions are necessary, and it is recommended that patients receiving more than 30 mc of I^{131} be hospitalized and that intracavitary colloidal gold instillation should always be a hospital procedure. If the gold procedure is safely completed there will be no leakage or elimination of isotope. If the wound should leak, warning is immediately given by the staining of the linen; the radiation safety officer should be summoned and his instructions carried out.

In the case of a large dose of I^{131}, usually for treatment of thyroid cancer, the patient will excrete a considerable part of the isotope by way of the kidneys during the first 24 hours. It is frequently desirable to save the urine in order to check excretion and retention. Instructions as to handling it must be given to nurses or orderlies. In hot weather an individual who perspires profusely may eliminate an appreciable amount of radioactive iodine by this route, and the bed-clothes should be checked for possible contamination.

The patient with 100 mc of Au^{198} in her abdominal cavity is emitting radiation at the rate of 235 r per hour at 1 cm (point source). At 50 cm, a survey type measuring instrument indicates about 100 mr per hour from such a patient immediately after the treatment; the dose rate will, of course, decrease with decay of the isotope. Personnel caring for these patients can carry out all indicated procedures, but should not spend unnecessary time about them (see below). A patient in a neighboring bed, say 2 meters away, would receive about 8 mr in the first hour, and this would decrease so that in a week her total dose would be about 650 mr, if both patients stayed constantly in these relative positions. This is more than the permissible annual dose for non-occupational exposure. If the patient in the next bed is beyond the reproductive age, there is no cause for concern, but young people, and particularly pregnant women should not be thus exposed. In this connection it should be remembered that an ordinary building partition of hollow tile or plaster board is not sufficient to stop the gamma rays. Putting radioactive patients in individual rooms is often advocated, and this is frequently desirable. But it should be ascertained that patients in the next room are not being irradiated. Bed heads are often in contact with the common wall, and patient-to-patient distances not as large as they should be.

Instructions for Personnel Caring for Radioactive Patients. Except for patients who have received large therapeutic doses of radioactive material, there is no hazard to personnel. Even in the case of these patients, the hazard is insignificant if simple instructions are carried out. Detailed notes covering various situations are available in various publications. Some general information may be given here.

If the procedure has been carried out without mishap, and the patient has not vomited or been incontinent, the first question which arises is the length of time which may be spent near the patient for ordinary nursing care. Table 12 gives maximum daily times which may be spent at different distances from patients who have received radioactive material. For radioactive gold or iodine (I^{131}) these times apply only to the first two post-treatment days. After the second day times may be doubled and after the fifth, doubled again. In the case of the gold, the half period is just over two days, and for the iodine there will have been a good deal of excretion during the

Table 12. Permissible Times for Nurses to Spend with Radioactive Patients

Radio-Nuclide	Initial Millicuries	Maximum Daily Hours at Specified Distance*			
		2 Feet	3 Feet	4 Feet	6 Feet
I^{131}	200	$\frac{1}{2}$	1	2	4
or	150	$\frac{3}{4}$	$1\frac{1}{2}$	3	6
Au^{198}	100	1	2	4	8
	50	2	4	8	Over 12
	25	4	8	Over 12	Over 12
Co^{60}	100	$\frac{1}{6}$	$\frac{1}{3}$	$\frac{2}{3}$	$1\frac{1}{3}$
	50	$\frac{1}{3}$	$\frac{2}{3}$	$1\frac{1}{3}$	$2\frac{1}{2}$
	25	$\frac{2}{3}$	$1\frac{1}{3}$	$2\frac{1}{2}$	6
	10	$1\frac{2}{3}$	$3\frac{1}{2}$	6	Over 12
Radium	100	$\frac{1}{4}$	$\frac{1}{2}$	1	2
	50	$\frac{1}{2}$	1	2	4
	25	1	2	4	8
	10	$2\frac{1}{2}$	5	10	Over 12

* Note that for iodine and gold these times apply only to the first two days. On the third day then may be doubled, and on the fifth day doubled again.

initial period. In the case of radium or radioactive cobalt the daily time remains the same throughout the treatment period, since there is neither elimination nor appreciable decay. It is not generally necessary to limit visitors to these patients, except for children and pregnant women. Others may be cautioned to sit at a little distance from the patient's bed.

In any hospital where radioisotope therapy is administered, there will be a radiation safety officer who will be responsible for instructing personnel in necessary precautions, and to whom all unusual situations must immediately be referred. However some general precautions may be listed: Radioactive materials should not be allowed to come into contact with the skin. Rubber or plastic gloves should be worn whenever such contact is possible, as for instance in handling bedpans for these patients. Articles or utensils suspected of being contaminated should be turned over to the safety officer for monitoring; disposable materials such as paper handkerchiefs should be put into non-porous paper garbage bags until they can be thus disposed of. No precautions are usually necessary for dishes, instruments, or utensils, unless contamination (as by vomiting) is known to have occurred. Standard items of nursing care, such as basins and bedpans, should be thoroughly washed with soap and running water; the nurse or orderly should wear heavy rubber gloves while doing this. The same items should be used for an individual patient until his treatment is considered terminated. If they were used for a patient who had received a large dose of I^{131} they should be monitored before being returned to stock. If the patient vomits, is incontinent, or leaks material from a drainage wound (especially in the case of radioactive gold) the radiation safety officer should be summoned at once. In the meantime all unnecessary people should be removed from the contaminated neighborhood, and every effort made to confine the contamination until it can be dealt with as discussed in "spills" above.

Handling of Bodies Containing Radioactive Isotopes. It will occasionally happen that a patient requires emergency surgery shortly after receiving a therapeutic dose of radioactive isotope. Or the patient may die, in which case an autopsy may be desired, or the body will be embalmed. The handling of such bodies may pose problems of radiation exposure for the surgeon, the pathologist, or the embalmer. This subject is treated in detail in National Bureau of Standards Handbook 65, *Safe Handling of Bodies Containing Radioactive Isotopes.*

Here it may be briefly stated that a patient whose isotope content is not more than 5 mc of any radioactive material does not constitute a hazard for any of these procedures. If surgery or autopsy is to be done on an individual at a time when the isotope content is greater than this, the radiation safety officer should advise as to procedures, in accordance with information in the handbook. A body may be embalmed without autopsy with an isotope content up to 30 mc, provided standard procedures are employed. If the body contains more activity, it is recommended that embalming be carried out in the hospital morgue, with the collaboration of the safety officer. (See page 158).

Safety Considerations for Isotopes Administered Internally. When radioactive nuclides are administered internally for therapeutic purposes, of course there is no thought of keeping the dose to the patient within the permissible levels. However, when they are used for diagnostic studies, and particularly for research in normal human beings, every effort should be made to maintain low levels. Certain recommendations for internal emitters (isotopes injected or ingested) are given in National Bureau of Standards Handbook 69, *Maximum Permissible Body Burdens and Maximum Permissible Concentrations of Radionuclides in Air and Water, for Occupational Exposure.* Here are listed maximum permissible body burdens, that is, amounts of isotope present continuously in the body, which will never deliver more than the permissible irradiation, and concentrations in air and water which may be continuously inhaled or ingested and maintain the same levels. There is no information about permissible occasional doses, such as tracers. In The ICRP report on the same subject (see reference 52), valuable data are given as to "critical organs," that is, organs in which radioactive material is concentrated, the percentage of the isotope deposited there, the metabolism and excretion or effective half life. Often, however, only the element is listed and it is not stated whether all compounds behave in the same manner, or to which ones the data apply. Therefore effective half lives thus listed should not be used without some indication as to their applicability. If there is uncertainty, the physical half life should be used. Any error will then be on the conservative side.

In Chapter 8 a formula was developed for the calculation of dose delivered during the first week from a quantity of isotope within the body:

$$D_{(\beta + \gamma)} (\text{1st week}) = C\ T\left[(73.8\ \overline{E}_\beta + 0.0346\ \Gamma g)\ (1 - \frac{1}{2^{\,7/T}})\right].$$

$$10-(3)$$

From this, the concentration of isotope to be deposited within a given tissue mass, to give a specified dose in the first week, can be obtained:

$$C = \frac{D_{(\beta + \gamma)}}{T(73.8\ \overline{E}_\beta + 0.0346\ \Gamma g)\left(1 - \frac{1}{2^{\,7/T}}\right)}\ \mu c\ \text{per gm.}\qquad 10-(4)$$

For permissible doses of nuclides having half period two weeks or less $D_{(\beta + \gamma)}$ may be taken as 0.3 rad; C gives the permissible concentration in μc per gram. This multiplied by tissue weight gives total μc to be administered. If effective half life is known, it should be used instead of T (physical). It is often more convenient numerically to multiply the numerator by 1000 and have the result in μc per kg. Instead of C in the formula it may be well to use C_p to indicate permissible concentration.

For example, the permissible dose of Na^{24}, considered to be uniformly distributed throughout the body, is obtained by

$$C_p = \frac{0.3 \times 1000}{0.625 \, (73.8 \times 0.55 + 0.0346 \times 18.7 \times 120)}$$

$$= 4 \, \mu c \text{ per kg.}$$

Since this is essentially all delivered in the first week, the second term in the denominator of the general formula is omitted. Thus for a 60 kg individual the permissible tracer dose is 240 μc.

If a single organ takes up most of the nuclide, or is particularly sensitive to radiation, this is called the "critical organ," and dose must be calculated for this rather than for the whole body. Reference has already been made to The ICRP report on permissible internal dose for information as to critical organs, percentage of dose in them, and so on. As an example, S^{35} may be considered. This is stated to concentrate in the skin, 0.17 of all in the body being there. The mass of the skin is 2 kg; $\overline{E}_\beta$ is 0.049 Mev; T_{eff} is 18 days. For the permissible dose

$$C_p = \frac{0.3 \times 1000}{(18 \times 73.8 \times 0.049) \left(1 - \dfrac{1}{2^{7/18}}\right)} = 20 \, \mu c \text{ per kg.}$$

The 2 kg of skin can use 40 μc and this is 17 per cent of the entire dose. The total which may be administered then is 235 μc.

For longer-lived isotopes the permissible weekly dose should be taken as 0.1 rad instead of 0.3, since the dose integration will extend over more than 13 weeks, and the total might be too high. For these nuclides it is simpler to find the dose per day and multiply it by 7 than to find the fraction decaying in the first week (See page 113). For instance, for Ca^{45}, T_{phys} is 164 days and T_{eff} is little if any less. If a soluble calcium salt is ingested about 50 per cent reaches the skeleton, which is the critical organ, weighing about 7 kg. $\overline{E}_\beta = 0.077$ Mev.

$$d_\beta \text{ (day)} = 51.2 \, \overline{E}_\beta \, C, \text{ whence}$$

$$C_p = \frac{0.1 \times 1000}{7 \times 51 \times 0.077} = 3.6 \, \mu c \text{ per kg retained} = 7.2 \, \mu c \text{ per kg ingested}$$

For the 7 kg skeleton the total permissible dose is 50 μc.

For long-lived materials about whose turnover rate there is insufficient information, a conservative estimate of permissible dose may be arrived at in a different manner. In Handbook 69, and in Part 20 of the Federal Register are given the maximum permissible concentrations of many radionuclides in water for continuous ingestion. It is assumed that the total 13-week intake on this basis would be a permissible dose for it should amount to

1.3 rads in that period. If there is contamination with a different radio-isotope of the element, its radiation must be considered; if the nuclide in question has a radioactive daughter, this must also be included.

An example illustrating these points is the determination of the permissible dose of Ca^{47} as received from Oak Ridge. The catalog states that the Ca^{47}/Ca^{45} content of the sample is 10 to 1. The material is also in equilibrim with the Sc^{47} daughter. The permissible concentrations of these nuclides, and the permissible 13-week intakes on a basis of 2 liters consumed per day, are given in Table 13, together with the Ca^{47} equivalent for the Ca^{45}. Obviously the scandium does not have to be considered. Its permissible intake for bone dose is many times larger than that for the calcium, with which it is in equilibrium. For the gastrointestinal tract as critical organ, the permissible calcium intakes are larger than for the bone, and the scandium is well within the limits.

Table 13.   Permissible Ingested Quantities of Ca^{45}, Ca^{47} and Sc^{47}

Nuclide	Permissible $\mu c/cc$ Water	μc 13-Week Intake at 2 Liters per Day	μc Ca^{45} equivalent to 1 μc Ca^{47}	Permissible Combined Ca^{45} and Ca^{47}
		For Bone as Critical Organ		
Ca^{45}	9×10^{-5}	16	6	6
Ca^{47}	5×10^{-4}	90		56
Sc^{47}	60	Large		
		For Gastro-Intestinal Tract as Critical Organ		
Ca^{45}	4×10^{-3}	730		
Ca^{47}	8×10^{-4}	144		
Sc^{47}	9×10^{-4}	160		

Since 16 μc of Ca^{45} give the same bone dose as 90 μc of Ca^{47}, it is 6 times as effective. In order to find the combined dose equivalent to 90 μc of Ca^{47} the procedure is to let $x = Ca^{47}$ μc. Since in the received material there are $\frac{1}{10}$ as many μc of Ca^{45}, the effectiveness of this isotope will be 0.1 x multiplied by the efficiency factor of 6. Then the total effective microcuries are $x + 0.6 x$, which must equal the permitted 90 μc of Ca^{47} alone. 1.6 $x = 90$, or $x = 56$ μc Ca^{47}, which will inevitably be accompanied by 5.6 μc of Ca^{45}.

It is apparent from the foregoing considerations that for any nuclide the permissible dose depends on the critical organ, the route of administration, the chemical form in which the material is administered, any accompanying radioactivity, and possibly other factors. Any attempt at a tabulation of permissible doses for many nuclides under practicable conditions of administration would involve a much broader survey of physiologic processes than can be undertaken in such a text as the present one. Formulae given above are in general satisfactory as a first approximation, but sometimes use of 1.3

rad in 13 weeks rather than 0.3 or 0.1 in the first week make possible a liberalization of a program. A few values calculated in this manner are given in Table 14, based on data in Handbooks 52 and 69, for ingested material. These values are not applicable to injected material, nor to any colloidal preparations.

It is seen that, according to these calculations, for very shortlived nuclides very considerable doses are permissible. However with modern instrumentation doses of this magnitude are not necessary and should not be considered. With these the entire 1.3 rads would be delivered in a very few days, and this should be avoided. However here the 0.3 rad in one week

Table 14.   Permissible Tracer Doses for Certain Radionuclides; Soluble Material Administered Orally.   Dose to Give 1.3 Rad to Critical Organ in 13 Weeks.*

Nuclide	Critical Organ† (Ingested Soln.)	Per Cent Administered Dose to Critical Organ	T_{eff} Days	Permissible Administered Dose Microcuries
$_{35}Br^{82}$	Total Body	100	1.5	910
$_{20}Ca^{45}$	Bone	50	151	65
$_{6}C^{14}$	Fat	50	35	230
$_{26}Fe^{59}$	Blood	80	27	12
$_{53}I^{130}$	Thyroid‡	30	0.5	15
$_{53}I^{131}$	Thyroid	30	6	2
$_{53}I^{132}$	Thyroid	30	0.1	40
$_{19}K^{42}$	Muscle	70	0.5	990
$_{11}Na^{22}$	Total Body	90	15	110
$_{11}Na^{24}$	Total Body	90	0.6	1160
$_{15}P^{32}$	Bone	20	14	63
$_{16}S^{35}$	Skin	20	18	200

† These values are not applicable to intravenous administration, nor to any type of colloidal preparation.

‡ The permissible dose for thyroid has been established as 8 rads in a 13-week period; accordingly the permissible doses are 6 times as high as those listed.

* It is permissible to deliver 3 rads in 13 weeks, if the dose for the rest of the year does not exceed 2 rads, (5 rads for annual total.) Therefore values in this table can be doubled if the total year's radiation can be controlled.

is a good basis for calculation. For a nuclide with a really long effective half life, the 13-week dose is 13 times the 1-week dose at 0.1 rad per week, since radiation continues to be delivered at that rate. For an intermediate effective half life of the order of a week or two, there may be an advantage to the 13-week calculation. For example, for Na^{22} with a listed T_{eff} of 15 days, the permissible 1-week, 0.1 rad dose is only $\frac{1}{4}$ of the permissible 13-week, 1.3 rad dose.

General Safety Routines.   It is a relatively simple matter to calculate barriers and working distances to control radiation levels. Shielded equipment and long-handled tools can be bought. But in the last analysis the safety of the worker depends on his understanding of the problem and his adherence to the rules. The following suggestions may be used as a basis for day-by-day procedure:

1. Maintain "good house-keeping" at all times. Keep the laboratory neat; wash glassware regularly; do not let waste or contaminated material accumulate.

2. Wear rubber gloves and laboratory coat for all operations in the "hot" laboratory.

3. Make all possible set-ups on easily cleanable trays.

4. Cover all trays and all other work surfaces with disposable absorbent paper. (Good material of this sort is commercially available.)

5. Make sure that all containers of radioactive material are properly labeled at all times, both with a statement of the kind and quantity of isotope, and with a suitable radioactivity label. (Such labels are commercially available.)

6. Keep all active solutions covered.

7. *Never* pipette solutions by mouth.

8. Have available a paper sack garbage can for immediate disposal of all contaminated waste, including paper wipes.

9. Try out all new procedures with dummy runs not involving radioactive material.

10. Never allow eating, drinking or smoking in the "hot" laboratory.

11. Monitor all work areas regularly.

12. Employ standard personnel monitoring with either film badges or monitor ionization chambers, and keep careful records of all exposures.

13. Give immediate attention to cleaning up any contamination. (See next chapter.)

The Atomic Energy Commission requires that in any institution where an isotope program exists there should be a radiological safety officer, whose duties are to make sure that all procedures with radioactive materials are safely carried out. He may be a staff member or a consultant; he may be a physicist, a radiologist, or other professional individual, but he must be thoroughly conversant with basic safety procedures. His name and qualifications are filed as part of any application for an isotope license. He is to be depended upon for checking all routine procedures and for advising on any new developments. He must know where to look for radiation hazards and how to avoid or overcome them. His duties cover the laboratory and clinical uses of isotopes, the disposal of radioactive waste, and the removal of radioactive contamination if it should occur. These last topics will be discussed in the next chapter.

The Federal Register, in Part 20, lays down regulations governing permissible levels, precautionary procedures, waste disposal, records and reports. Every isotope user should be familiar with these; the suitable excerpt from the Register is available from the Isotopes Division of the

Atomic Energy Commission. Every one holding a license to possess iso-topes is subject to inspection by the Commission's agents, and is expected to comply with these regulations.

Radioactive Fall-out from Atomic Bombs. Consideration of the hazards to the human race resulting from the peace-time testing of nuclear weapons has been confused by the tremendous emotional impact of the possibility of war. A dispassionate effort should be made to separate the two, and to look at such facts as are available regarding the irradiation from this source as a part of the general picture of irradiation of the population. Fall-out contributes a certain amount of external irradiation from radioactive material in the air and on the ground; it was earlier mentioned that this was equal to only a small part of the natural background. It is not expected to reach as much as 10 per cent of background unless the testing programs of all nations possessing nuclear weapons are markedly increased. It is evident therefore that as far as the external irradiation hazard is concerned, fall-out is negligible.

More serious fears arise from the fact that two of the principal com-ponents of fall-out, radioactive strontium and radioactive cesium, have long lives. After falling to the ground they are taken into growing plants, which serve as foodstuffs for man or cattle. In the latter case they enter the human foodchain via the milk. Strontium in particular, since it is metabolized in much the same way as calcium, is built into the bones and gives off its radiation there, becoming a long-time menace. The question is, how great a menace? Not genetic, for these materials do not deposit in the gonads, and do not deliver, from other sites of deposit, enough radiation to the gonads to be significant. The dangers usually spoken of are the production of leukemia and bone cancer, and possible life shortening. Calculations of dose from internally deposited fall-out products at levels prevailing in the United States in the last few years, lead to values of the order of 30 millirads per year to the bones or bone marrow, or a total of about 1 rad in 30 years. In the preceding chapter it was pointed out that no cases of leukemia or bone cancer had been demonstrated to follow less than a few hundred rads administered in a relatively short time. There is no evidence of life shortening resulting from chronic irradiation at or well above fall-out levels.

Those who maintain that these small doses can result in leukemia or bone cancer base their assertions on the (completely unproven) statement that there is no threshold dose which must be reached before the condition can develop, but that the incidence of these somatic changes, like genetic ones, is proportional to dose, down to the lowest possible levels. If this postulate is accepted, the number of additional cases of these two diseases to be expected annually can be calculated from presently available statistics regarding radiation-produced leukemia and bone cancer. These numbers turn out to be such small percentages of the present incidences that it would be statistically impossible to find them; year-by-year fluctuations in mortality statistics are greater. The difficulty of ever obtaining significant human data for such low doses is almost insuperable. The only permissible conclusion at present is that it cannot be demonstrated that these conditions *cannot* be produced by fall-out,—neither can it be demonstrated that they *can.*

REFERENCES

ADVISORY COMMITTEE ON BIOLOGY AND MEDICINE, G. Failla, Chairman. Statement on Radioactive Fallout. American Scientist, Vol. 46, pp. 138–150, June, 1958.

BRAESTRUP, C. B. and WYCKOFF, H. O.: *Radiation Protection*, Springfield, Ill., Thomas, 1958.

BRITISH MEDICAL RESEARCH COUNCIL. *The Hazards to Man of Nuclear and Allied Radiations. Second Report.* London, Her majesty's Stationery Office, 1960.

Federal Register, National Archives of the United States, Washington, D. C. (Part 20, 1956).

GLASSER, O., QUIMBY, E. H., TAYLOR, L. S., WEATHERWAX, L. J. and MORGAN, R. H.: *Physical Foundations of Radiology*, 3rd Ed., Chapter 20, New York, Paul B. Hoeber, Inc., 1951.

International Commission on Radiological Protection, Report of Subcommittee II on Permissible Dose for Internal Radiation. Pergamon Press, New York, 1959.

MORGAN, R. H., and CORRIGAN, K. E.: *Handbook of Radiology*, Section 6, Chicago, Yearbook Publishers, Inc., 1955.

QUIMBY, E. H., *Safe Handling of Radioactive Isotopes in Medical Practice.* New York, Macmillan, 1960.

SCOTT, W. G. (Editor): *Planning Guide for Radiologic Installations*, Chicago, Year Book Publishers, 1953.

VENNART, J. and MINSKI, M.: Radiation Doses from Administered Radio-nuclides. Brit. Jour. Radiology, *35*, 372, 1962.

National Bureau of Standards Handbooks:

    42. *Safe Handling of Radioactive Isotopes.*
    52. *Maximum Permissible Amounts of Radioisotopes in the Human Body, and Maximum Permissible Concentrations in Air and Water.*
    54. *Protection Against Radiations from Radium, Cobalt-60, and Cesium-137.*
    59. *Permissible Dose from External Sources of Ionizing Radiation.*
    65. *Safe Handling of Bodies Containing Radioactive Isotopes.*
    69. *Maximum Permissible Body Burdens and Maximum Permissible Concentrations of Radionuclides in Air and Water for Occupational Expense.*

11

Disposal of Radioactive Waste and
Removal of Contamination

General Considerations. For most medical users of radioactive nuclides, waste disposal problems will not be serious. Material to be disposed of will in general be short-lived; for longer-lived substances, quantities will be very small. Methods of disposal are by putting the radioactive waste into sewage or garbage, by incinerating it, by burying it underground or dumping it at sea, or by returning it to the Atomic Energy Commission. Factors influencing the choice of method will be the half life of the isotope, the chemical form and solubility of the material, and its bulk. (Bulky waste is generally limited to contaminated equipment and animal carcasses.)

There are two general methods of handling the material, which may be described as *dispersion* and *concentration*. The principle of disposal is so to manage that nobody can, under the worst circumstances, receive as much as a permissible dose of the isotope. *Dispersion* is accomplished by mixing the radioactive material with so much diluting substance—water, air, or other—that constant intake of the diluted mixture will not result in accumulation of a permissible dose. This is the basis in the first three methods mentioned above. *Concentration* is accomplished by reducing the volume as much as possible, and is the necessary first step for burial or sea disposal.

Atomic Energy Commission Rules. At the present time the Atomic Energy Commission has control over waste disposal of all radionuclides obtained from its facilities. They accept only two procedures without special permission, release into sanitary sewage systems, or burial in the soil.

Sewage disposal is applicable to soluble or readily dispersible material, so long as certain specified concentrations are not exceeded. These are tabulated in Title 10, Part 20 of the Federal Register, and are in general the concentration for constant intake for a 40-hour week (Hb 69). The disposer must therefore know the average water flow from his institution, and the proposed disposal of all radionuclides. In the United States the average hospital water flow is about 1000 liters per day per bed. It is apparent that except for very small institutions or very large disposals, hospital and laboratory waste, if it is soluble, presents no problem. The matter is further simplified by the fact that excreta from individuals under-

11 (161)

going medical diagnosis or therapy with radioactive materials are exempt from even these limitations.

Burial in soil is permissible under conditions which would be restrictive in practically any urban institution. It would be useful for large laboratories located in the country, with extensive grounds over which complete control could be exercised.

Incineration would appear to be the logical method for disposal of combustible materials, and similar considerations could be applied to the exhaust stack gases as to the water outflow from the institution. Permissible concentrations of gaseous radionuclides in air are also listed in the Federal Register. However the possible radioactive residual in the ashes must be considered, as well as deposits in chimney soot. Therefore in any particular institution the problems must be analyzed as to quantity and type of radionuclide, final disposal of ashes, nature of prevailing winds, vicinity of other buildings, and so on, and application made to the ACE for permission to incinerate under these conditions. While this can usually be obtained, sometimes after various adjustments in the procedures, it is sometimes simpler, for small quantities of short-lived nuclides, to store the waste until its activity is only slightly above background, and then burn it. For paper wipes used in procedures with I^{131}, for example, storage for a few weeks is seldom a problem. On the other hand, for animal carcasses with appreciable quantities of P^{32}, several months in a freezer might be necessary, and this puts a strain on facilities.

Because of these problems, certain commercial waste disposal groups have been authorized by the AEC to collect waste materials from institutions and dispose of them according to procedures set up under their licenses. This type of service is very useful in the institution where a good deal of research is carried out with long-lived nuclides, or resulting in insoluble waste—animal carcasses, insoluble chemicals, and so on.

Stable Isotope Dilution. A disposal method sometimes practicable for relatively small quantities of isotopes of common elements is stable isotope dilution. The AEC does not recommend it, but under certain circumstances might accept it. To any preparation of a radioactive isotope enough "carrier," stable isotope of the same element in the same chemical form, can be added, so that if this mixture furnished the whole source of the element for an individual, his body burden would never reach the permissible level. In this case, no disposal precautions are necessary. With small quantities of long-lived materials this is a desirable procedure. Dilution by sewage water may be adequate at the date of disposal, but if successive quantities are thrown away, there may be a reconcentration in the sludge of a sewage treatment plant, such as would not develop with a short-lived isotope.

Data in Handbook 52 facilitate the calculation of the necessary amount of carrier. This may be illustrated with Ca^{45}. The handbook gives the daily intake of calcium as 0.8 gm, of which all is in the 7000 gm of skeleton, in a concentration of 0.15 gm Ca per gm of bone. There are therefore $0.15 \times 7000 = 1050$ gm of calcium in the body. The permissible body burden of Ca^{45} is 65 μc, or 1 μc for every 16 gm of stable calcium. Admixture of carrier at this level would do away with need for *any* disposal precautions. At a somewhat lower level it might be a worthwhile precaution against too severe reconcentration.

Cadavers Containing Appreciable Quantities of Radioactive Material. As stated in the last chapter, this matter is treated in detail in National Bureau of Standards Handbook 65. Bodies containing less than 5 mc need no precautions for any type of handling. Those containing between 5 and 30 mc may be buried or cremated with no preparation, or embalmed according to standard injection procedures without special precautions. If the body is to be subjected to autopsy, the radiation safety officer will designate any special precautions. A body containing more than 30 mc can be buried or cremated with no preparation, but if embalming is to be carried out, it should be with the guidance of a radiation safety officer.

Radioactive Contamination and Decontamination. Where procedures with radioactive materials are carried out in accordance with the rules suggested in the last chapter, there is little likelihood of serious personnel contamination. Apparatus and floors may be contaminated by an occasional accidental spill, patients who vomit or are incontinent may present major problems in the hospital. The entire subject is dealt with in National Bureau of Standards Handbook 48, *Control and Removal of Radioactive Contamination in Laboratories;* familiarity with this should be mandatory for all isotope users.

Certain general rules may be indicated. In the laboratory, if bottles and equipment are maintained on trays as suggested, contamination, if it occurs beyond the tray is likely to be at a low level. If it is on person, clothing, or floor:

1. Drop towels or absorbent material on spill.

2. Get out of contaminated clothing; put it on a large paper for future check. Put on a clean laboratory coat.

3. Scrub hands well with soap or detergent, not highly alkaline and not abrasive. Do not scratch the skin surface.

4. Put on fresh rubber gloves.

5. If the spill is on floor or table, take up as much as possible with blotters or absorbent paper, using forceps to hold the material. Place it immediately into a receptacle for radioactive waste. Clean further with a damp cloth and detergent; avoid spreading the contamination by sloshing water. Levels to which cleaning must be carried are given in the Handbook.

6. Monitor contaminated material to determine whether clothing may go to the laundry and mopping material to the incinerator, or whether they must be stored for decay. The Handbook gives suitable levels.

If a larger contamination occurs in the hospital as a result of vomiting or excretion after a large dose of I^{131} or a leak or spurt back from an injection of radioactive colloid, so that patient and bedding are involved, the following procedures are indicated:

7. All personnel involved in the clean-up—laboratory workers, nurses, orderlies—put on laboratory coats or coverall protective aprons, and rubber gloves.

8. If the patient is ambulatory, get him immediately into a bathtub, have him wash well with soap and water and rinse the whole body and tub. Check local contaminations and re-wash if necessary. If the patient is not ambulatory, remove all bedding down to and including the rubber sheet, shifting him onto a clean rubber sheet. Give him a careful bed bath, with monitor control of all steps in the procedure.

9. Put all contaminated bedding and patient's clothing onto a large paper or into an impervious waterproof container, to be dealt with later.

10. Return patient to bed.

11. Treat contaminated floors and furniture as described in rule 5.

12. Take contaminated material to the "hot" laboratory, spread on large piece of paper, separate out severely contaminated pieces, handling everything with forceps. It may be desirable to try to dispose of these immediately rather than store for decay. They can be dropped into a utility sink filled with water and detergent, lifted, stirred and manipulated with sticks, rinsed and rewashed until the remaining activity is low enough to permit sending them to the laundry. (See Handbook.) If such levels cannot be obtained, they can be dried on disposable lines, with pans and paper to catch the drippings, and stored for decay. Individuals carrying out these procedures should be constantly monitored; if levels are high the work should be done by a team. At the end of the procedure, careful monitoring should be done of everyone involved.

Special Case of Internal Personnel Contamination. If good housekeeping practices are adhered to in the "hot" laboratory, no one will ever ingest radioactive material. If pipetting by mouth is done, sooner or later radioactive material will be swallowed. If smoking is permitted during isotope handling, it is inevitable that contamination will go from fingers to cigarette to mouth. Measurable levels of I^{131} have repeatedly been found in the thyroid glands of some individuals who persisted in this practice, insisting that they could do it "cleanly." It is desirable to monitor at intervals the thyroid glands of all those who work regularly with radioactive iodine.

REFERENCES

National Bureau of Standards Handbooks:

42. *Safe Handling of Radioactive Isotopes.*
48. *Control and Removal of Radioactive Contamination in Laboratories.*
49. *Recommendations for Waste Disposal of Phosphorus-32 and Iodine-131 for Medical Users.*

52. *Maximum Permissible Amounts of Radioisotopes in the Human Body and Maximum Permissible Concentrations in Air and Water.*
53. *Recommendations for the Disposal of Carbon-14 Wastes.*
58. *Radioactive Waste Disposal in the Ocean.*
65. *Safe Handling of Bodies Containing Radioactive Isotopes.*
69. *Maximum Permissible Body Burdens and Maximum Permissible Concentrations of Radionuclides in Air and in Water for Occupational Exposure.*

Federal Register (Part 20) National Archives of the United States. Washington, D. C., 1956.

Part II
INSTRUMENTATION AND
LABORATORY METHODS

Sergei Feitelberg

12

Radiation Detectors: Principles of Operation

Each disintegration of a radioactive isotope is accompanied by a burst of radiant energy. This radiant energy may be electromagnetic radiation of very short wave length (gamma rays), it may consist of elementary particles like electrons (beta rays), nuclei of helium (alpha rays), or any combination of some of them in extremely rapid succession. The interaction of these types of radiations with matter makes them detectable although the power of each burst is almost inconceivably small when compared to the power of events with which we deal in everyday experience. The disarrangement of orbital electrons when radiation interacts with gases is basically liberation of electrons from the confines of the gas atoms, which is called ionization, and which permits gases to conduct electricity although they are ordinarily non-conductors. The conductivity of gases due to ionization by radiation is one of the basic processes used in the detection of radiation bursts accompanying the disintegration of radioactive isotopes and hence in the observation of the occurrence of such disintegrations. The processes involved in the interaction of ionizing radiation with solid matter are more complex, but the sequelæ of a variety of these processes can be also observable. A number of crystals, for instance, emit visible light when ionizing radiation is absorbed, and this light can either be observed directly or be measured by devices sensitive to visible light. Halogen salts of photographic emulsions form latent development centers which can be transformed by reducing agents to visible agglomerations of metallic silver (photographic image). In a variety of substances the disarrangement of orbital electrons results in a change of color.

Radiation detectors have been made using any of the mechanisms listed above. The selection of the type of detector will depend on a great variety of factors as, for instance: whether the *number of disintegrations* in a given sample or the *overall intensity* of the radiation has to be determined; whether the radiation consists of penetrating gamma rays or of easily absorbed beta particles.

An understanding of the mechanism of radiation detectors is therefore essential not only for their intelligent and efficient use, but also for the selection of the best instrument for a given problem.

Ionization Chambers. We shall examine first the detection of radiation in a gas. When a beta particle with a range of several feet traverses air, it will ionize a large number of air molecules. This number will be different if one foot or two feet of its path are observed. To eliminate this first and elementary ambiguity, the volume of air under observation must be defined; the simplest way of doing it is by using some container of definite volume. This container or its inner walls must be an electric conductor, since the ionization produced will have to be observed by induced conductivity of the enclosed air. In order to observe this conductivity, a second piece of conducting material has to be introduced into the box and insulated from it. Conductivity of air will be measured by connecting the wall of the box and the second component (electrode) to a source of electric potential, for instance to a battery, and to a measuring instrument which will indicate the flow of electric current (see Fig. 40).

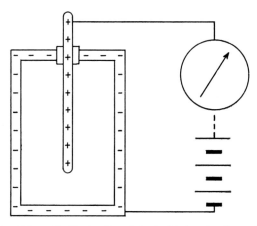

Fig. 40.—Schematic illustration of an *ionization chamber* and of the associated electric circuit.

If there is no ionization inside the box, no current will flow and the meter will show no deflection. When a beta particle traverses the air, a large number of air molecules will be ionized: there will be floating along the paths of the beta rays free electrons and the remainders of gas molecules. The gas molecules were originally electrically neutral; since they have lost negative electrons, they have now positive charges. Ion pairs have been formed, consisting of a (negative) free electron and the positively charged residue of the molecule.

Two different things can happen to the ion pair. The two parts, coming originally from the same or from different molecules, may meet; they are attracted to each other as are any opposite electric charges and they may recombine to form again a complete and electrically neutral gas molecule. An event of this sort will not affect the electric circuit and will not be observable on the meter. It is possible, however, that free electrons which are repelled by the negative electrode, the box wall for instance, and attracted by the positive electrode, which may be a rod inside the box, will reach the rod and be drawn into the electric circuit. The positive remainder of the molecule will drift to the negative wall and become neutral by getting an electron from the conducting wall, since this, being negative, has a supply of free electrons. In this second case there will be a current pulse in the electric circuit and this could be detected in the meter if it were sensitive enough.

Which of the two possible processes will occur—inside recombination or external collection—will depend on the electrostatic attraction by the electric charges in the box. If this charge is increased by increasing the battery voltage, for instance, the free electrons will be collected more quickly by the central rod, and they will have less time and therefore less chance to recombine with the positive remainders of the molecules. A larger proportion of the ion pairs formed during the passage of a beta ray will contribute to the current flowing through the electric circuit and indicated on the meter. Thus with increasing voltage, the ratio of collected to recombined ion pairs increases, until almost all ion pairs produced are collected, and the deflection on the meter becomes a good measure of the total ionization produced. At this point a further increase of voltage will have no appreciable effect on the collection efficiency nor on the current in the circuit. The device has been saturated as seen from the external circuit, and the voltage range for this condition is called *saturation voltage*. The changes in current intensity for each beta ray traversing the box for varying voltage are represented in Figure 41.

This figure also indicates the relative magnitude of current bursts which would occur if different rays pass through the air. Ionization density (number of ion pairs per unit length) along the path of a gamma ray is very much less than for a beta ray, since less energy from the more penetrating radiation is absorbed by the air. This means, in other words, that fewer ion pairs are produced and therefore there are fewer of them to be collected and detected by the electric circuit. The current bursts are therefore smaller, but they show a similar saturation effect when the voltage is high enough to collect all ion pairs formed.

Alpha particles have ionization density higher than beta rays. If they reach the inside of the box, even more ion pairs are produced and the current pulses in the circuit are greater than those for either beta or gamma rays.

The device discussed here has therefore one very remarkable and useful property: when it is operated with saturation voltages, the current going through the meter is a direct measure of the total number of ion pairs produced per unit time in the enclosed air space, and is therefore a measure of the ionization due to radiation. It is called an *ionization chamber* and it is one of the best instruments for the measurement of ionization. One of the problems which we are trying to solve here, however, is to observe each radiation burst separately; and for this purpose the current pulses occurring in the external circuit, even when an alpha particle is the radiation to be ob-

served, are much too small for any available electric meter. The limitation
of electric meters is not so much their sensitivity, but the speed of their
response to a fast electric pulse; as a general rule the sensitivity can be increased only at the expense of speed. Ionization due to a radiation burst
from a disintegrating isotope occurs over an extremely short interval of
time; the collection of ion pairs takes more time, but is is also accomplished
very quickly. When a large number of ionizing events occurs in the ionization chamber, electric measuring instruments of several kinds can be used

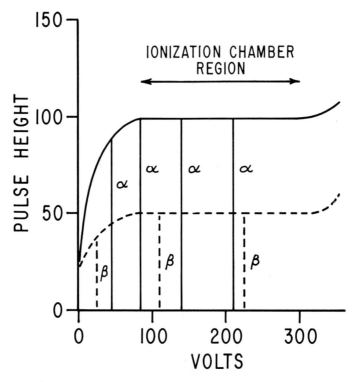

Fig. 41.—Electric pulses due to passage of beta and alpha particles through an
ionization chamber (pulse height scale in arbitrary units, as in Fig. 42 and Fig. 43).

to measure either the amount of electric charge equivalent to the total
number of ion pairs produced during the time of observation (total ionization, which is a measure of radiation exposure dose), or the current, which is
equivalent to the number of ion pairs produced per unit time (a measure of
the dose rate).

To summarize: an ionization chamber is an instrument which is well
suited to measure dose and dose rate of ionizing radiations, but the current
pulses due to radiation bursts, produced when individual disintegrations
of radioactive atoms take place, are too small to be observed.

Proportional Counters. The latter difficulty can be overcome by taking advantage of a phenomenon occurring in the gas during the ionization process, when the applied voltage is increased beyond the saturation range.

Ion pairs are produced due to radiation; the free electron and the positive remainder of the molecule are attracted towards the cathode and anode. The positive remainder of the molecule, which is heavy (nucleus of the atoms plus whatever orbital electrons are left) drifts relatively slowly towards the cathode. The electron, however, being very light, will acquire a considerable velocity which will depend on the potential acting on it: this velocity will be therefore increased when the voltage is raised. When the velocity of these electrons reaches a value at which their kinetic energy is high enough to ionize in their turn the gas in the chamber, such electrons, produced during the primary ionization process will form secondary ion pairs, that is, liberate secondary electrons. These secondary electrons will be accelerated also and produce tertiary ion pairs resulting in more free electrons; this process will continue in the form of an avalanche until a whole cone of ionized gas is formed, starting at the site where each primary electron was formed and ending at the anode. The ionizing effect of electrons accelerated by the increased collecting voltage may seem puzzling at first, but it is the same effect which is observed when beta particles pass through a gas, since beta particles are also electrons of high energy, moving at a high speed.

The crucial result of the avalanche formation in so far as it affects the current through the external circuit of Figure 40 is that for each primary liberated electron, a large number of additional electrons is liberated, and the current pulse through the electric circuit, and hence through the meter, is greatly amplified. Since this amplification occurs in the gas of the detector itself, it is called the gas amplification factor.

This gas amplification factor depends on the energy which was imparted to the liberated electrons by the electric field and therefore on the applied voltage. The electric pulse through the circuit will therefore increase with higher voltage, as illustrated in Figure 42.

The current pulse will also depend on the total number of avalanches occurring simultaneously; and since each primary ion pair gives rise to an avalanche, the current pulse will depend on the intensity of primary ionization produced by the passage of the radiation burst through the gas. Since this ionization is higher for a beta ray than for a gamma ray, and even higher for an alpha ray, the amplified current pulse will be also greater for a beta ray than for a gamma ray; the pulses will be proportional to the primary ionization. This device is therefore called a *proportional counter.*

The great advantage of a proportional counter is that the current pulse produced by the ionizing event due to the passage of a single radiation burst is much greater than in an ionization chamber; it is large enough to be detected by available electric devices. Since the pulse height or intensity is proportional to the ionization, the pulses can be sorted out in the electric measuring device, and alpha particles, for instance, can be observed separately and independently of beta particles. There are, however, two disadvantages. First, the electric pulses, though amplified, are still quite small and their observation requires rather elaborate and somewhat delicate

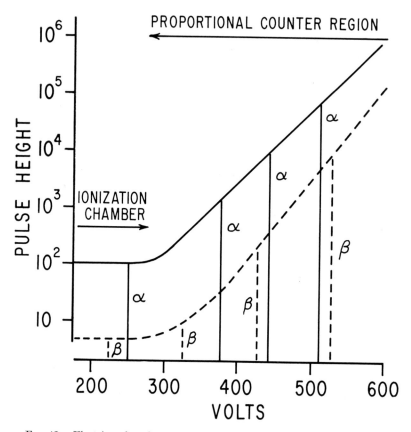

FIG. 42.—Electric pulses due to passage of beta and alpha particles through a *proportional counter* (see legend to Fig. 41).

electronic devices. Second, the magnitude of the electric pulses, as seen in Figure 42, varies with the applied voltage, and unless this voltage is maintained sufficiently constant, the pulse intensity will vary with it and affect the observations.

Geiger-Mueller Counters. If the voltage applied to the counter is increased still further, a third process begins to play a significant role which at the lower voltage occurs so infrequently that it can be neglected.

This process has to do with other interactions of electrons with atoms than those leading to ionization. When the energy of secondary electrons is high enough, radiative collisions with gas atoms will occur and Bremsstrahlung of low energy photons (visible and ultra-violet light) will be produced.

With higher applied voltage the number of secondary electrons in each avalanche increases, as can be seen in the increased intensity of the electric pulse. The number of radiative collisions will also increase. These photons of visible and ultra-violet light will traverse the counting volume, and when they reach the enclosing walls they will be absorbed and may release electrons by the photoelectric effect. These electrons will be accelerated by the potential inside the counter and form avalanches in their turn.

When this process begins to occur with significant frequency, the number of avalanches becomes greater than the number of the ion pairs formed during the primary ionization process due to the radiation bursts, which we are interested in detecting. The proportionality between the primary ionization and the electric pulses is lost. The counter does not behave any longer strictly as a proportional counter and this region is called that of limited proportionality. Further increase in voltage will lead to an even more frequent occurrence of radiative collision within the avalanches; there will be more and more avalanches due to photoelectrons released by light photons from these collisions, and finally these processes will increase to a point when ionization will spread through the whole enclosed gas volume. Beginning at this voltage, the device is called a Geiger-Mueller counter. It shows quite a remarkable behavior: once any ionizing event occurs in the gas, ionization is no longer localized. The electric pulse through the electric circuit will have a higher value than in the proportional region; a very high gas amplification factor is reached, of the order of a million to a billion. This pulse will be independent of the intensity of the original ionizing event (all proportionality is lost); it still will be dependent on applied voltage, but much less than in a proportional counter. The advantages are therefore the high intensity of the electric pulse, which is easy to observe, and the decreased dependence on the variations in the voltage supply. The disadvantage is that there is no proportionality between pulse height and the intensity of the ionization produced by the radiation bursts under observation: the pulses are the same whether they are released by alpha, beta or gamma radiation. The voltage at which the porportionality between the intensity of the primary ionizing event and the intensity of the electric pulse is lost, and where the Geiger-Mueller region begins, is called the *threshold voltage* (*See* Fig. 43 and 56).

The voltage cannot be increased indefinitely beyond the threshold value without destroying the ability of the counter to detect radiation, since eventually the electric potential will reach a value at which it has enough force to tear away by itself an orbital electron from an atom. Depending on the pressure, either an electric spark or a gas discharge will occur, and current will flow through the electric circuit without external ionization due to radiation. The voltage at which this occurs is called the self-discharge voltage.

The positive ions have been neglected so far, but they play also a relevant role in the behavior of a Geiger-Mueller counter. Since they are much heavier than the electrons, they acquire a correspondingly lower velocity and move relatively more slowly towards the cathode than the electrons towards the anode, and therefore arrive later at their destination. The

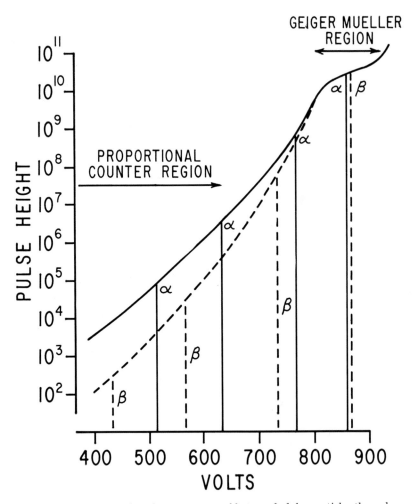

Fig. 43.—Electric pulses due to passage of beta and alpha particles through a *Geiger-Mueller counter* (see legend to Fig. 41).

presence of such an accumulation of positive ions in the counter volume creates a cloud of positive charge which counteracts the potential gradient created by the applied voltage. This can effectively stop the discharge; when this happens, the positive ions will reach the cathode and become neutralized. Until this occurs, the counter has effectively no potential-gradient inside the gas and it cannot respond to another ionizing event; it is "dead" and the time which this neutralization takes is called its "dead time."

The neutralization of positive ions at the cathode can occur in two ways. One is by disassociation, if the gas contains polyatomic molecules. Such disassociation occurs without the emission of any radiations, and the counting discharge is quenched as described in the preceding paragraph. Such counters are called *self-quenching*. But in some other gases, a radiative neutralization may also occur which acts in the same way as radiative collisions in the avalanches: ultraviolet and visible light quanta (photons) are emitted, and they release photoelectrons which form additional avalanches. The discharge process perpetuates itself and continues until it is quenched externally by disconnecting or reducing the voltage applied to the counter; this is called a non-self-quenching counter. Most counters in use today are of the self-quenching type.

In order to recapitulate what happens in an enclosed gas volume when an ionizing ray passes through it, the processes are listed in the following paragraphs. The voltage applied to the electrodes in the gas volume is increased for each subsequent paragraph:

1. Some of the ion pairs formed are collected; some recombine.

2. Ionization chamber at saturation voltage. All ion pairs formed are collected. Current is proportional to ionization. Current pulses due to single quanta (radiation bursts) are too small to be detected individually.

3. Proportional Counter. Acceleration of primary electron is great enough to produce secondary ionizations and localized avalanche discharges. Primary ionization pulse is amplified by this gas amplification factor and is large enough to be detected; it is proportional to the intensity of the primary ionizing event. Pulses due to rays of different ability to ionize gases can be differentiated and observed independently.

4. Geiger-Mueller Counters. Radiative collisions in the avalanche become sufficiently frequent to release enough photoelectrons from the cathode so that ionization spreads through the whole counter volume. Maximal gas amplification and highest electric pulses are independent of the intensity of the primary ionizing event. Positive ion cloud terminates the discharge in self-quenching counters. In non-self-quenching counters, discharge is self perpetuating due to radiative recombination and must be quenched externally.

Scintillation Counters. So far, ionization processes in radiation detectors have been discussed as they take place in gases. They are comparatively simple, since ion pairs formed can move freely in a gas. But the density of a gas is low, the energy absorbed from a beam of γ or X radiation is therefore small, the interactions are infrequent and the inherent sensitivity of such gas detectors is not high. Greater energy absorption takes place in solid matter of similar volume, so that solid radiation detectors are potentially much more sensitive. This is particularly important in the detection

12

of highly penetrating gamma radiation. The phenomena involved are, however, more complex than in a gas.

The molecules of a variety of organic and inorganic crystals undergo a process which is analogous to what was called radiative collision in gases; they emit photons, quanta of visible light, as a result of absorbing ionizing radiation. This luminescence is one of the oldest known effects of radiation on matter; its observation lead Roentgen to the discovery of x-rays; it was the phenomenon by means of which Rutherford originally investigated the nature of radium disintegrations, and it is in everyday medical use in fluoroscopy.

When a crystal, which has this property of emitting light when absorbing radiation, is hit by a single burst of radiant energy, and some or all of this energy is absorbed by it, a light pulse of short duration is produced. If the crystal is transparent, the light pulses occurring not only on its surface, but also inside of the crystal will become visible. Such light pulses are called *scintillations*; they are often of sufficient intensity to be seen. This intensity is proportional to the energy absorbed by the crystal from the impinging radiation. The number of pulses is a measure of the frequency with which radiation bursts impinge on the scintillating crystal, and therefore a measure of the disintegration rate of a radioactive isotope, if this is the source of the radiation.

Visual observation and counting of these scintillations are obviously too laborious and too slow for practical purposes. For this reason, scintillating crystals were not generally used as radiation counters until a way was found to observe and register the occurrence of scintillations automatically.

The obvious way to achieve this is to use a photoelectric cell for the conversion of light pulses into electric ones. The difficulty was, however, that photoelectric cells were not sensitive enough to translate scintillations into electric pulses of useful intensity, even with the use of electronic amplifiers. It was only after the invention of the photomultiplier tube that the potentially extremely useful property of scintillation detectors could be employed in practice.

A photomultiplier tube utilizes secondary emission of electrons. Figure 44 illustrates schematically a single stage photomultiplier tube. Let us examine first the cathode and the first electrode; they form a conventional photocell. The cathode is formed by a thin, transparent coating of a conducting material on glass and a potential of about 100 volts is applied between this coating and the first electrode. The whole glass envelope is evacuated to a high vacuum. The electric change attracts the electrons from the cathode, but is not strong enough to pull them out. When light strikes the photocathode, some of its energy is transferred to the electrons, and this added energy makes it possible for the electric charge to liberate them from the coating. These electrons will fly towards the first electrode, attaining a given speed and hence energy when they impinge on it. This will allow some current to flow in the circuit formed by the photocathode, the battery and the first electrode.

The next step involves events between the first and second electrode which characterize the photomultiplier. Let us examine what happens when a single electron, emitted from the photocathode and accelerated by the first battery, impinges on the first electrode. It will be absorbed, that is its energy will be transferred to the atoms and electrons in the first electrode. These electrons, however, are attracted by the second electrode which has, due to the second battery, a positive charge with respect to the first electrode. Again, this charge by itself cannot pull electrons out of the first electrode, but when they acquire additional energy from the electrons arriving from the photocathode, they are able to leave and fly to the second

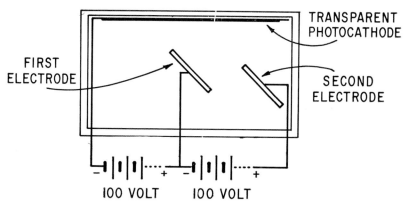

FIG. 44.—Schematic illustration of a *photomultiplier tube.* Only one multiplier electrode is shown; in actual design there are usually ten such electrodes.

electrode. A single photoelectron can set free several of them. Then the current which will flow through the circuit formed by the second battery and the first and second electrodes will be several times greater than the current flowing between photocathode and first electrode. This secondary emission has *amplified* the original photocurrent. The amount of this amplification is determined by the applied voltage; it cannot be increased indefinitely, however; if the voltage is too high it will be able to pull out electrons from the electrodes without help from electron bombardment, current will flow without light and will be, therefore, no measure of light intensity. In practice, four secondary electrons for one primary electron is approximately the limit. But further amplification is possible by arranging an additional electrode after the second one, with an additional battery as another voltage supply. This will give again an amplification of four, or a total amplification of sixteen. This can be repeated and practical photomultiplier tubes contain usually ten such electrodes and have a total amplification of over a million. When the light flash of a scintillating crystal reaches such a phototube, the electric pulse has a value approaching the output of a Geiger-Mueller counter.

The ability of emitting light pulses after absorbing ionizing radiation is not limited to solid crystals. A variety of solutions, both in solid plastic materials and in liquid solvents, is available, although the light output is usually smaller than that of crystals.

Other Solid State Detectors. The main advantage of scintillation counters over gas detectors is that the crystal is a solid and absorbs, therefore, much more energy from an impinging radiation than a gas of equal volume. Its disadvantage is the complexity of the mechanism which consists in the three steps: 1. Absorption of ionizing energy, 2. Conversion of this energy into light pulses, and 3. Conversion of the light pulses into electric pulses by a photocell. It would be desirable to have a solid state detector which combines the advantages of high absorption for ionizing radiation with the simplicity of a gas detector which converts the absorbed energy directly into an electric pulse.

It appears that the search for such a detector is succeeding. A device closely related to transistors is in development, in which a highly purified semiconductor like silicon is modified by the addition of controlled impurities and which changes its conductivity when it absorbs ionizing radiation. When connected to an external source of voltage, such a solid state detector behaves exactly like an ionization chamber; the electric pulse is proportional to the energy absorbed and is largely independent of the applied voltage. Since the energy absorbed is larger in a solid, the electric pulses are larger then in an ionization chamber and can be counted. The mechanism of ionization is, however, different. The mobile negative ion is identical in the solid state detector and in a gas detector; it is the electron. However, the positive ion formed is different; it is not the positive remainder of a gas molecule, but what is called "a positive hole" in the semiconductor. These holes are mobile like ions and are collected by the cathode in the same way as the electrons are collected by the anode. The result is an electric current or an electric pulse. A phototube is no longer needed. The elimination of the phototube allows the detection of much lower energy radiations. Sensitivity is further increased since the same amount of absorbed energy produces about ten times more electron-hole pairs in this type of detector than ion pairs in a gas.

Since this type of detector is in the process of development and has not been used at this time in medical or biological work, it will not be discussed any further in this book.

Photographic Emulsions. The blackening of a photographic plate by x-rays and by other ionizing radiations is at least as familiar to the reader as luminescence, although the processes involved are far from simple. The essential difference between the two mechanisms is that in a scintillating counter the changes due to absorption of radiation are fully reversible. After the emission of a light pulse the original state of the crystal is restored, while the phenomena which occur in the photographic emulsion are longer lasting chemical changes. For this reason, a photographic emulsion is of no use when the rate of radioactive disintegrations has to be detected, but it is a simple and convenient device to measure the accumulated amount of radiation, that is, the dose. It is of course also of unique value in the determination of the spatial distribution of radiation sources.

The first step in the absorption of radiation by a photographic emulsion is probably the emission of an electron from the electronegative halogen ion. This electron is then captured by an electropositive silver ion. Capture of an electron is chemically a reduction. The reduction of electropositive silver ions in the silver-halogen molecule forms development centers of the latent image. The latent image is made visible by further reduction during the development, when metallic silver particles are produced in visible conglomerations. The amount of metallic silver can be measured quantitatively by a densitometer. The observed density is a measure of the total radiation absorbed by the emulsion.

Summary. Some general properties of the different types of radiation detectors can now be summarized.

Photographic emulsions can be used only to measure directly the total dose, in addition to their particular properties of localizing radiation sources by image formation.

Ionization chambers can be used to measure both dose rate and total dose.

Neither of the two allows the observation of single radiation bursts during the disintegration of a radioactive isotope.

Proportional counters give electric pulses when they are traversed by radiation bursts. The height of the electric pulse is proportional to ionization occurring during such bursts.

Geiger-Mueller counters give electric pulses when ionizing events occur in the sensitive volume in a similar manner to a proportional counter, but the pulse height is independent of the ionization intensity of the initiating radiation burst.

Scintillation counters which are made of solids or liquids absorb more radiation energy than the devices containing gas; they have the highest sensitivity for penetrating radiation such as gamma or x-rays. The light intensity of each scintillation depends on the absorbed energy of the radiation.

13

Auxiliary Instruments

THE description and explanation of auxiliary apparatus for nuclear measurement present a dilemma. At first it seems reasonable and perhaps necessary to offer a complete presentation of function, design and construction to satisfy an interested and critical reader. But on second thought the background of the reader has to be considered. The training of a physician covers some physics, but no electrical engineering. Knowledge of electronics, vacuum tube amplifiers, transistors, cannot be presupposed. The first part of this chapter ought to contain, therefore, an elementary treatise on this branch of engineering. It is not possible to do this satisfactorily without disrupting the framework of the present book. Such attempts have been made in the past, but without much success. Cursory explanation of the basic functions of a vacuum tube is usually quickly followed by diagrams of flip-flop circuits, which remain mysterious to the neophyte and which are too elementary for the engineer. The technical complexities of the instruments are too great for a casual, semi-popular short treatment.

The approach selected for this chapter is perhaps best explained by an analogy. To drive a modern automobile well it is not necessary to understand the construction of cam shafts, the design of the automatic gearshift, the intricacies of the electric ignition system, the response and damping of the suspension springs and shock absorbers. What is necessary is a full understanding of the functions and controls of the car: conversion of combustion energy of fuels into mechanical power; what happens when accelerator, brake and steering are operated. Knowledge beyond these functional operations is not necessary for driving, but is essential of course for repairs when the car breaks down. However, cars are today quite reliable pieces of machinery: they do not break down often when they get adequate servicing, and when they do break down, there are enough service stations to get them going again. Neither was true forty years ago. At that time a driver had to know a great deal about the mechanism, or he would too frequently get stranded and helpless on the road.

The situation with nuclear equipment has had a very similar development. About fifteen years ago this equipment was rather experimental. It would have been foolhardy to use it without knowing how to take it apart and how to repair it. Its use was limited to technically trained people or those who were willing to get this technical training. Today this equipment is reasonably reliable and service facilities are becoming increasingly available, so that knowledge of the engineering construction is no longer essential.

It is still essential, however, to understand the functions of the various controls and components. This is so because otherwise the instruments cannot be used intelligently and reliably, malfunctions will not be detected and observations may become misleading.

During the past year or two a minor revolution in nuclear instrumentation has been in progress. Vacuum tubes are being replaced by transistors and an increasing number of instruments appear on the market which are either partially or almost fully transistorized. It becomes, therefore, necessary to discuss the reasons for this trend.

Within the self-imposed limitation of technical descriptions only some functional features of transistors and transistorized equipment will be given.

The basic difference between transistors and vacuum tubes is that conduction of electricity in transistors does not take place in vacuum by electrons liberated from a heated filament but in a solid semiconductor. No power to heat a filament is required and only a few volts are necessary to operate a transistor, instead of a few hundred needed for a vacuum tube. The result is that less power is dissipated, less heat is produced and the instrument operates at lower temperature. Lower temperature insures longer life of all electric circuit elements, which leads to longer periods of reliable operation and permits the use of smaller components. Smaller components permit miniaturization, which is not a virtue in itself for medical instruments used in the laboratory but which permits construction that makes repairs easier. More about servicing will be said in Chapter 21. Another advantage of transistors is that they have potentially longer life than vacuum tubes, and when they stop working they do so suddenly and completely, while vacuum tubes deteriorate gradually. It is easier to notice when some function of an instrument stops completely; when the deterioration is gradual it is possible to work for some time with an apparatus without realizing that it is not working right and is giving erroneous readings.

These remarks appear to indicate an unequivocal preference for transistorized instruments. This conclusion is however only conditionally true. Transistors are relatively new, technological experience with their utilization is only in the process of being accumulated and actual design not infrequently results in poor engineering vitiating potential advantages. Only field experience during the coming years will tell whether and how far transistorized nuclear instruments will supplement or replace vacuum tube operated devices.

This chapter will be devoted, therefore, mainly to the functional description of the auxiliary instruments and to the purpose of their different components. The reader who would like to gain insight into the actual mechanisms and technical details is referred to specialized textbooks on electronics and instrumentation.

Ionization Chambers. Ionization chambers are not suitable for the observations of single radiation bursts occurring during the disintegration of a radioactive nuclide, but they are inherently stable and simple devices to measure dose or dose rate, a problem which is of great practical importance in isotope work, particularly for purposes of health protection. We shall discuss first methods of measuring dose rate and then methods of measuring total dose.

Dose Rate Meters. The three integral parts of such an instrument are, (a) ionization chamber, (b) source of electric potential, and (c) sensitive current measuring device.

The ionization chamber itself is an enclosure, defining the gas volume in which ionization occurs. The larger the gas volume, the more ion pairs it will contain when it is exposed to a given intensity of radiation, and the larger therefore, will be the current observed. The sensitivity of the whole instrument can be increased by increasing the volume. This is limited by inconvenience of handling a bulky chamber, and the size of practical ionization chambers is usually not larger than a sphere of several inches in diameter or a cylinder about 6 to 8 inches long and a few inches in diameter. The ionization chamber must contain two conducting electrodes; as a rule the inside walls of the chamber are made conducting and serve as one electrode, and a metal or graphite rod in the center of the chamber serves as the second. The walls of the chamber have to fulfill a variety of physical conditions in order that they do not affect unduly the measurements. One such condition is that the walls have proper thickness. Absorption of primary γ radiation, production and absorption of secondary electrons by walls of different thicknesses and material may give a wide variation of ionization in the chamber when it is exposed to the same radiation intensity of different γ ray energies. By suitable choice of wall thickness and material, ionization chambers can be made largely independent of gamma ray energy between about 0.1 Mev. and a few Mev. Beta rays present a different problem due to their low penetration and limited range. In order to make an ionization chamber sensitive to beta radiation, there must be in the wall a thin window which can be closed by some sort of a slide in order to protect it from damage when it is not needed.

A few hundred volts are required to obtain saturation in an ionization chamber. In portable instruments this is usually supplied by dry cells, like B batteries in a portable radio.

For radiation intensities of interest to us, the current through an ionization chamber cannot be measured directly by ordinary pointer type meters, since they are not sensitive enough, and amplifiers have to be used. Such amplifiers can have a wide range of sensitivity and complexity. They can be made to give readings with a current flow of only a few electrons per second (vibrating reed electrometers, stationary vacuum tube electrometers), but then they are quite expensive, bulky and heavy. Less sensitive portable amplifiers can be made using special miniature vacuum tubes, which are sensitive enough for health protection measurements. Such an instrument is illustrated in Figure 45. It weighs only a few pounds and radiation intensities down to about 1 mr per hour can be measured.

Dose Meters. The total dose, as observed in an ionization chamber, is proportional to the total number of ion pairs produced in a given volume and it is independent of the time during which such an ionization occurred. The technical problem in measuring the total dose is therefore the measurement not of current (amperes, electrons per second) but of the number of electrons, which is expressed as "charge" and may be measured in several

Fig. 45.—Portable ionization chamber *survey meter*. The ranges are 2.5, 25, and 250 milliroentgens per hour full scale. The large ionization chamber of 500 cc volume can be removed and a small chamber of 5 cc (illustrated under the instrument) plugged in; this increases the range to 2.5, 25, and 250 roentgens per hour full scale (courtesy of Nuclear-Chicago Corporation).

units. The unit corresponding to the ampere is a coulomb, which represents a charge equal to 6.25×10^{18} electrons. The unit of radiation exposure dose, a roentgen, is defined as such an amount of x or gamma radiation as will produce in the volume of 1 ml of air (at standard temperature and pressure) ionization corresponding to 2.1×10^9 electrons (this is equal to another unit of charge called esu, see page 108). If we use, as an example, an ionization chamber of 10 ml volume, 1 roentgen will produce 2.1×10^{10} ion

pairs, or a charge of $\dfrac{2.1 \times 10^{10}}{6.25 \times 10^{18}} = 3.3 \times 10^{-9}$ coulombs. This charge,

small as it is, can be measured by a comparatively simple and robust device,

a combination of a small electric condenser and an electrostatic voltmeter (Fig. 46).

Condensers can be easily made of such a small capacity that a voltage
of the order of 200 volts will store in them not more than about 10^9 electrons;
this also means that if 10^9 electrons are accumulated in such a condenser,
the voltage will go up to 200. Since 1 roentgen will produce in a 10-ml
ionization chamber 2.1×10^{10} electrons, this number of electrons would
raise the voltage on the selected condenser to over 4000 volts, or one-tenth

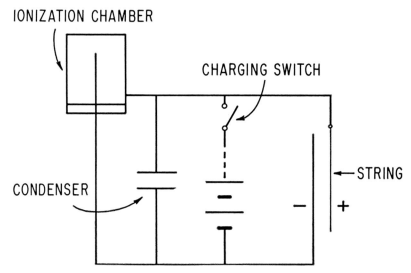

IONIZATION CHAMBER

FIG. 46.—Schematic illustration of a condenser type ionization chamber with string
electrometer for total dose measurement.

of a roentgen would raise it to over 400 volts. Such a voltage can be measured by observing through a low power microscope the electrostatic attraction of a thin quartz string to an oppositely charged support. Rather small
doses can be measured, therefore, with such an arrangement. The inconvenience of the device shown in Figure 46 consists in the need for a steady
supply of high voltage (a battery, for instance). This inconvenience can be
reduced by changing the arrangement slightly as illustrated in Figure 47.
Here the source of voltage is separate from the ionization chamber and the
electrometer, and is connected only for charging. The string will indicate
when the desired charge is reached. As soon as this charge is accomplished,
the charging device is disconnected and can be removed entirely. Another
way to handle the problem of a bulky charging device is that for the measurement process of this sort, only a small amount of "electricity," that is of
electrons, is needed, and this can be supplied by electrostatic friction
generators of a simple kind. The charge on the ionization chamber, and
hence the string deflection, will remain unchanged as long as no ionization

occurs, provided insulation in the instrument is perfect and no leakage takes place. As soon as ion pairs are produced in the ionization chamber, they will be collected by the electrodes, neutralize the charge on the condenser and reduce the potential (voltage). The degree of this discharge will be a measure of ionization produced and it can be observed on the electrometer string. The microscope scale can be calibrated in milliroentgens directly. The notable feature of this scale is that zero radiation dose corresponds to full charge, that is to a full deflection of the string: this position is marked "O," corresponding to "no radiation received." As radiation

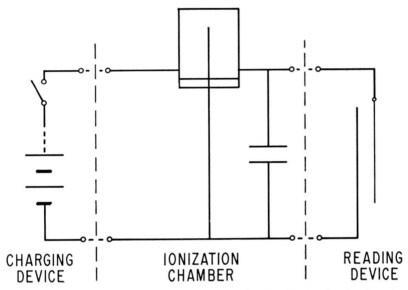

CHARGING
DEVICE

IONIZATION
CHAMBER

READING
DEVICE

Fig. 47.—Condenser type ionization chamber as in Fig. 46, showing the three basic components as they can be separated in actual construction. Such instruments have been designed in every possible combination of the components.

dose increases, the string moves towards the discharge position and the scale markings show *increasing* dose reading, while the charge decreases (see Fig. 48).

A dose rate instrument is necessarily self-contained: ionization chamber, voltage source, amplifier and meter are one integral unit. A dose measuring instrument, which consists of an ionization chamber, condenser, charging device and electrometer, can be made in separate parts. The condenser and ionization chamber are usually combined in one unit (hence the common name: "condenser chamber") but otherwise the following combinations will be found:

a. Ionization chamber separate, charger and reading device combined.

b. Ionization chamber and reading device combined, charging device separate.

c. All three elements combined.

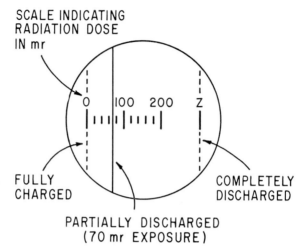

SCALE INDICATING
RADIATION DOSE
IN mr

0   100   200   Z

FULLY
CHARGED

COMPLETELY
DISCHARGED

PARTIALLY DISCHARGED
(70 mr EXPOSURE)

Fig. 48.—Reading scale of an ionization chamber electrometer. String position on scale indicates an exposure of 70 milliroentgen.

The first arrangement allows for optimal precision and reliability and is generally used for dosage purposes in radiotherapy. The second and third arrangements are preferable for health protection measurements, where precision better than 10 to 20 per cent is not essential, but portability and convenience are important. The ionization chamber and reading device are made in the size of a fountain pen for personnel monitoring.

Counting Circuits. Radiation detectors with sufficient sensitivity to record single bursts of radiation of a disintegrating element have the purpose of determining the disintegration rate of the isotope sample. Not every disintegration will reach the detector and produce a "count," but as a rule there will be a straightforward, proportional relationship between the disintegration rate, or activity in millicuries, and the counting rate as observed by the detector and associated counting circuit. This relationship will be discussed in detail in later chapters. In this chapter we will discuss how the counting rate can be observed and determined.

A radiation detector, whether it is a proportional counter, a Geiger-Mueller counter or a scintillation counter, needs a supply of constant voltage of about one to two thousand volts. The pulses which occur when the counter "sees" radiation are rather small and must be amplified. An amplifier will increase not only the pulses produced in the counter, but all other electric "noises" which may originate in the electric circuit, so that a device must be incorporated after the amplifier to pass the counting pulses only and to block, or to discriminate against artificial noise. Finally, when clean, amplified pulses are obtained, they must be counted, and the time for such counting determined. The counting rate is finally obtained by dividing the observed counts by the time of observation and expressing it as counts per second or counts per minute. The electric counting apparatus is generally called a "scaler," or scaling circuit. However, it has become accepted usage to describe the complete "black box" containing all auxiliary devices just mentioned as "scaler." We shall discuss these separate components of the scaler in a little more detail.

High Voltage Supply. The simplest source of high voltage is a dry cell battery, like several B batteries of a portable radio in series. This is occasionally used in portable counters, but not in standard stationary laboratory scalers because it is quite expensive in use and requires continuous replacement. The conventional way to get the high potential is to step up the alternating line voltage of 110 volts by a transformer to about 2000 volts and then to rectify it and smooth and stabilize it against line voltage fluctuations by suitable electronic methods. The voltage attained in this way fluctuates as a rule less than about $\frac{1}{2}$ per cent, although this stability is occasionally increased to 0.1 per cent, as commonly required for proportional counters and for spectrometers. The voltage necessary to operate a given counter varies for different types of radiation detectors and for individual tubes. A Geiger-Mueller tube may require a supply of from 900 to 1500 volts, whereas a scintillation counter or a proportional counter may require up to 1000 volts more. A scaler must be able to supply, therefore, a variable potential. A coarse and fine control of this voltage is provided on the panel, and a voltmeter is built in so as to read the voltage used and to make it possible to adjust this whenever necessary.

Amplifiers. Amplifiers used to increase the pulse output of a radiation detector are needed to increase the electric pulse from about 0.3 volt to about 100 volts, a factor of about 300, which can be easily achieved by a simple two stage amplifier. Such amplifiers are more complex when the amplification has to be rigorously linear, as in spectrometers; this corresponds to low distortion in a high fidelity audio amplifier and does not present serious engineering difficulties. The frequency response of the amplifier is also of some importance, depending on the speed with which the counter pulse rises and decays. In ordinary Geiger-Mueller counters this time is of the order of about 100 μs (1 μs = 10^{-6} seconds), and a frequency response of 10,000 cycles per second is required, which is within the ability of a medium fidelity phonograph amplifier. In fast scintillation counters, this time interval may be much smaller, of the order of 1 μs. Then a frequency response of a million cycles per second is needed, which can be obtained by amplifiers such as those used in radio receivers.

Preamplifiers. Proportional counters have a pulse output very much smaller than the pulses of a Geiger-Mueller counter or a scintillation counter and they would not operate with an ordinary amplifier as discussed previously. These small pulses must be first amplified to about 0.3 volts in a preamplifier. Since such preamplifiers have to handle small input pulses they must be designed with a very low inherent noise level. This is achieved by the use of specialized tubes and circuits.

Discriminator. The function and the purpose of a discriminator are identical to the threshold phenomenon in sensory perception, it passes on to the counting circuit proper only pulses which exceed a certain ("threshold") value. Thus spurious pulses originating within the measuring device itself and not coming from the outside are not counted. The equivalent purpose served by the visual and acoustic threshold is to prevent the cortex from being swamped by endoptic and endaural phenomena. It is always desirable to set the discriminator threshold as high as possible in order to have maximum rejection of unwanted electric noise; but it is of course not possible to set this threshold too close to the value of the counter pulse itself, since one has to be sure that all proper counts are transmitted. With Geiger-Mueller counters it is easy to find a compromise; most scalers have, therefore, no external control for the discriminator, which is preset internally by the manufacturer. In scintillation counters, where the pulse size depends on the energy of gamma radiation, the setting of the discriminator is more critical and it is desirable to have an adjustable control. Tests for suitable discriminator settings will be described in the next chapter.

Counting Mechanisms. After the electric pulses are amplified and "cleaned" from electric noise by the discriminator, they are counted in the scaling circuit in the narrow sense of the word.

Basically the scaling or counting circuit has the same function as a hand tally counter, used for the counting of blood cells. This is a device with a set of numerals which advance by one unit whenever a lever is depressed by the finger. The only difference is that in the counting circuit this advance is achieved electrically. In its simplest form an electromagnet performs this function. Although such an electromechanically operated counter is very simple, it has one serious limitation: it is slow, and it cannot follow counts which occur more frequently than 10 to 20 times per second (some specially constructed ones have achieved maximum speeds of 130 counts per second). Disintegration rates in samples to be observed are frequently much higher; counting rates in radiation detectors therefore exceed usually the limitations of electromechanical counters. Electronic devices using vacuum tubes or other similar electric components are capable of much higher speeds and can be built to approach a counting rate capacity of about one million per second.

From the point of view of the user, the electronic counters can be divided into two classes: decade and binary.

A decade counter displays the result in our conventional decimal notation in several ways. It may have a row of lights, labelled from 1 through 9 for each decade (a zero light is usually not provided; it is indicated by all lights being off). There are also several special counting and indicating tubes where either a light dot moves from side to side or around the periphery of the tube, and each position is labelled by the numbers 0 to 10 (glow transfer tubes). Recently indicator tubes have been introduced which actually show the illuminated arabic numerals. The advantage of these decade counters is that they indicate the counts in the conventional, decimal notation. The disadvantage is the complexity of the electric circuits.

Electrically the simplest counting circuit is the binary counter; its disadvantage is that the binary system of notation is not familiar, and rather puzzling at first, although it is basically simpler than our decimal system. It is in general use in electronic computing machines.

It can be best explained by an examination of the decimal notation. What do we mean by writing down say:

$$8052?$$

We know the answer of course:

$$8 \times 1000 + 0 \times 100 + 5 \times 10 + 2 \times 1$$

Or, remembering that any number raised to the power zero equals one, so that $10^0 = 1$:

$$8 \times 10^3 + 0 \times 10^2 + 5 \times 10^1 + 2 \times 10^0$$

We see that the *position* of a digit designates the power of ten by which it has to be multiplied:

$$
\begin{array}{cccc}
8 & 0 & 5 & 2 \\
10^3 & 10^2 & 10^1 & 10^0
\end{array}
$$

If there are five digits, the first on the left, which will be the fifth from the right or unit digit, will indicate ten thousands or 10^4 and so on. To summarize: in the decimal system the position of each digit indicates by what power of ten it has to be multiplied. This is of course what we are doing when we use this system.

In the binary system powers of two are used instead of powers of ten. If we write

$$1011$$

the positions will denote

$$
\begin{array}{cccc}
1 & 0 & 1 & 1 \\
2^3 & 2^2 & 2^1 & 2^0
\end{array}
$$

or, if the powers of two are spelled out:

$$
\begin{array}{cccc}
1 & 0 & 1 & 1 \\
8 & 4 & 2 & 1
\end{array}
$$

which means, in complete analogy to decimal notation

$$1 \times 8 + 0 \times 4 + 1 \times 2 + 1 \times 1 = 8 + 0 + 2 + 1.$$

We can, if we wish, add this up in decimal notation ("translate") to 11. There are naturally no limitations to the number of digits; the number 1430 can be written down in binary notation as 10110010110:

$$
\begin{array}{ccccccccccc}
1 & 0 & 1 & 1 & 0 & 0 & 1 & 0 & 1 & 1 & 0 \\
2^{10} & 2^9 & 2^8 & 2^7 & 2^6 & 2^5 & 2^4 & 2^3 & 2^2 & 2^1 & 2^0
\end{array}
$$

$$1024 + 0 + 256 + 128 + 0 + 0 + 16 + 0 + 4 + 2 + 0 = 1430$$

There are two features about binary notation which must be noted: First that we need more "places" to write out a given number: in the example four places are needed in the decimal notation and eleven places in the binary. This complication is one of the reasons why the binary system did not find use prior to the introduction of electronic computers. Second we must note that only two "numbers" are needed, 0 and 1, instead of ten, 0 to 9. This alone permits a tremendous simplification in a counting circuit: we need no device to write out or to indicate the ten numbers of the arabic decimal notation and we can indicate every digit by a single lamp, by using for instance the code: lamp *off* indicates "0," lamp *on* indicates "1." The number 1430 would then appear on the scaler panel as

on	off	on	on	off	off	on	off	on	on	off
2^{10}	2^9	2^8	2^7	2^6	2^5	2^4	2^3	2^2	2^1	2^0
1024 +	0 +	256 +	128 +	0 +	0 +	16 +	0 +	4 +	2 +	0

The greatest advantage of the binary system goes much deeper, however, than the simplicity of the indicating system: the electric circuitry is inherently simpler; for the same capacity it requires fewer components (tubes, etc.) than a decimal scaler and is therefore cheaper and more trouble free. The complication of translating the binary numbers into decimal ones is unquestionably a nuisance, since necessary calculations have to be done in the decimal system (slide rule scales are of course so divided). Some methods of counting, however, do not require such translation (preset count method, for instance, which will be discussed in a subsequent section), and here the binary system presents little difficulty.

Electronic counting circuits have no limitations in capacity, any number of counts can be counted by increasing the number of "digits," that is binary or decimal scaling stages. But it must be recalled that the purpose of using electronic counting stages was their high speed. The ultimate speed in measuring disintegration rates is limited, due to the limited ability of the radiation detectors themselves to record excessively high counting rates (see section on resolving time, p. 226). Most counters have a maximum counting rate limitation of between a few hundred and a few thousand counts per second. A number of electronic counting stages which have a capacity of about 200 to 500 counts will reduce the counting rate of a detector of *e.g.* 2,000 counts per second to less than 10 pulses per second, so that subsequent counting stages need not have a high speed response and electronic counting stages can be replaced by much simpler and cheaper electromechanical tally type counters. Most modern scaling circuits have, therefore, a combination of electronic and electromechanical counting elements: the pulses arriving from the radiation detector are first counted by electronic counting stages; when these stages have divided the counts sufficiently so that the pulses passed by them are slow enough to be handled by electromechanical counters, these counters take over and carry out the further extension of the counts.

One common arrangement consists for instance in eight binary stages. The eighth stage lights up when 128 counts have been accumulated, and goes out after 256 counts; each time the signal lamp of this stage goes out, an electromechanical counter registers and the number indicated on it increases by one unit. After 1024 total counts, this counter will show the number 4. If it indicates say 11, it means that $11 \times 256 = 2816$ counts have been registered; to this number the indication of the binary stages, if any, will have to be added.

Timing Mechanisms. The final purpose of nuclear measurements is the determination of the number of radiation bursts per unit time, and the purpose of the scaling circuit is to determine the counting rate. To achieve this, it is necessary to find in addition to the counts observed, c, also the time, t, in which the counts, c, accrued. Every reader is familiar with the measurement of time intervals with a stopwatch, and this is also used in scaling circuits; an electric stopwatch is either built into the instrument or it can be plugged in externally. The stopwatch is started and stopped simultaneously with the counting mechanism. The counting rate, R, is then calculated by dividing the observed counts by the elapsed time:

$$R = c/t.$$

It might be noted that time may be measured in seconds, minutes or hours, and the counting rate calculated in counts per second, counts per minute, or counts per hour. There is no theoretical reason to prefer any one of the units and the only guide for selection is convenience. For high counting rates, counts per second are more convenient since the numbers will have fewer zeros; for low counting rates, counts per minute are preferable since there will be fewer decimal places. Frequently the best guide to the selection of the units is the way the stopwatch happens to be calibrated. If it is calibrated in minutes and decimal fractions of a minute, counts per minute should be used, otherwise every result will have to be multiplied by 60, in order to convert it into counts per second.

For convenience and for reducing errors in starting and stopping, the counting mechanism and the stopwatch are electrically coupled in such a way that a single switch actuates both. Provision is further made to reset the counter and the timer to zero before a new observation is started. The resetting can be made in some instruments by operating a single switch or button, in others the timer and the counter are reset separately; the electromechanical counter has to be reset in some instruments mechanically. Separate resetting is a minor inconvenience.

Preset Time and Preset Count Features. A considerable inconvenience in working with scaling circuits is the necessity to watch the counts or the time and to stop the measurements when one of the two has reached the required reading. This is eliminated in most scalers by incorporating an automatic stopping of the measurement after the required time has elapsed or after the required number of counts have accumulated. The first is

13

achieved by one of the familiar interval timers, which are suitably connected into the circuit to stop the counts when the preset time has elapsed; this is called the *preset time method*. The advantage of this method is that the timer can be preset for a convenient integral interval, say one or ten minutes. The calculation of the counting rate is then simply the division of the observed counts by one or ten. The second method is to stop the stopwatch after the desired number of counts has been accumulated. This is electrically as simple as the use of an interval timer. It is called *preset count method*, and it has two advantages. One of the advantages is that it permits convenient use of binary counting stages. The timer is stopped after the selected single power of two, say 256 or 1024 counts have been observed, so that no interpolation of binary lamp indicators is necessary: the number of preset counts is always 32, 64, 128, 256, etc. This particular advantage is of course irrelevant with straight decimal counters. The second advantage is of more basic nature: by presetting a number of counts the precision of the observations is also preset, as will be discussed in the section on counting statistics. When making a series of measurements, a comparable precision of each measurement is usually desirable; preset count method can insure this automatically.

Time and Count Printers. With the scaling circuits discussed so far, after every measurement the elapsed time and the accumulated counts have to be read off the instrument panel and written down. Even with preset time or preset count circuits, the time or the counts have to be read and noted. When a large series of counting measurements have to be performed with an automatic sample changer, it is necessary also to record the readings automatically. For this purpose some scalers have provision for the connection of automatic printers, which print out on adding machine paper tape either elapsed time for a preset number of counts or the accumulated counts for a preset time interval. The advantage of such auxiliary printing devices is obvious with automatic sample changers: once such a sample changer is loaded, the instrument makes the observations automatically, it can operate during the night, and the results are recorded numerically. There is a further use of such printers not only where they are a convenience and a time and labor saving device, but where the required result cannot be obtained by simple manual counting. This situation presents itself if a phenomenon has to be observed where the radiation intensity changes so rapidly that it cannot be followed by manual counting. Several such examples will be encountered in clinical diagnostic studies, for instance in using radioactive sodium in peripheral vascular disease. A radiation detector is placed over some location of the human body and the appearance, increase and eventual decrease and disappearance of radioactivity is to be observed; these changes with time are the relevant information which is sought. If the time during which these changes occur is short, say a few minutes, it is difficult to count manually and to keep track of the time elapsed from the beginning of the experiment. An automatic printer, however, will register this information continuously and will give a record from which as many points for plotting a graph can be calculated as are desirable and as can be obtained with the average counting rate in the given experiment.

Rate Meters and Recorders. Sometimes the variations of radiation intensity are so rapid that it is inconvenient or perhaps impossible to observe them even with a printing device. In such situations rate meters can be used. A rate meter is an instrument which is basically different in design and construction from a scaler. It has in common with it a high voltage supply for the operation of the radiation detector, an amplifier and a discriminator; but instead of a counting circuit (the "scaling circuit" in the narrow sense of the word) it has a circuit which is made sensitive to the average frequency of the electric pulses, that is to the counting rate. Such electric and electronic circuits are well known and commonly used in electric engineering as frequency meters. Their electric output, usually in milliamperes, is proportional to the counting rate. If this output is connected to a meter, the counting rate at any given instant can be read on a dial. The output can be also connected to a strip chart recorder, which is essentially identical to the recording part of an electrocardiograph, so that the time plot of radiation intensity is obtained directly. There is one feature of the rate meter circuit which should be clearly understood for its proper use and that is that it performs basically the same function as a scaling circuit: it observes counts and elapsed time and computes the ratio (counts per unit time) by electric means. It does this in a manner essentially similar to the preset time method. The parameter in a rate meter which is analogous to time for which a scaler is "preset" is usually called "time constant." The longer the time constant, the more counts will the rate meter accumulate with a given counting rate to reach its final deflection, and the slower will its pointer or recording pen deflect in response to a change in radiation intensity. The time constant is also one of the factors which determine the precision; this will be discussed in the next section. It may be useful to anticipate here the conclusion: the larger the time constant, the greater the statistical precision of the readings for a given counting rate; the higher the counting rate, the greater the precision with a given time constant. This determines the limitations of a rate meter in recording rapidly changing phenomena; a small time constant is required to observe rapid changes and this can be achieved only at the expense of precision, unless the observed counting rates are high.

One common use of counting rate meters is in radiation survey instruments. In this application low radiation intensities are of interest, and low counting rates have to be measured. The requirements for precision on the other hand are quite modest. A workable compromise between time constant and precision can therefore be easily achieved.

Coincidence and Anticoincidence Circuits

In certain counting applications it is required that not every pulse arriving from a radiation detector or some part of the auxiliary circuit is counted but only those pulses which occur simultaneously with some other pulse: coincidence counting, as for instance in positron scanning (see page 302). There are also applications where an opposite function is required, that is when only such pulses must be counted as occur alone and which should not be counted when they occur simultaneously with another pulse: anticoincidence counting, as for example in some background reduction circuits (see page 259) and in spectrometers (see page 262).

Coincidence Circuit. Figure 49 illustrates the principle of operation in a coincidence circuit by an electromechanical model.

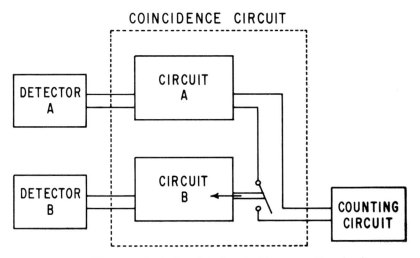

Fɪɢ. 49.—Electromechanical model of a coincidence counting circuit.

Two radiation detectors A and B are connected to two circuits A and B. The detectors A and B produce electric pulses and it is required that the pulse from detector A is counted only when detector B also produces a pulse simultaneously with the pulse of detector A, and that when a pulse occurs in detector A only, no count is registered in the counting circuit. The sources of pulses A and B need not necessarily come from two different detectors; they may be generated in an auxiliary circuit source which produces two different pulses depending on the operating conditions of a single detector.

The pulses A and B are handled in circuits A and B, which contain, as required, power supplies, discriminators and amplifiers.

Circuit A passes the pulse from detector A after amplification and discrimination to the counting circuit, but there is a switch (relay contact) in series with this connection.   This contact is normally open so that the pulses from circuit A cannot reach the counting circuit and be counted, unless this contact is closed.

Circuit B operates the relay and closes the contact when and only when a pulse occurs in detector B, which after amplification passes through the discriminator of circuit B.

The result is that pulses originating in circuit A reach the counter only when the relay contact is closed by circuit B, due to a pulse in that circuit. Counts are registered therefore only when detector A with circuit A operate simultaneously (in "coincidence") with detector B and circuit B.

While it is quite feasible to build a coincidence circuit with a relay, as described, the usefulness of such an arrangement is limited due to the relatively slow action of an electromechanical relay. In actual practice the same result is achieved by electronic means, which operate at the required high speed.

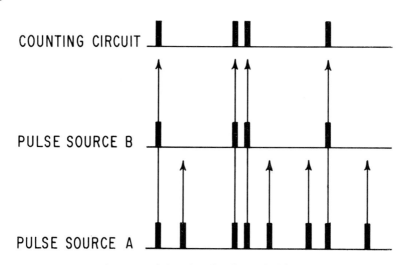

Fig. 50.—Diagram of electric pulses in a coincidence circuit.

Figure 50 illustrates the performance of a coincidence circuit.

Anticoincidence Circuit.   Figure 51 illustrates a model similar to that shown for the coincidence circuit, arranged for anticoincidence operation.

Pulses passed by circuit A are here normally free to reach the counting circuit since the relay contact of circuit B is closed, unless circuit B produces a pulse originating in source B.   When this occurs, the relay contact opens and the pulse from source A—circuit A is blocked from the counting circuit and no counts can be registered.   The performance of the anticoincidence circuit is illustrated in Figure 52.   As in a coincidence circuit the actual instruments use high speed electronic devices to block the pulses from circuit A when a pulse occurs in circuit B.

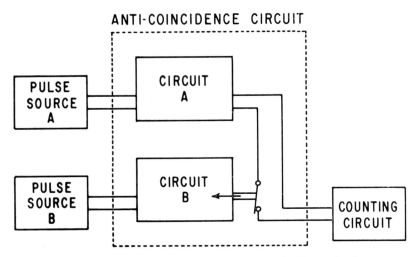

FIG. 51.—Electromechanical model of an anticoincidence circuit.

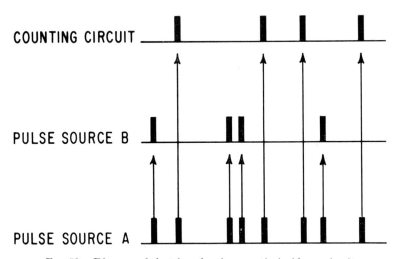

FIG. 52.—Diagram of electric pulses in an anticoincidence circuit.

14

Basic Measurements With Radiation Detectors

Statistics of Nuclear Counting. Radioactive disintegrations occur in a completely random manner. There is no way of predicting when a given individual atom will disintegrate; the only information we have about such an atom is that it has a 50-50 chance to disintegrate during the next half-life. The reliability of predictions about half-lives and disintegration rates of radioactive samples is based on the fact that even a minute fraction of a millicurie contains an extraordinarily large number of atoms, and that statistical predictions approach certainty when large numbers of events are involved.

Principles. When measurements of radioactive samples are made, the actual numbers of disintegrations which are observed by counting are not necessarily very large. Let us consider the measurement of a radioactive sample with some counting arrangement in which about five counts per second are observed. If we were to carry out our measurements until one million counts were accumulated, the error due to the random nature of radioactive decay, that is the statistical fluctuations, would become negligible for any practical purpose. But such an observation would take 200,000 seconds, or over 55 hours. This is obviously impractically long, and therefore a certain amount of statistical error will have to be accepted in order to reduce this time.

The magnitude of the error which is acceptable is determined by the particular experiment. In measuring blood pressure for instance the acceptable error is a few mm of mercury, since physiological variations are of this order of magnitude and only larger deviations from the normal values have clinical significance. It is easy to build a manometer, which has an error of less than $\frac{1}{2}$ mm mercury, but the increased cost compared to a conventional sphygmomanometer will be wasted since the increased precision would be of no diagnostic value. On the other hand an error exceeding 10 mm mercury would not be acceptable, since such a difference approaches clinical significance. Similar consideration must lead us to decide what the tolerable limits of error are in any particular use of radioactive materials. Counting statistics will then give us information about the number of counts to be accumulated and the required counting time.

Let us assume that in our example the required precision corresponds to a standard deviation of 3 per cent. The statistical problem is then to decide how many total counts should be collected, in order to find the counting rate with an error not exceeding 3 per cent.

This is possible since it is known how the statistical fluctuations change when the number of the observed random events is increased. The relation is given by the "Poisson Distribution": *the standard deviation is equal to the square root of the number of the observed events.*

This deduction from the random nature of radioactive decay and the application of Poisson's distribution plays a considerable role in nuclear measurements. It will have to be examined in some detail before it can be applied to the proposed specific problems.

At first the statement about the standard deviation will be expressed algebraically. We shall call the total number of counts N, and the standard deviation σ. Then

$$\sigma = \sqrt{N} \tag{1}$$

The standard deviation is a measure of the error in the determination of N, and we employ it in expressing the true value of N as $N \pm \sigma$. When we have to discuss errors in measurement quantitiatively, σ has to be defined with more precision. One suitable definition is that if the measurement of the quantity under observation is repeated many times, 68 per cent of these measurements will deviate from their mean by an amount which is smaller than the standard deviation. An extension of this statement, which follows from elementary probability theory and which applies to nuclear counting, is that about 95 per cent of all observations will have deviations less than twice the standard deviation, and over 99.7 per cent will have less than three times the standard deviation.

Let us return to the example in which the counting rate was known to be roughly 5 counts per second and the question was how much and how long to count so that the error will be 3 per cent. If we assume tentatively that we want the standard deviation σ to be equal to 3 per cent of the accumulated total counts, N, we have the equation:

$$\sigma = \frac{3}{100} N$$

which expresses the stipulation that σ should be 3 per cent of N.

Substituting σ from (1) we get

$$\sqrt{N} = \frac{3}{100} N$$

and

$$N = \left(\frac{100}{3}\right)^2 = 1,111 \text{ counts}$$

This will take about 200 seconds, or only a little over three minutes. It is, however, very important to realize that a standard deviation of 3 per cent means only that our chances to obtain a value of N within 3 per cent of the presumably correct value every time we count for 200 seconds, is about 2 to 1. This is certainly poor betting odds. If we want to have a value of N less likely to differ from the correct value by as much as 3 per cent, we have to recall that these chances increase as we reduce the value of the standard deviation.

If we make σ half the desired error of 3 per cent, that is

$$\sigma = \frac{1.5}{100} N$$

we get for the required N the value

$$N = 4,444$$

The chances now will be 20 to 1 that the observed N does not differ by more than 3 per cent from the correct value. And if σ is reduced to one-third of the required error of 3 per cent, we get

$$\sigma = \frac{1}{100} N$$

and

$$N = 10,000$$

In this case our chances of being within the 3 per cent limit of error are 370 to 1.

It is frequently convenient to express an error in per cent of the measured magnitude. The error corresponding to the standard deviation in per cent will be designated as V (this is called the coefficient of variation)

$$V = 100 \, \frac{\sigma}{N} \tag{2}$$

Since $\sigma = \sqrt{N}$, V can be expressed as

$$V = 100 \, \frac{\sqrt{N}}{N} \qquad \text{or}$$

$$V = \frac{100}{\sqrt{N}} \tag{3}$$

If we want to find the value of N, which assures a given coefficient of variation V, we get from (3):

$$N = \frac{10,000}{V^2} \tag{4}$$

The use of this per cent error or coefficient of variation has an advantage beyond mere convenience. Later the errors in counting rates will be discussed. If they are to be determined from the standard deviation, σ, of the total number of counts, N, some additional mathematical operations will be needed: the standard deviations of the total counts, N and of a counting rate R, are not the same, whereas the per cent error has the same value for both N and R, under certain conditions, which usually obtain.

From equation (4) the required number of counts can be calculated which are needed to have the actual per cent error within a given limit with a given confidence. *If this error is designated as P per cent*, then in order to have 2 out of 3 observations with an error not to exceed P, we have to make V = P; in order to have about 20 out of 21 such observations V should be = P/2 and to have 370 out of 371 observations within the limits, we need V = P/3.

This gives the rule for determining the required coefficient of variation to be used in equation (4) for a given per cent error:

$$\text{Low reliability:} \qquad V = P \tag{5}$$

$$\text{Medium reliability:} \quad V = P/2 \tag{6}$$

$$\text{High reliability:} \qquad V = P/3 \tag{7}$$

By substituting V in (4) we get the required number of counts:

$$\text{Low reliability:} \qquad N = \frac{10,000}{P^2} \tag{5a}$$

$$\text{Medium reliability:} \quad N = \frac{40,000}{P^2} \tag{6a}$$

$$\text{High reliability:} \qquad N = \frac{90,000}{P^2} \tag{7a}$$

It will be noted that increase in reliability is achieved at a considerable cost in time: almost 10 times as many counts and hence time is needed to achieve high as compared to low reliability!

This discussion demonstrates that after deciding on the required precision, we still have to make the further decision about the degree of assurance so that the limits of the selected error are not too frequently exceeded in the measurements. There is no hard and fast rule in this respect, and the only simplifications which can be given are some practical guides:

For preliminary information the standard deviation or coefficient of variation may be made equal to the desired error (low reliability).

In everyday work, when a compromise has to be made between available time and the reliability of individual measurements, a standard deviation or coefficient of variation equal to half the accepted error is a reasonable compromise (medium reliability).

When the conditions of the observation are such that a high order of confidence is needed in keeping the errors within the stipulated limit then the standard deviation or coefficient of variation should be made equal to one-third of that error (high reliability).

Different levels of reliability are described as "confidence limits." Confidence limit means the probability for the error in a given observation not to exceed the desired error. We can express our descriptive terminology quantitatively:

Low reliability corresponds to confidence limit of 0.68

Medium "   "   "   "   "   " 0.95

High   "   "   "   "   "   " 0.997

Background.   Whenever a radiation detector is used to measure a radioactive sample, it will receive, in addition to the radiation emitted by this sample, radiation coming from the outer space ("cosmic radiation") and from naturally occurring radioactive materials in the earth. To these two extraneous sources of radiation is added whatever may have been introduced in and around the laboratory, as for instance other samples in the vicinity, radioactive sources in storage, and x-ray machines. All these sources create a radiation background which affects a detector and is observed by counts even when no sample is introduced into the measurement arrangement. This background, or background counting rate, can be reduced but not completely eliminated when an observation is made, so that whenever a sample is actually "counted," the sum of the sample counts and of the background counts is obtained. The background counting rate has to be determined separately and the counting rate of the sample itself can then be obtained by subtracting the background counting rate R_b from the combined or gross counting rate R_c. The sample or net counting rate R_s is therefore

$$R_s = R_c - R_b \tag{8}$$

This introduces a new complication to the statistical considerations discussed in the preceding section: the required counting rate R_s depends actually on two distinct and separate magnitudes, that is, on the background as well as on the combined or gross counting rate.

This complication disappears if the background is negligibly small compared to the sample count; in this case gross and net counts are practically identical. But when the background is significant in comparison with the combined count, it will contribute to the error in the determination of the sample counting rate.

The statistical rule for the determination of the standard deviation σ_d of a sum or a difference of two other magnitudes which themselves have the standard deviations σ_1 and σ_2 is:

$$\sigma_d = \sqrt{\sigma_1^2 + \sigma_2^2} \tag{9}$$

In order to apply this equation to the calculation of the standard deviation of the net sample counting rate R_s, we have to know the standard deviations of the gross and background counting rates R_c and R_b.

From equation (1) we know that the standard deviations of the total accumulated gross counts N_c and the background counts N_b are $\sqrt{N_c}$ and $\sqrt{N_b}$ respectively. If the time to accumulate the gross counts is t_c, and the time for the background counts is t_b, then the counting rates are

$$R_c = \frac{N_c}{t_c} \tag{10}$$

$$R_b = \frac{N_b}{t_b} \tag{11}$$

From this it follows that

$$\sigma_c = \frac{\sqrt{N_c}}{t_c} \tag{12}$$

and

$$\sigma_b = \frac{\sqrt{N_b}}{t_b} \tag{13}$$

where σ_c and σ_b are the standard deviations of the gross and background counting rates respectively. Equation (9) can now be used and we get for the standard deviation σ_s of the net or sample counting rate

$$\sigma_s = \sqrt{\sigma_c^2 + \sigma_b^2} \tag{14}$$

and by substituting (12) and (13)

$$\sigma_s = \sqrt{\frac{N_c}{t_c^2} + \frac{N_b}{t_b^2}}. \tag{15}$$

By substituting N_c and N_b from (10) and (11), equation (15) can be written also in the form:

$$\sigma_s = \sqrt{\frac{R_c}{t_c} + \frac{R_b}{t_b}} \tag{16}$$

which will be useful in a different connection, to be discussed later.

Or finally by substituting t_c and t_b in (16) from (10) and (11):

$$\sigma_s = \sqrt{\frac{R_c^2}{N_c} + \frac{R_b^2}{N_b}} \tag{17}$$

The per cent standard deviation of the sample counting rate V_s is now, according to (2) and since σ_s is known from (14), (15), or (16):

$$V_s = \frac{100\sigma_s}{R_s}. \tag{18}$$

The equation (15) will permit calculation of the standard deviation of the sample counting rate, when the total counts and times of the gross and background measurements are known, but it still leaves open the answer to the following important problem: how many counts should one accumulate for gross and for background counting in order to achieve a desired precision, that is, a selected value of standard deviation? The answer is too complex for a complete treatment here.

A rigorous solution of this problem was given by Loevinger and Berman*). Since the numerical calculations from their equations are somewhat lengthy and a graph of a family of curves is used, a simplified assumption will be used in the following presentation. The limitations of this simplification will be also discussed.

It can be seen from the equations (14) and (15) for σ_s that it is pointless to count background to a higher precision than the gross counts, since, however small the background errors become, the final error in the sample counts will not be reduced below the error in the gross counts. The errors in gross counts and background counts should be balanced. The simplest approximation to such a balance is to make them equal, that is to have

$$\sigma_c = \sigma_b \tag{19}$$

On the basis of this approximation, it is possible to determine the number of counts to be accumulated for gross and for background counting, provided we know *approximately* these counting rates from a preliminary rough measurement. Let these approximate counting rates be R_c' and R_b'. We have from (12)

$$\sigma_c^2 = \frac{N_c}{t_c^2} \tag{20}$$

and by substituting t_c from (10)

$$\sigma_c^2 = \frac{R_c'^2}{N_c} \tag{21}$$

and similarly from (13) and (11):

$$\sigma_b^2 = \frac{R_b'^2}{N_b} \tag{22}$$

Since we decided to use the assumption of equation (19), it follows from it and from (14) that

$$\sigma_s^2 = 2\sigma_c^2 \tag{23}$$

and also

$$\sigma_s^2 = 2\sigma_b^2 \tag{24}$$

*See R. Loevinger and M. Berman: Efficiency Criteria in Radioactivity Counting Nucleonics *9*, 26–39, 1951. The graph and instructions for its use are now conveniently available in: "A Manual of Radioactivity Procedures," National Bureau of Standards Handbook 80, 1961. For sale by the Superintendent of Documents, Washington 25, D.C., price 50 cents.

Equations (23) and (21) give

$$\sigma_s^2 = 2 \frac{R_c'^2}{N_c} \tag{25}$$

and equations (24) and (22) give

$$\sigma_s^2 = 2 \frac{R_b'^2}{N_b} \tag{26}$$

Finally we can calculate the required number of counts to be accumulated in order to have a standard deviation σ_s of the net counting rate: From (25) we get the gross counts

$$N_c = 2 \frac{R_c'^2}{\sigma_s^2} \tag{27}$$

and from (26) the background counts

$$N_b = 2 \frac{R_b'^2}{\sigma_s^2} \tag{28}$$

We decide on the value of σ_s on the basis of the per cent standard deviation which has been selected. Let this be V; we have then from (18)

$$V = \frac{100\sigma_s}{R_s}$$

$$\sigma_s = \frac{VR_s}{100}$$

R_s is known approximately from R_c' and R_b' as their difference. Hence

$$\sigma_s = \frac{V(R_c' - R_b')}{100} \tag{29}$$

We can express now the combined counts N_c and background counts N_b which must be accumulated in order to insure the coefficient of variation V, by substituting the values for σ_s from (29) in the equations (27) and (28):

$$N_c = 20{,}000 \left[\frac{R_c'}{V(R_c'-R_b')} \right]^2 \tag{30}$$

and

$$N_b = 20{,}000 \left[\frac{R_b'}{V(R_c'-R_b')} \right]^2 \tag{31}$$

The two equations (30) and (31) are useful when preset count technique is used. For preset time technique the counting times for combined and background counting t_c and t_b can be calculated by substituting $N_c = t_c R_c'$ in (30) and $N_b = t_b R_b'$ in (31). This gives

$$t_c = \frac{20,000 \ R_c'}{[V(R_c'-R_b')]^2} \tag{32}$$

and

$$t_b = \frac{20,000 \ R_b'}{[V(R_c'-R_b')]^2} \tag{33}$$

Equations (32) and (33) are also useful for estimating the time which will be required in order to obtain the error V. This total time is obviously $t_c + t_b$.

Whether preset time or preset count technique is used, it is essential to keep in mind that the preceding four equations are calculated from counting rates which have been determined only roughly from preliminary experiments. The standard deviation σ_s and the coefficient of variation V of the final determination of R_s will be only approximately of the desired magnitude. It is useful therefore to check their value on the basis of the finally observed t_c and t_b if N_c and N_b were preset, or on the basis of the observed N_c and N_b if t_c and t_b were preset. σ_s can be calculated from (15). V can be calculated by substituting in (18); σ_s from (15) and R_s from (8), (10) and (11):

$$R_s = \frac{N_c}{t_c} - \frac{N_b}{t_b}$$

$$V = 100 \ \frac{\sqrt{\dfrac{N_c}{t_c^2} + \dfrac{N_b}{t_b^2}}}{\dfrac{N_c}{t_c} - \dfrac{N_b}{t_b}}$$

This can be simplified by algebraic manipulations to

$$V = 100 \ \frac{\sqrt{N_c t_b^2 + N_b t_c^2}}{N_c t_b - N_b t_c} \tag{34}$$

The use of the equations will be illustrated by an example in which the approximate gross counting rate is $R_c' = 150$ counts per minute and background counting rate is $R_b' = 100$ counts per minute; the required coefficient of variation is $V = 5\%$.

We obtain the needed total counts from (30) and (31)

$$N_c = 20,000 \left(\frac{150}{5 \times 50}\right)^2 = 7,200 \text{ counts}$$

$$N_b = 20,000 \left(\frac{100}{5 \times 50}\right)^2 = 3,200 \text{ counts}$$

and the counting times from (32) and (33)

$$t_c = \frac{20{,}000 \times 150}{(5 \times 50)^2} = 48 \text{ minutes}$$

$$t_b = \frac{20{,}000 \times 100}{(5 \times 50)^2} = 32 \text{ minutes}$$

The total counting time will be 80 minutes. If the finally observed counting rates should turn out to be exactly $R_c = 150$ and $R_b = 100$, then V will be necessarily 5 per cent. Should the observed counting rate differ from the approximately estimated values, the obtained per cent error can be calculated from (34) and compared to the required value of $V = 5$. Should the actually obtained error be too large, it will indicate that R_c' and/or R_b' were too poor approximations. The calculations will have to be repeated using the newly obtained combined and background counting rates as R_c' and R_b' and the counting done again.

Let us compare the above result with the Loevinger-Berman method. The example given in Handbook 80 (see footnote page 205) corresponds to our example. The values obtained from the graph are in our notation:

$$N_c = 6{,}600 \text{ counts}$$

$$N_b = 3{,}600 \text{ counts}$$

The counting time would be

$$t_c = 44 \text{ minutes}$$

$$t_b = 36 \text{ minutes}$$

or the total of 80 minutes, identical with ours. This agreement is fortuitous and is due to small errors in reading the graph. The superiority of the Loevinger-Berman method should appear in a smaller error obtained in the same counting times. If the actually observed counting rates were identical to the assumed ones, the final errors due to both methods could be calculated from (34), and it would show that the error is less than 5 per cent by a negligible amount.

A mathematical comparison of the two methods shows that the gain in time with the Loevinger-Berman method is negligible, when combined counting rate is less than twice background. The choice between the two methods may be left therefore to personal preference. When combined counting rate is greater, the time saving may become significant, though the counting times will be progressively shorter, so that absolute time saved will be significant only when many samples are to be counted. Under such conditions the examination of the data by the Loevinger-Berman method will be advisable.

If the background in the example discussed above were 0.1 count per minute, it is obvious that it could have been disregarded, gross counts considered equal to sample counts and the calculations simplified. The decision between disregarding and not disregarding the background may be difficult in a borderline situation, for instance if in the above example the background rate were two counts per minute. It is of course possible to calculate generally the error introduced by disregarding the background, but the resulting equations are of moderate practical use. A simple rule may be given instead: background can be disregarded when the background counting rate does not exceed one-fifth of the desired per cent error as calculated from the gross counting rate. If the desired per cent error is V, then background may be disregarded when R_b is equal to or smaller than $\dfrac{1}{5} \times \dfrac{R_cV}{100}$. If this rule is followed, disregarding the background will not increase significantly the expected error. The suggested factor of one-fifth is somewhat arbitrary, one-third may be used for less critical work and one-tenth when greater reliability is required. The more stringent criterion will cost somewhat more in terms of time spent in counting.

The rule for neglecting background may be formulated as subject to the condition that

$$R_b \lessgtr \frac{R_cV}{500} \text{ counts per minute} \tag{35}$$

Let us apply this rule to the example with combined counting rate $R_c = 150$, required error $V = 5$ per cent.

$$\frac{R_cV}{500} = 1.5 \text{ counts per minute}$$

According to the rule of equation (35), background could be neglected in this example if it were 1.5 counts per minute or less.

The equations for required number of counts and for the counting time are very much simplified when background can be neglected. R_s becomes R_c; instead of (23) we have $\sigma_s = \sigma_c$, and not $\sigma_s^2 = 2\,\sigma_c^2$, so that the factor 2 becomes 1 in the following equations in which also σ_b, N_b and t_b vanish, and we return to (4) in the form

$$N_s = \frac{10,000}{V^2} \tag{36}$$

It will be noted that N_s is now independent of estimated counting rates, which cancel out in the modified equation (30). The required counting time is from the modified equation (32):

$$t_s = \frac{10,000}{V^2 R_s'} \tag{37}$$

which is dependent on the preliminary determination of the approximate counting rate.

If the standard deviation σ_s of the observed counting rate R_s is needed, it follows from the definition of coefficient of variation and equation (3)

$$\sigma_s = \frac{R_s V}{100} = \frac{R_s}{\sqrt{N}}$$

σ_s can be expressed directly in terms of the observed counts and counting time, since $R_s = N_s/t_s$

$$\sigma_s = \frac{\sqrt{N_s}}{t_s} \tag{38}$$

Preset Time and Preset Count Methods of Counting. After the discussion of the statistics of counting, the basic advantage of counting for a preset and therefore constant number of counts is obvious; by presetting the total number of counts to be observed and by measuring the time required for their accumulation, a constant counting error is maintained. An added advantage was mentioned in the discussion of binary scalers; preset counting makes it unnecessary to translate a complicated binary number into decimal form for calculation. This second point is irrelevant when a decimal scaler is used.

A disadvantage of preset count technique is that the scheduling for counting a large number of samples is difficult. If it is important to have the counting of a given number of samples finished within a certain time, preset time technique is to be preferred at the expense of some non-uniformity of the experimental errors.

One potential pitfall of preset counting technique should be mentioned, which sometimes occurs with high counting rates. Let us consider a sample which gives 100 counts per second, and a required error of 3 per cent. This will mean that a total of 1000 counts is needed, or that a binary scaler will have to be set at 1024 counts. Time for this number of counts will be ten seconds. A stopwatch is usually reliable at best to 0.2 seconds. Ten seconds will be measured therefore with an error of about 2 per cent, which will increase the "preset" statistical error. This means that the error in measurement of time cannot be neglected when the time intervals become short, and that we shall have to increase the preset count setting in such a way that this error becomes negligible. As a rule, it can be neglected when times of one minute or longer are measured. When the preset time method is used, it is possible that small time intervals of less than one minute or so may introduce timing errors in addition to the statistical errors determined by the number of counts accumulated during this interval.

The role of background in radiation measurements can now be summarized. Background counting rate, when it is of comparable magnitude to sample counting rate, increases the time required to make the determination with a desired precision. Under these conditions, precision of the sample measurement depends on the reliability and hence the constancy of the background. Attention must be directed therefore to the constancy of the background, unless it is so small in relation to the sample count, that it can be disregarded. The constancy of the background depends to a large degree on environmental conditions such as proximity of x-ray generating equipment which is turned on and off, radioactive sources which are moved around (patients with tracer and therapeutic amounts of radioisotopes should not be overlooked), or sample containers which are reused and may contain traces of previous radioactive samples. The shielding of counting devices by lead enclosures serves therefore a twofold purpose: to reduce the background due to cosmic and terrestial radiation and to reduce fluctuations of this background produced by changing levels of radiation in the laboratory. Shielding will not affect variations of background due to contamination of sample containers; this can be accounted for only by checking the background with the empty individual containers and by either using this background as determined for each container, or by discarding or storing contaminated containers until they are either decontaminated or the radioactivity has decayed.

The Use of Rate Meters and Recorders. Counting rate meters and recorders have been mentioned in the section on scaling circuits. Since the evaluation of the statistical errors and hence the reliability of observations with these instruments presents some special aspects, they must be discussed separately from ordinary scalers. On the first casual inspection of a rate meter, it will not be apparent how the general rule of statistics of random events can be applied to it. If such a meter is connected to a radiation detector and a radioactive source brought into its vicinity, it will be noticed that the deflection does not occur instantaneously but slowly until it reaches a final value around which the pointer of the instrument (or the line traced by a recorder) will oscillate. In most rate meters a selector switch will be found on the panel which permits variation in the response speed. This speed of response is a characteristic value of a rate meter; it is usually called its "time constant." The functional role of this time constant corresponds to the time interval selected in a scaling circuit, when it is used with preset time method of counting. To be more precise, the inherent "preset time" of a rate meter is equal to twice its "time constant." If the time constant of a rate meter is thirty seconds, for instance, and if the observed counting rate is 50 counts per second, a total of 3000 counts have been "collected" for this reading since the equivalent "preset time" is sixty seconds. The 3000 counts correspond to an error of about 2 per cent for the observation of a source of constant activity. When the radiation intensity changes, it will again take the instrument some time to reach the new deflection; this time will have a value between its response time and twice its response time, depending on the magnitude of the change.

Counting Statistics in Rate Meters and Recorders. In ordinary counting the operational controls on the scaling circuit are 1. Manual, where a switch is operated to start and to stop the counting with a read-out for time and total counts. 2. Preset counts, with a read-out for elapsed time. 3. Preset time with a read-out for accumulated counts. The controls on a rate meter are different. There is a selector switch for "response time" and one or two switches or controls for "range" or "sensitivity." The read-out is either a meter or a strip chart recorder, with some scale or chart divisions, indicating the counting rate directly. The sensitivity or range control permit changing the calibration of the meter or recorder in the sense that the rate corresponding to a given deflection (for full scale or per division) may be made larger or smaller. This is a different way to present the results than in a scaling circuit. We shall designate the result of given settings of these two controls as *sensitivity of the instrument S, which is defined as the change in counting rate which produces a deflection of one division.*

The statistical counting errors will appear as fluctuations of the pointer or of the record, superimposed on the actual changes of counting rate with changes of activity in the observed sample (organ or animal for instance). These fluctuations, as we actually observe them, are best described by the number of divisions over which they are spread. If we express the standard deviation in a rate meter as σ_d divisions, we shall know that one third of the fluctuations will be larger and two thirds smaller than $2\sigma_d$ since the errors will be $\pm \sigma_d$ from the mean deflection.

We shall express the fluctuations in term of scale divisions, since this is what we actually observe on the recording.

In the ratemeter, background appears as a baseline deflection and cannot be subtracted except by reference to this base line. All deflections are a measure of "combined" counting rate, which will be designated in the following paragraph simply as R. The response time will be designated as t_r. The equivalent preset time is then equal to $2t_r$.

The standard deviation of the counting rate R will be as in (12)

$$\sigma_R = \frac{\sqrt{N}}{2t_r}$$

and since $N = Rt = R \times 2t_r$:

$$\sigma_R = \sqrt{\frac{R}{2t_r}} \text{ counts per second} \tag{39}$$

or, since we want to know the standard deviation in scale divisions:

$$\sigma_d = \frac{1}{S} \sqrt{\frac{R}{2t_r}} \text{ divisions} \tag{40}$$

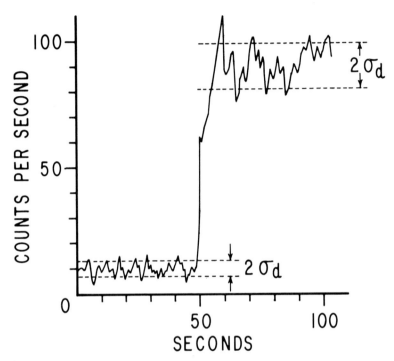

FIG. 53.—Diagram of a rate meter record with a time constant of $\frac{1}{2}$ second and a full scale range of 100 c/s (1 scale division = 10 c/s). In the beginning the counting rate is 10 c/s. After 50 seconds it rises suddenly to 90 c/s. σ_d calculated from equation (40). $2\sigma_d$ in the first half = 0.6 div; in the second half it is = 1.8 div.

Figure 53 illustrates an example. The graph paper has 10 divisions, full scale deflection corresponds to 100 counts per second (S = 10) and response time is set to $\frac{1}{2}$ second. For a counting rate of 10 per second we get

$$\sigma_d = \frac{1}{10} \sqrt{\frac{10}{1}} = 0.3 \text{ divisions}$$

and when the counting rate goes up to 90 per second

$$\sigma_d = \frac{1}{10} \sqrt{\frac{90}{1}} = 0.9 \text{ divisions}$$

Two characteristics of the rate record, which can be seen in the illustration, must be pointed out:

1. Standard deviation means that about one-third of the observations will deviate by more than this amount from the mean value. The band which encloses fluctuation equal to or smaller than σ_d is $2\sigma_d$ wide . (0.6 div for R = 10 and 1.8 div for R = 90).

2. This band becomes wider, as the counting rate increases.

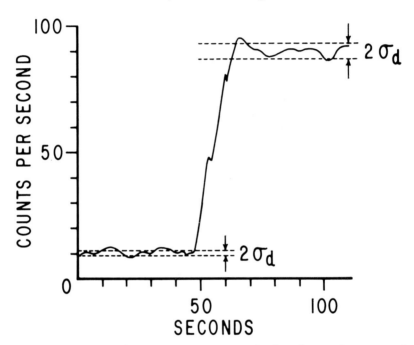

Fig. 54.—Same as in Figure 50, but the time constant has been increased to 5 seconds. $2\sigma_d$ in the first half is now = 0.2 div, and in the second half it is = 0.6 div.

Figure 54 illustrates the same observation made with an increased response time t_2 = 5 seconds. Here for R = 10:

$$\sigma_d = 0.1 \text{ div}$$

and R = 90

$$\sigma_d = 0.3 \text{ div}$$

It will be seen that the fluctuations have decreased in magnitude according to (40). Due to the increased response time they also become less frequent, but the deflection to the higher counting rate takes longer.

Figure 55 shows the effect of reduced sensitivity to a full scale value of 1000 counts per second with t_2 = 10, for the two rates used in Fig. 54 and for R = 900. From (40) we calculate the expected fluctuations σ_d, considering that S is now equal to 100 c/s. We get ± 0.01; ±0.03 and ±0.1.

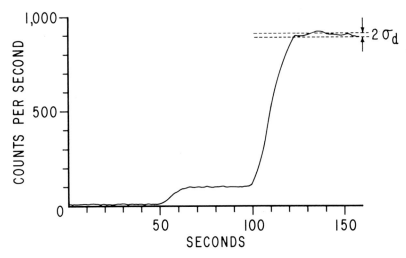

FIG. 55.—For the first 100 seconds this is the record of the same counting rates as in Figures 53 and 54. The time constant is the same as in Figure 54, 5 seconds, but the scale has been changed so that full deflection corresponds to 1000 c/s (1 scale division = 100 c/s). $2\sigma_d$ during the first 50 seconds is now = 0.02 div and between 50 and 100 seconds it is = 0.06 div. After 100 seconds the counting rate rises suddenly to 900 c/s; $2\sigma_d$ is here = 0.2 div, or one third of what it was in Figure 54 when the deflection was also 9 divisions.

Equation (40) and the illustrations show that fluctuations are reduced when longer response times are used and when strong samples permit a less sensitive setting of the range. The experimental conditions determine here, as in all counting, the acceptable error, which appears as fluctuation in a rate meter: the changes to be observed must be larger than the fluctuation, since otherwise they would be masked by them. Increase in response time is limited by the experimental conditions also: if response time is longer than the time in which the relevant changes of counting rate take place, these changes will not be registered.

It may appear at first that a rate meter is an ideal substitute for a scaler, if preset time method of counting is desired. This is not quite true, because of one inherent technical limitation of electronic rate meters: the longest practical time constant is limited to not more than a few minutes, while no such limitation exists with an ordinary scaler. This limitation of time constant means a limitation of total counts determining a single reading, so that when the counting rate is low, precision is also quite low.

The use and the limitations of a rate meter can now be summarized:

When the counting rate is high enough to give the required precision within the given time constants of the instruments, a rate meter is a useful and simple device. When the counting rate is too low to satisfy this requirement, a conventional circuit is preferable, although when a rate recorder is used, it is possible to recapture some of the lost precision by a graphical interpolation of the recorded wavy line; this corresponds to the taking of a mean of several readings made with low preset time on a scaler.

A recording meter is of very great usefulness when a rapidly changing source of radioactivity is under observation, as for instance in observing the circulation time with sodium-24 or another physiological mechanism with a rapid turnover. A printing counter, which prints either the time elapsed with a preset count circuit or counts accumulated with preset time mechanism, can also be used, but this will require a manual plotting of the data to obtain a graphic representation, whereas a rate recorder produces such a plot directly. Whenever a rate recorder is used, it must always be taken into consideration that on the one hand response time limits the precision of the reading or recording, if it is short compared to the counting rate, and that on the other hand, if the response time is long compared to the speed with which the observed physiological phenomena change, such changes will be masked by the slow response. A compromise will have to be made under many circumstances between the speed of response and the attainable precision. For a given time constant, the precision can be increased by increasing the counting rate, which can be achieved either by using a counting arrangement of higher sensitivity or by administering a higher dose of the isotope. When neither is possible, either some degree of precision has to be sacrificed, or a longer time constant must be used, although this may involve getting inherently less frequent readings; a smooth record may deceive one in this case; there are no more frequent readings ("points on the chart") than the response time offers, the smooth line is simply a form of electrical interpolation. If a time constant longer than a few minutes is acceptable and higher precision is required than can be attained with a rate meter, a printing scaler can be used instead of a recorder.

Evaluation of Equipment Performance Using Counting Statistics. Since nuclear events as seen by a properly functioning radiation detector are of purely random nature and as such subject only to the Poisson distribution, the proper function of a counting set-up can be tested by investigating whether the variations of observed counting rates follow the Poisson distribution or not.

A casual way of doing this test consists of taking two consecutive readings. As an example, let us consider a counting set-up with a given radioactive sample which gives 8000 gross counts in ten minutes (sample and background counts need not be considered separately in this connection) on the first observation and 8100 counts on the second observation in the same interval; the question is now whether this observation agrees with the theoretical expectation. The theoretical error should be $\sqrt{N}$ counts. The mean of the two observed counts is 8050, its square root is 90. The difference between this mean and the two counts is 50, smaller than what was expected. The statistical meaning of the standard deviation has to be recalled in this connection: this is the deviation which has the odds of 2 to 1 to be observed. In other words, we should expect in 2 out of 3 observations to have a difference of 90 counts or less and in 1 out of 3 to observe a larger difference. If the equipment is working properly, we should expect in 2 out of 3 measurements to have the observed result. This is of course not very meaningful. If we had observed a difference of 270 counts between the two measurements and their mean, this would have meant that if the equipment were working properly, such a result might occur once in over 300 measurements, or would be quite unlikely; the conclusion would be that that instrument is *not* working well. This example shows that two observations alone will never reassure us that an instrument performs well, but can only indicate when it malfunctions rather badly. A test by two observations is only a very rough check.

A more reliable procedure is to repeat the observation about 10 times, to obtain for instance N_1, N_2, N_3, N_4, N_5, N_6, N_7, N_8, N_9, N_{10} counts for the same time interval t; to calculate the mean counts $N_{mean} =$

$$\frac{N_1 + N_2 .. + N_{10}}{10} = \frac{\Sigma N}{10},$$ to obtain the deviation of the counts from this

mean: $N_1 - N_{mean}$, $N_2 - N_{mean}$, $N_3 - N_{mean}$, etc. and to compare these deviations with the standard deviation $\sqrt{N_{mean}}$. Table 15 gives a numerical example. The expected deviation is $\sqrt{2992} = 55$; there are two deviations larger than this (#3 and #9) and eight which are smaller. The theoretical expectation is to find about three larger and seven smaller deviations. The observed result is not significantly different from the expected one and it is reasonable to assume that the apparatus is working properly. What result would indicate the opposite? A rigorous answer is not possible, but a practical guide may be given: if six or more of the observed deviations are larger than the expected value or if only one or none exceed it, one should question the performance and repeat the series of observations; if

Table 15. Counts Observed in 5-minute Intervals

#	N	Deviation
1	2940	− 52
2	3020	+ 28
3	3065	+ 73*
4	3010	+ 18
5	2980	− 12
6	2970	− 22
7	3025	+ 33
8	3030	+ 38
9	2890	−102*
10	2985	− 7
Sum:	29915	
Mean:	2992	

Expected standard deviation 55

*Observation with a deviation exceeding the expected value

the second series gives the same result, something is probably wrong with the equipment.

It may be surprising to read the statement that something is wrong not only when errors are larger than expected, but also when they are smaller than expected, since it is unusual to complain when errors are too small. It must be realized, however, that the "expected" deviations under discussion are not human or instrumental errors, but are inherent in the random nature of radioactive decay. As long as our observations reflect nuclear disintegrations only, they must fluctuate within the range of the Poisson distribution. If our observations have smaller or larger fluctuations, both can take place only if something other than nuclear disintegrations influences them: either can be due only to an artifact.

The given example was for preset time counting technique. For preset counts technique, the arithmetic is a little more involved, since the standard deviation is determined as always by the total number of counts accumulated, while the variable in this technique is the time required to accumulate these counts. The difficulty is handled easily if we use the per cent standard deviation, since this applies equally to counts in a given interval or to time for a given number of counts.* If we accumulate N counts, the per cent standard deviation is

$$V = \frac{100}{\sqrt{N}}$$

If the mean interval is t_{mean} and the expected standard deviation of the time intervals σ_t,

$$\sigma_t = \frac{t_{mean} \, V}{100} = \frac{t_{mean}}{\sqrt{N}} . \tag{41}$$

Table 16 illustrates an example where time required to accumulate 6400 counts has been measured. The mean time $t_{mean} = 68.3$ (it is immaterial for this purpose whether it was measured in seconds or in minutes); the expected standard deviation in time is from (41) $\sigma_t = 0.85$. It can be seen that this value is exceeded in 3 out of the 10 observations (#6, #7 and #9). The conclusion is that the equipment works properly.

The described method of checking the randomness of results and hence of equipment testing is reasonably rigorous and is suitable in practice. It may leave a feeling of dissatisfaction in the reader, however, since it does not lead to a definite number expressing the probability that the equipment is performing properly or odds against such a conclusion. A way to obtain a numerical expression of this sort is indeed available in statistics as the chi square method. Its presentation in sufficient detail would go beyond the scope of the present book. The interested reader is referred

---

* This statement has been occasionally questioned; rigorous proof will be found in Robley D. Evans: "The Atomic Nucleus," New York, McGraw-Hill Book Co, 1955, page 797-798.

to standard textbooks on statistics* for general description and to Evans†
for its application in nuclear counting. The more simple procedure discussed above will be found sufficient for most applications encountered
in clinical use of counting circuits.

When a statistical check of a counting set-up reveals that something is
wrong with the apparatus, it must be determined first whether the source of
trouble is in the radiation detector or in the electronic scaling circuit. For
this purpose there is frequently provision for the "calibration" of the scaler,
consisting of a switch which disconnects the detector and applies electrically
a uniform counting rate of 60 counts per second to the scaler. If the scaler

Table 16.   Time Required to Accumulate 6400 Counts

#	Time	Deviation
1	68.0	−0.3
2	68.9	+0.6
3	67.6	−0.7
4	68.8	+0.5
5	68.3	+0
6	69.2	+0.9*
7	67.3	−1*
8	69.1	+0.8
9	67.3	−1*
10	68.3	0
Sum:	682.8	
Mean:	68.3	

Expected standard deviation 0.85
*Observations with a standard deviation exceeding the expected value.

counts this incorrectly, the trouble is in the electronic circuit. A correct
counting rate indicates that the trouble is probably in the radiation
detector part of the apparatus.

Selection of Operating Voltage.   *Voltage Characteristic.* The fundamental
role of the high voltage applied to a Geiger-Mueller counter and to the
photomultiplier tube of a scintillation counter has been discussed in considerable detail (p. 175ff). It will be recalled that the Geiger-Mueller region
is defined as that range of applied voltage where every ionizing event reaching the counter produces an electrical pulse of equal amplitude independent
of ionization intensity of the event. In this region the total number of
pulses (or counts in reference to a scaling circuit) observed from a source
with a constant disintegration rate is independent of the voltage, or largely
so. Similar independence exists for a range of voltages applied to a scintillation counter. Below this range the pulse amplitude is too small to activate
the counting circuit. Above it spurious pulses occur due to a variety of
causes which are inherent in the detector itself and are not due to ionizing

* For instance: M. Bancroft: *Introduction to Biostatistics*, New York, Hoeber-Harper,
1957
† See footnote page 218.

events reaching it. Reliable information on this useful range of voltages and its limitation is essential for the operation of a radiation detector. The curve representing this information is called the "*Voltage Characteristic*" of a counter.

If a radiation detector is connected to a scaling circuit and a suitable source of radioactive material is placed near it, no counts will be observed until the voltage reaches a certain value. If the voltage is gradually increased, occasional counts will be observed at a certain value called the *starting voltage*, as indicated in Figure 56. It should be noted that the ordinates in Figure 56 represent counting rate, and are different from the ordinates in Figure 43, where they represent pulse height or amplitude.

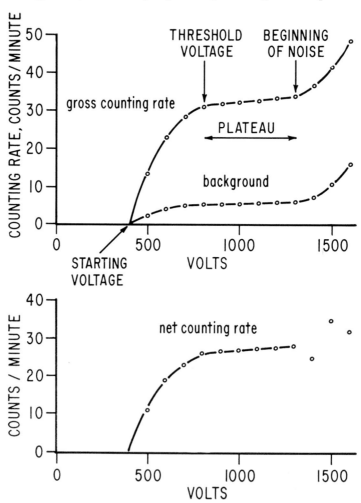

Fig. 56.—Voltage characteristic of a Geiger-Mueller counter. The bottom curve of the net counting rate was obtained as difference of the two curves in the top graph; note that it is difficult to find the beginning of noise in this curve.

As the voltage is increased, the counting rate will at first also increase and then level off. The voltage range where the counting rate levels off is called the *threshold voltage* or simply "threshold." It will be noted that this threshold does not have a precise value, since there is no sharp kink in the voltage characteristic; nevertheless a value can be assigned to it within about ± 10 volts.

Further increase of voltage will not produce marked changes in the counting rate in a well-functioning counter for a few hundred volts. This region is called the *plateau.*

The end of the plateau occurs at a voltage where the counting rate begins to increase at first slowly and then quite rapidly. This increase is due to spontaneous discharges produced in the Geiger-Mueller counter or in the phototube by the excessive voltage, and is called *noise.* The excessive voltage in this region can easily damage the radiation detector, therefore it should be approached slowly in determining the voltage characteristic. Readings should not be taken beyond the voltage at which the counting rate is about two times that in the plateau region.

The whole voltage characteristic can be determined and plotted with a radioactive sample giving a few thousand counts per minute. The higher the counting rate (within the limits of resolving time, which will be discussed later), the easier it is to observe starting and threshold voltage and the less time it will take to get data of desired precision. A high counting rate, however, may mask the beginning of noise, and a low counting rate (preferably background alone) will permit a more precise determination of noise voltage. When a radioactive sample is used for the plateau determination, the gross counting rate must be plotted; if the net counting rate is used for plotting, the noise may become completely masked or it may appear at a misleadingly high voltage.

Three basic data about a counter can be derived from the voltage characteristic: length and slope of the plateau and correct operating voltage.

The *length of the plateau* is simply the difference between noise voltage and threshold voltage. It is usually a few hundred volts. A counter with a plateau less than 100 volts long is considered, as a rule, unsatisfactory, unless it has some other especially desirable properties. The plateau length becomes shorter as a counter ages; usually the noise appears at lower voltage, but the threshold may also go up on occasion. Periodic determination of the plateau and its length is the best way to anticipate a counter breakdown. As a general rule, a counter should be replaced when its plateau reaches 100 volts.

The *operating voltage* is the voltage at which the counter is used. It may be placed anywhere on the plateau, but for optimal reliability a few rules should be followed. Since noise voltage goes down with aging, it is poor practice to operate a counter close to the upper limit. It may be used nearer to the threshold voltage, but not too near either, since this also may shift. For these reasons the best operating voltage is close, but not too close to the threshold, and as far below noise voltage as this recommendation permits. To give a specific rule: when plateau length is less than 200 volts operate the counter at the voltage corresponding to the center of the plateau; if the plateau is 200 volts or longer, use as operating voltage the threshold plus 100 volts.

The *slope of the plateau* is a measure of the independence of the counting rate from changes and fluctuations in the high voltage supply. This voltage is stabilized in the scaling circuit to minimize such fluctuations but they can never be reduced to zero. As a rule they vary from about 0.5 to 1 per cent, which means 5 to 10 volts for an operating voltage of 1000 volts. Plateau slope is expressed as the per cent increase of the counting rate, when the high voltage is increased by 100 volts. For example: a counting rate of 127 counts per second is measured at 1000 volts and 134 counts per second at 1100 volts. An increase from 127 to 134 counts per second is observed for a 100 volt increase in voltage. The per cent increase is then $100 \times \dfrac{134-127}{127} = 5.5\%$. This counter has a plateau slope of 5.5 per cent.

Good Geiger-Mueller counters have an average slope between 1 and 5 per cent while scintillation counters show values between 5 and 10 per cent, although with technical improvements this slope is gradually decreasing. It can be seen that a counter with a 10 per cent slope will have fluctuations of 1 per cent in the counting rate, when high voltage varies from the 1000 volts selected operating voltage by 10 volts. This error will be added to the statistical errors, and cannot be reduced by increasing the number of accumulated counts. This consideration demonstrates the importance of good stabilization of high voltage supply, and the justification of expending considerable effort and expense for improving this component when critical work is to be carried out. The slope also may change with aging or other deterioration in the detector. In scintillation counters a common cause for increased slope is leaking out of the oil or grease which establishes the optical connection between the crystal and phototube, or dirt and dust penetrating into this oil. A periodic check of plateau slope and of plateau length is a valuable element in preventive maintenance, since help can be summoned before an actual breakdown occurs.

Energy Dependence of the Voltage Characteristic and Discriminator Setting. The voltage characteristic of a Geiger-Mueller counter is independent of the nature and energy of the primary ionizing event. Once a primary ion pair has been produced, the avalanche discharge and the spread of the discharge are determined only by the counter properties and the applied voltage: the pulse height does not depend on the primary ionizing event. If the voltage characteristic of such a counter has been determined with one radioactive isotope, or even on background alone, the same plateau length, slope, operating voltage, etc. will be observed with any other isotope.

This is not quite true for a proportional counter, in which the pulses depend on the number of ion pairs produced in the counter volume. In most β emitting isotopes the β range is much greater in gases even at atmospheric pressure than the dimensions of the counter. The number of primary ion pairs produced in the counter depends, therefore, largely on the linear ionization density which does not vary by more than a factor of 10 over a β energy range from about 10 kev to several Mev. Since the plateau of proportional counters is as a rule quite long, about 500 volts, and has a low slope, the difference in threshold for different β energies with conventional operating voltage plays a small role. The voltages used with proportional counters are higher than for Geiger Mueller counters. Compare Fig. 56 and 57. This situation is quite different when other nuclear par-

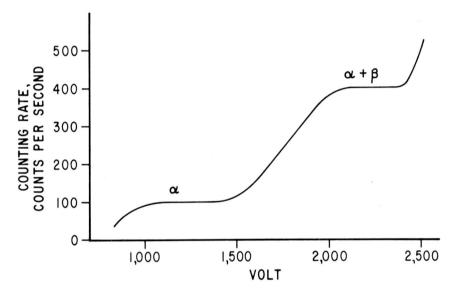

FIG. 57.—Voltage characteristic of a proportional counter with a sample of Radium D plus E. The first plateau is due to α radiation. The second plateau is due to $\alpha + \beta$ radiation.

ticles are emitted by the sample. α particles for instance have a very much higher linear ionization density than β particles, they produce much higher pulses which will override the threshold of the scaling circuit (when the same preamplification is used) at much lower voltage applied to the counter. Figure 57 shows the voltage characteristic of a proportional counter for a Radium D and E mixture which emits both α and β radiation. The first "plateau" is due to α counting; β pulses are too low at these voltages to override the discriminator. A second "threshold" appears around 1500 volts in the illustration, when some β particles begin to be counted. At the second plateau almost all α and β particles are counted. The β counting rate alone is equal to the difference between the counting rates of the two plateaus.

The situation is quite different with a scintillation counter. The light pulse intensity during the absorption of radiation depends on its energy. A low energy gamma ray will usually produce a weaker light pulse than a high energy gamma ray. The photomultiplier will therefore also produce electrical pulses of varying energy, which will be fed into the scaling circuit. It will be recalled that one of the essential components of a scaling circuit is the discriminator (threshold device, bias) which has the purpose of discriminating against random electrical noise and which operates by letting through to the actual counting circuit only pulses which exceed a selected

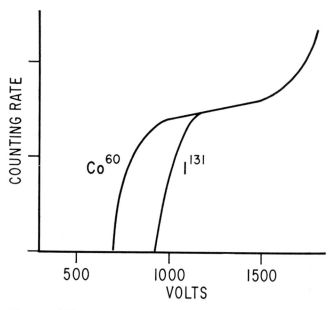

Fig. 58.—Voltage characteristic of a scintillation counter with an improperly adjusted discriminator.

minimum level. The electrical output of a phototube depends not only on the intensity of the light pulse, but also on the applied voltage, which determines the phototube sensitivity. If we consider now the voltage characteristic of a scintillation counter obtained with a high energy gamma emitter, for instance Co^{60}, we may obtain such a curve as is illustrated in Figure 58. The light pulses have somewhat varying amplitudes, but on the average they are relatively high, due to the high gamma energy of Co^{60}. These light pulses are of course not affected by the voltage applied to the phototube. When this voltage is too low, however, the phototube sensitivity is low, and the electrical pulses from the phototube to the scaler are also small; they are too small to be passed by the discriminator and no counts are observed (voltage below starting value). When the voltage is high enough for the phototube to produce electrical pulses which will be passed by the discriminator, counts will be observed; the starting voltage has been reached, but pulses will be sufficiently great only for the largest light flashes in the crystal. As the voltage is further increased, gradually most light flashes cause sufficiently high electrical pulses to pass the discriminator and to cause counts to be registered; the threshold voltage and plateau are reached.

This sequence of events will be modified if lower energy gamma radiation, as for instance from I^{131}, is absorbed in the crystal. Light pulses are weaker, hence the electrical pulses produced by the phototube are smaller, and at an applied voltage, at which counts were observed with Co^{60}, with I^{131} all pulses may be still below the discriminator threshold. Under these conditions the starting voltage and the threshold voltage will be higher with I^{131} than with Co^{60}, and the plateau will be shorter (*see* Fig. 58). The voltage at which noise occurs and the plateau ends will be the same, since this is inherent in the phototube and not due to the external radiation.

The practical consequence of this discussion is that the voltage characteristic of a scintillation counter should be determined with the isotope for which the counter will be used. A convenient radium or cobalt standard may give a misleading voltage characteristic, if the instrument is actually used for I^{131} measurements. A modern and well-designed counter may not show this difference. Whether this is the case or not should be established for every scintillation counter and scaling circuit by determining the plateau for various isotopes in use and also with a radium or Co^{60} source. Should a difference be found, a counter can still be useful, if the plateau is long enough and of sufficiently low slope. For periodic checks it is advisable to use the isotope with the lowest gamma energy available, since this will offer a more sensitive way to demonstrate faults when they begin to appear.

Since the reason for different starting and threshold voltages for isotopes with different gamma energies is due to the intensity of light flashes (scintillations), this difference can be minimized by lowering the discriminator setting (threshold). In some scaling circuits this is possible from the front of the panel where a knob is provided for this purpose. The practical limitation for such lowering is set by internal electrical noise, which appears as an increased background. Some experimentation in this direction is possible and useful without specialized servicing of apparatus. Voltage characteristics are determined with I^{131} and with radium or Co^{60} at progressively lower settings of the discriminator control; the background for each setting is determined also. The optimum setting is where there is no difference between the voltage characteristics in Figure 58 with the two isotopes, provided there is no appreciable increase in background. Apart from reducing energy dependence of the voltage characteristic, a change of discriminator setting affects the ratio of sample and background counting rates. For a given isotope the best conditions are given when the ratio R_s^2/R_b is a maximum. This maximum frequently extends over some range in the discriminator setting; the lowest setting within this range will offer the least energy dependence of the plateau.

15

Resolving Time. In the discussion of the mechanism of counters, mention was made of a time interval immediately following the occurrence of a pulse, during which a Geiger-Mueller counter is insensitive and does not respond to ionizing events; this was called "dead time" of a counter. A similar dead time exists also in scintillation counters. This is, however, very much shorter, so short in fact that the response speed of the electrical or electromechanical counting mechanisms becomes the limiting factor. Whatever the cause of the overall "dead time" of a counting set-up may be, it will put an upper limit on the counting rate which can be measured accurately. It will influence the observed counting rate when it is high enough, and it is necessary to have information about this dead time, or "resolving time."

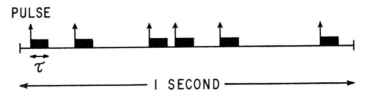

Fig. 59.—The sequence of pulses and the ensuing "dead times" (resolving time) of duration τ in a radiation detector.

In Figure 59 a time interval of one second is charted, with several pulses occurring during this time. The dead time or resolving time is called τ. If a second pulse occurs within this time after a first pulse, it will not be recorded; the counting set-up will "miss" it. If R counts per second have been observed, some radiation bursts may have been missed. The true counting rate R_t will be larger than the observed counting rate R_o by the number of counts which will have occurred during the dead time and therefore missed. The duration of the total dead time during each second will be $R_o\tau$. The number of counts missed will be the number of radiation events which actually occurred during this time, that is $R_t R_o \tau$. Since by definition the number of counts missed is also $R_t - R_o$, we have the equation

$$R_t - R_o = R_t R_o \tau \qquad (42)$$

A careful inspection of (42) will reveal what appears to be a dimensional discrepancy. The units on the left are in counts per second; the units on the right are in counts squared per second. The answer is simply that "counts" are dimensionless numbers, so that both sides have the dimension of "per second," that is sec^{-1}.

Solving for R_t we get

$$R_t = \frac{R_o}{1 - R_o \tau} \qquad (43)$$

The true counting rate can be calculated from the observed counting rate by using (43) if the resolving time is known. It is frequently convenient to know also the per cent correction which has to be added to an observed counting rate to obtain the true counting rate. This per cent correction, C, is

$$C = 100 \frac{R_t - R_o}{R_o} \tag{44}$$

and can be calculated from (42) by substitution:

$$C = 100 \frac{R_o \tau}{1 - R_o \tau} \tag{45}$$

When C is calculated from (45) the counting losses $R_t - R_o$ and the true counting rate can be calculated from (44):

$$R_t - R_o = \frac{C R_o}{100} \tag{46}$$

and

$$R_t = R_o \left(1 + \frac{C}{100} \right) \tag{47}$$

In Table 17 the per cent correction and true counting rate are calculated for a series of observed rates with a resolving time $\tau = 200$ microseconds, which is a representative value for a Geiger-Mueller counter. When high counting rates are a frequent occurrence, it is convenient to use the actual resolving time of the given counter, to calculate a similar table; and to plot the results on graph paper with the observed rates as abscissas and the

Table 17. $\tau = $ **200 Microseconds (Resolving Time)**

Observed Counting Rate	% Correction	True Counting Rate
R	C	R
50	1	50.5
100	2	102
150	3	155
200	4	208
250	5.2	263
300	6.4	319
350	7.5	376
400	8.7	435
450	9.9	495
500	11	555

true rates as ordinates as in Figure 60. The true counting rate for any observed rate can be read directly from such a graph.

One word of caution should be mentioned at this point on the use of such high counting rates that the per cent correction is excessive, say about 20 per cent.

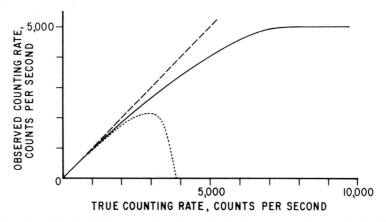

FIG. 60.—Relationship between the observed and the true counting rate. Dashed line: no counting losses, resolving time is zero. Solid line: hypothetical, not paralizing counter. Observed counting rate reaches assymptotically a maximum. Dotted line: actual counter, which shows paralysis at high counting rate. Note that near the origin all three lines coincide and that over a part of the range the solid and dotted lines coincide. Note also that for any observed counting rate in the range of the dotted curve there are two possible corresponding true counting rates; for any true counting rate above the intersection of the descending limb with the abcissa the observed counting rate is zero (jamming).

The basic assumption in setting up equation (42) was that the resolving time is a constant. Counting detectors and scaling circuits which behave according to this assumption are called "non paralyzing" counters. This term becomes clear from Figure 60 which is a rough plot for Table 17 extending the calculation to extreme counting rates. By solving (42) for R_o we get

$$R_o = \frac{R_t}{1 + R_t\tau} \tag{48}$$

This can be also written in the form

$$R_o = \frac{1}{1/R_t + \tau} \tag{48a}$$

From (48a) it can be seen that

$$\lim R_o = \frac{1}{\tau} \tag{49}$$

when $R_t \to \infty$.

which means that when the true counting rate increases to infinity, the observed counting rate approaches asymptotically a steady value of $1/\tau$ counts per second. In the example of Table 17 with $\tau = 200$ μs, R_o would approach 5000 c/s when R_c approaches infinity. The counter continues to count, however high the true counting rate may be: it is not blocked or jammed, it is "non paralyzable." Practically no counter behaves this way. Actually, when a pulse occurs during a dead time interval something does happen in a counter and counting circuit which prolongs the dead time. By how much depends on whether the new impulse occurs at the beginning or the end of the dead interval. The mathematical handling of this phenomenon is difficult and of little value since it is rarely possible to determine the relevant parameters experimentally. The result, however, is of great practical importance: when the prolonged dead times merge into each other and encroach upon each other, counting stops and the counter shows no counts at all: it is blocked or jammed, it is "paralyzed." The dotted line in Figure 60 illustrates the actual behavior of a counter. At first observed counting rate is linearly proportional to the true counting rate (negligibly small resolving time correction). With increased counting rate, resolving time correction becomes significant and for a limited range the correction agrees with the assumption of non-paralyzable counting behavior (both correction curves are close together). After the resolving time correction C reaches roughly 25 per cent, the deviation of the curve from non paralyzable behavior begins to be significant, and soon after a maximum observed counting rate is reached, it begins to drop, the counter becomes partly paralyzed and soon afterwards it jams completely.

It is useful to express the conditions of validity of equations (43) and (47) in terms of the maximum permissible value of the observed counting rate R_o. We get this by calculating R_o from (44) for C = 25:

$$25 = 100 \; \frac{R_t - R_o}{R_o} \tag{44a}$$

$$R_t = 1.25 \; R_o \tag{44b}$$

by substituting R_t from (43):

$$\frac{R_o}{1 - R_o\tau} = 1.25 \; R_o$$

and we get the condition under which resolving time correction may be made

$$R_o < \frac{0.2}{\tau} \tag{50}$$

Let us summarize the practically important points of this discussion:

1. Resolving time correction beyond about 25 per cent is not reliable, equations (43) and (47) are not valid when C > 25. See equation (50).

2. When the true counting rate becomes very high, the counter may jam and it will behave as if there is no radiation at all present. This may lead on occasions to grave errors. Whenever there is some suspicion of jamming, a simple test can be performed: slowly remove the sample from the counting position. Increased distance will reduce the true counting rate and if jamming took place the counter may resume counting at some greater distance.

Modern scaling circuits combine electronic counting stages with electromechanical counters. Particularly when binary counters are used there is usually a switch which permits connecting the electromechanical counter to any one of the binary stages so that the electromechanical counter will count on every 8, 16, 32, 64 and so on counts. The purpose of this arrangement is to give flexibility in selecting a convenient preset count number. This creates a source of serious errors, since the electromechanical counters have a low resolving time, usually about 0.1 second. If they are connected to a low scaling stage, this mechanical resolving time may be exceeded at a relatively low counting rate and the electromechanical counter will jam. Let us examine the counter of Table 17. We may have a counting rate of 200 c/s, quite within the validity of the resolving time correction, but if we

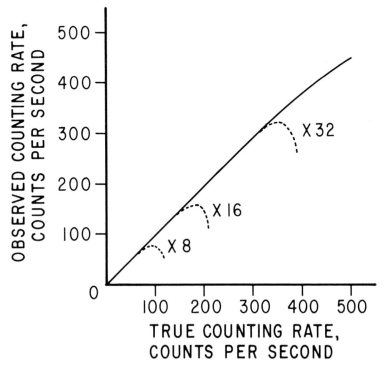

Fig. 61.—Plot of observed counting rate against true counting rate according to Table 17 (solid line). Dotted lines show incipient jamming due to blocking of the electromechanical counter when low scaling factors (8, 16 and 32) are used.

connect the mechanical counter to the scaling stage 16, the counter will have over 12 pulses per second and will jam, since it cannot follow more than 10 pulses per second.

Figure 61 illustrates the effect. The solid line is plotted according to Table 17. The dotted lines show how much the observed counting rate will deviate from the expected line when lower scaling factors are used. The consequence is that the highest possible scaling factor should be used and that the operating rate of the electromechanical counter should be less than 10 per second. The mechanical counter operates with a loud audible click, and it is strongly recommended to train and sensitize one's ear to the danger signal of a high clicking rate, say about 3 to 5 per second.

Determination of Resolving Time. The experimental determination of resolving time for a given counter and circuit combination is done by using two sources of radiation which give sufficiently high counting rates to show observable counting losses between the sum of separately determined counting rates R_1 and R_2 for each of the two sources, and the counting rate for the two sources counted simultaneously, R_{12}. In other words, the counting rates should be such that $R_1 + R_2$ is appreciably larger than R_{12}. A quantitative evaluation is possible only if the separate and the simultaneous counts are done with the sources in identical positions with respect to the counter. A simple way to achieve this is shown in Figure 61. In addition

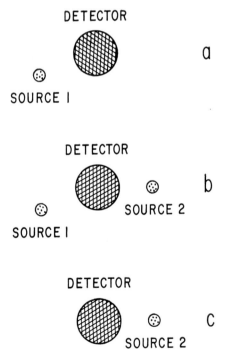

Fig. 62.—Three successive arrangements a, b, and c, of two radioactive sources 1 and 2 for the determination of resolving time.

to the three determinations illustrated, the background R_b has also to be determined.

If it is considered that the true net counting rate R_{t12} for the two sources counted together must be equal to the sum of the net counting rates R_{t1} and R_{t2} of the sources counted separately and that the same background appears whenever the two sources are counted together and when they are counted separately:

$$R_{t12} + R_b = R_{t1} + R_{t2} + 2R_b$$

and that the observed counting rates R_1, R_2 and R_{12} give each an equation for R_{t12}, R_{t1}, and R_{t2} from (43), a set of four equations with the unknowns R_{t12}, R_{t1} R_{t2} and resolving time τ will be obtained. The solution requires a somewhat lengthy but straightforward calculation,* with a solution for τ:

$$\tau = \frac{R_1 + R_2 - R_{12} - R_b}{R_{12}{}^2 - R_1{}^2 - R_2{}^2} . \tag{51}$$

It may be noted that when the difference between $R_1 + R_2$ and R_{12} is much larger than the background, this background can be ignored, and (51) is then simplified to

$$\tau = \frac{R_1 + R_2 - R_{12}}{R_{12}{}^2 - R_1{}^2 - R_2{}^2} . \tag{52}$$

A still further simplification is possible under certain assumptions, which leads to the often encountered equation

$$\tau = \frac{R_1 + R_2 - R_{12}}{2R_1 R_2} . \tag{53}$$

It is however infrequent that the assumptions leading to (53) are justified. The simplification of (52) compared to (51) is not very great. It is therefore advisable always to use equation (51) in determining the resolving time; this is simpler in routine work than to study and evaluate the justification for the use of the simplified formulæ.

Efficiency and Sensitivity of Radiation Detectors. The terms efficiency and sensitivity as applied to nuclear measurements are sometimes confusing. Since they describe two different aspects of the response of a counter to radiation bursts accompanying the disintegration of radioactive samples, they are very useful indeed and the confusion has to be untangled.

Efficiency in the narrow sense of the word refers to the ratio of actually observed counts to the total number of radiation bursts *reaching the counter*, expressed in per cent. Not all gamma rays traversing a Geiger-Mueller counter interact with the counter walls and filling gas to produce a discharge, in fact usually less than 1 per cent of them do so. If one count is observed per 100 gamma rays traversing the counter, we say that the effici-

---

* See G. Friedlander and J. W. Kennedy: "Nuclear and Radiochemistry," New York, 1955, John Wiley & Sons Inc. page 265.

ency is 1 per cent. Beta rays interact much more frequently with the filling gas and produce counts, but they are much more easily absorbed by the walls and so prevented from interaction. For thin counter walls, beta efficiency is usually higher, but for walls which are thicker than the beta range, the efficiency may be close to zero (it will not be zero because of bremsstrahlung). Evidently the efficiency of any radiation detector depends on the energy of the measured radiation. The efficiency of any counter may be different for the softer gamma radiations from I^{131} than for the harder radiation from radium; a counter with reasonably thin walls will be highly efficient for beta radiation from P^{32} and it may have diminishingly small efficiency for C^{14} beta radiation.

Efficiency of a Geiger-Mueller counter to gamma radiation can be increased by coating the counter walls for instance with bismuth or by inserting metal baffles in the counting volume; this increases the production of secondary electrons and is particularly useful in I^{131} measurements.

Efficiency is also used in a wider sense of the word, applied not only to the number of counts observed per hundred *radiation events reaching the counter*, but also with reference to the number of counts observed per 100 disintegrations *occurring within a given radioactive sample*. This use of the term efficiency is not quite rigorous, but it is becoming so rapidly a part of technical language in this field that it will be used here also. Efficiency in this sense depends not only on the efficiency of the detector in the strict meaning of the word, but also on the overall counting set-up, that, is distance of the sample from the counter and a variety of other factors. Efficiency used in this second way has always a smaller value than the first. Let us say that a counter shows a counting rate of 60,000 counts per second when 111,000 beta particles per second, emanating from a source of I^{131}, impinge on it; its efficiency is then 54 per cent. In a practical counting set-up the source of I^{131} will be at some distance from the detector, and many of the rays emitted by the source will go into space and miss the detector. The actual counting rate observed may be only 5,000 counts per second, and the efficiency is then 4.5 per cent. This efficiency is closely related to the calibration of a counting set-up for a given isotope. Radioactive isotopes are measured in curies. One microcurie has 37,000 disintegrations per second. The sample in our example contains 3 microcuries. The counting set-up gives a counting rate of 5,000 counts per second for 3 microcuries. The calibration is then expressed by the calibration factor: 1670 counts per second for 1 microcurie. When a counting set-up is used for actual measurement, its calibration factor indicating the counting rate per microcurie is the basic and essential datum.

Knowledge of the efficiency provides some information on the ultimate possibility of improving the counting set-up by changing the physical arrangement or by substituting a more efficient for a less efficient counter. If the efficiency is around 1 per cent, a great deal may be done in improvement. When the efficiency reaches the neighborhood of 50 per cent, nothing will improve matters by better than a factor of 2, which would give the theoretical maximum of 100 per cent.

Efficiency and calibration factors contain also information on the sensitivity of a counting set-up, although discussion of sensitivity in nuclear measurements is complicated by the random nature of the events under observation. Let us compare this with an everyday measurement procedure, such as weighing with a balance. Here sensitivity is expressed simply in terms of the number of scale divisions the balance pointer deflects when the weight of 1 milligram is put on a balance pan. It may also be necessary to know the ultimate sensitivity, that is the precision, of a balance. This can be achieved by determining that weight which corresponds to the standard deviation in weighing, or that weight in milligrams which can be detected in about half the trial weighings and will be missed in another half (for a more precise definition of standard deviation, this ratio will be two-thirds and one-third). Since the weight equivalent to the standard deviation will frequently remain undetected, it has been more recently proposed to use not one but three standard deviations in describing sensitivity of nuclear counters (NBS Handbook 80, footnote page 205). Such a quantity will be almost always detected. It might be compared with the weight on a balance which causes the deflection of one full scale division. In the following the sample which gives a counting rate equal to 3 standard deviations will be used as the smallest detectable amount to express precision.

If we try to use a similar approach with nuclear counting, we encounter some difficulties. Let us consider a counting set-up with an efficiency of 50 per cent, that is a calibration factor of 18,500 (counts per second for 1 μc). In analogy with the balance, we may equate sensitivity and calibration factor and say that this counting set-up has a sensitivity of 18,500 counts per second for 1 microcurie. This would correspond to a complete description of the sensitivity of a balance, but gives only partial information for a nuclear counter, since nothing has been said about the background. In our example we may have two different counters with different backgrounds, but with the same calibration factor, one with a background of 1 count per second and another with a background of 10,000 counts per second. The first counter should have been described as having a much higher precision than the second, since less time will be required to achieve a comparable error with the same sample, due to the lower background. The time element and its relation to background are essential in nuclear counting and cannot be disregarded if statements about sensitivity are to be of use in comparing different counting set-ups and in evaluation of their performances and limitations.

The application of the second method of describing the performance of a balance by indicating its ultimate sensitivity, its precision, appears more complicated, but it can be applied unequivocally to nuclear counters. Precision was defined as the magnitude equal to 3 standard deviations (the smallest "detectable" amount). In a nuclear counter it can be defined as 3 standard deviations in counting rate and it can be expressed in units of activity (microcuries for example). Let us examine equation (16) for standard deviation of net counting rate:

$$\sigma_s = \sqrt{\frac{R_c}{t_c} + \frac{R_b}{t_b}} \ .$$

Here σ_s is the standard deviation in counts per second. $3\sigma_s$ when expressed in microcuries, corresponds to precision as defined in the preceding paragraph.

$$\text{Precision} = \frac{3\sigma_s}{\text{calibration factor}} \ \mu c. \tag{54}$$

The usefulness of this concept of precision in nuclear counting becomes apparent when we consider that it depends not only on the calibration factor, but also on the background and on the time spent in counting $(t_c + t_b)$. Since precision depends on counting time, some time interval must be agreed upon for intercomparison of counters. In the following, as a somewhat arbitrary compromise, the value of ten minutes $(t_c + t_b = 600$ seconds) will be used as total counting time for both sample and background; it will have to be remembered that higher precision can be obtained by using longer counting times.

A precise calculation of the counting rate for the minimal detectable sample, which is equal to three standard deviations leads to somewhat involved calculations. But the equation (16) for σ_s can be simplified. The combined counting rate R_c will be only a little larger than the background counting rate R_b, since a minimal sample will be used. The difference between R_c and R_b will be small and will be neglected by substituting R_b for R_c. For the same reason the difference between the necessary counting time for combined and background counts will be neglected and t_b substituted for t_c. This gives the equation

$$\sigma_s = \sqrt{2\frac{R_b}{t_b}} \ . \tag{55}$$

It was decided to use a total counting time of 600 seconds: $2t_b = 600$; $t_b = 300$. With this assumption we get

$$\sigma_s = \sqrt{\frac{2}{300}} \ R_b = 0.08 \sqrt{R_b} \tag{56}$$

and an expression for precision, by substituting this in (54) and multiplying it by 3.

$$\text{precision} = \frac{0.24 \sqrt{R_b}}{\text{calibration factor}} . \tag{57}$$

Let us consider an example: a counting set-up with a calibration factor of 70 counts per second for 1 μc and a background of 0.5 counts per second. The standard deviation when counting a very small sample for a total of ten minutes (combined and background counts) is, according to (56)

$$\sigma_s = 0.08 \sqrt{0.5} = 0.058 \text{ c/s}.$$

Therefore we have from (57)

$$\text{precision} = \frac{0.17}{70} = 0.0024 \ \mu c.$$

This indicates that we shall be able to detect the presence or absence of 0.0024 μc = 2.4 nanocuries*, if ten minutes are spent for each observation. In a counter with the same calibration factor, but a background of 5 counts per second, the calculation will lead to a precision of 0.0075 μc = 7.5 nano c, by using (57). With the higher background, the smallest detectable activity is considerably higher.

The great practical value of knowing the precision of a counter is that it tells the order of magnitude of the smallest sample that can be detected and makes it possible to estimate approximately, but rapidly, the size of sample needed for a measurement of given reliability. In the first example the precision was 0.0024 μc. If a measurement with 10 per cent error has to be made, a sample of about ten times precision, that is 0.024 μc will be needed with ten-minute counting. This sort of estimate is not possible with the calibration factor, which has of course its own use and importance. The calibration factor permits the interpretation of observed counting rates in terms of millicuries or microcuries. It also permits the estimation of the sample strength required to obtain desired counting rates, which is necessary in order to determine required counting times. The calibration factor can be used finally for the determination of the sample strength needed so that background can be disregarded.

In describing the characteristics of counters the concept of *background equivalent activity* is sometimes used. This is the activity of a radioactive material in μc which will give a counting rate equal to the background.

$$\text{Background equivalent activity} = \frac{R_b}{\text{calibration factor}} \qquad (58)$$

The various concepts presented above will be illustrated by the following example.

A sample of about 0.001 μc is to be measured within about 10 per cent (V = 10). The following 3 counters are available, and the question is which counter should be selected for this measurement.

---

* 1 nanocurie or 1 nano c $= \frac{1}{1000}$ μc. From greek "nanos," meaning, "dwarf."

Counter 1: Calibration Factor 165 c/s for 1 μc; $R_b = 0.4$ c/s
"   2:   "   "   1650 c/s " " "; $R_b = 4$ c/s
"   3:   "   "   50 c/s " " "; $R_b = 0.03$ c/s

Let us tabulate the smallest detectable amount, (precision) from (57) and background equivalent from (58):

Counter	Precision μc	Background Equivalent μc
1	0.0009	0.025
2	0.0003	0.025
3	0.001	0.007

The selection of counters would be different, depending on the criterion used. Precision recommends counter 2. Background equivalent recommends counter 3 (it also appears to indicate that counters 1 and 2 are equal).

We shall calculate the required total counting time for the given sample and for the required error with the three counters from (32) and (33):

Counter	$t_c + t_b$
1	2 hours
2	12 minutes
3	$2\frac{1}{2}$ hours

Counter 2 is unquestionably superior; counter 1 is almost as bad as counter 2. In this example it is obvious that precision is a good guide.

These considerations are valid, however, only when the background is constant. We are faced with an entirely different problem when background fluctuates and these fluctuations cannot be eliminated (this is frequently the case, for instance, in a clinical laboratory where treated patients come and go, and where there is a structural or economical limit to the weight of the lead shielding). Here there may be little advantage in the second counter. It may be necessary to use stronger samples than the one mentioned in the example to override the uncertainty of the fluctuating background.

The effect of background variations is of course eliminated when background may be neglected altogether under the condition of (35), assuming that the value assumed for background counting rate is near to the maximum background observed. By dividing this equation by the calibration factor we get:

$$\text{Background equivalent} = \frac{V}{500} \times \text{sample activity} \quad \text{or in a more useful}$$

form as the condition for neglecting background

$$\text{sample activity} \gtrless \frac{500}{V} \times \text{background equivalent}$$

This equation indicates what the smallest sample activity is that for which the background can be neglected.

Following is a listing of this activity for the 3 counters:

Counter	Minimum sample activity for neglecting background for $V = 10$
1	1.25 μc
2	1.25 μc
3	0.35 μc

It is seen that the background could be neglected for the smallest sample when using the third counter. This demonstrates the value and use of background equivalent activity in selecting a counter when the possibility of performing a measurement is not limitation in time but fluctuations of the background.

Since the terms introduced and discussed in this section will be used frequently in the following chapters, they will be recapitulated and summarized:

1. *Counting efficiency in the narrow sense of the word*: number of counts registered by the detector, per 100 ionizing events reaching the counter or entering its sensitive volume.

2. *Counting efficiency in the broader sense*: Number of counts registered by the counting device, per 100 disintegrations occurring in the radioactive sample under observation.

3. *Calibration factor or sensitivity* (sometimes also called "response"): Counting rate (counts per second or per minute) per unit of radioactive material (in millicuries or microcuries). The use of the term "sensitivity" for this factor may be misleading, since it does not contain consideration of background or counting time.

4. *Precision*: the smallest detectable amount of radioactive material, expressed in microcuries or other suitable conventional unit. It can be calculated from the calibration factor, background and an arbitrarily assigned total counting time (in this text this time has been assigned the value of ten minutes, for counting both sample and background).

5. *Background equivalent activity*: that amount of radioactive material which will give a net counting rate equal to background. In other words, that amount which will give a combined counting rate two times as large as background. (background doubling activity).

Table 18.   Formulae in Counting Statistics

No.	Purpose	Formula	Units	Equation # in text
	I. General			
1.	Standard deviation of accumulated counts (preset time)	$\sigma_N = \sqrt{N}$	counts	(1)
2.	Standard deviation of counting time (preset counts)	$\sigma_t = \dfrac{t}{\sqrt{N}}$	time	(41)
3.	Coefficient of variation	$V = \dfrac{100}{\sqrt{N}}$	%	(3)
4.	For an acceptable error of P% make the coefficient of variation:			
	For low reliability	$V = P$	%	(5)
	For medium reliability	$V = P/2$	%	(6)
	For high reliability	$V = P/3$	%	(7)
	II. Counting Equations when Background can be neglected			
5.	Background may be neglected when:	$R_b' \lesssim \dfrac{R_c'V}{500}$	$\dfrac{\text{counts}}{\text{time}}$	(35)
6.	Counts to be accumulated	$N_S = \dfrac{10{,}000}{V^2}$	counts	(36)
7.	Counting time	$t_S = \dfrac{10{,}000}{R_S'\ V^2}$	time	(37)
8.	Coefficient of variation as in formula 3	$V_S = \dfrac{100}{\sqrt{N_S}}$	%	(3)
9.	Standard deviation of observed counting rate	$\sigma_S = \dfrac{\sqrt{N_S}}{t_S}$	$\dfrac{\text{counts}}{\text{time}}$	(38)
	III. Counting equations when Background cannot be neglected			
10.	Background cannot be neglected when:	$R_b' > \dfrac{R_c'V}{500}$	$\dfrac{\text{counts}}{\text{time}}$	—
11.	Combined counts to be accumulated	$N_c = 20{,}000\left[\dfrac{R_c'}{V(R_c'-R_b')}\right]^2$	counts	(30)

Table 18.   Formulae in Counting Statistics (Continued)

No.	Purpose	Formula	Units	Equation # in text
12.	Background counts to be accumulated	$N_b = 20,000 \left[\dfrac{R_b'}{V(R_c' - R_b')} \right]^2$	counts	(31)
13.	Combined counting time	$t_c = \dfrac{20,000 \, R_c'}{[V(R_c' - R_b')]^2}$	time	(32)
14.	Background counting time	$t_b = \dfrac{20,000 \, R_b'}{[V(R_c' - R_b')]^2}$	time	(33)
15.	Standard deviation of observed sample (net) counting rate	$\sigma_S = \sqrt{\dfrac{N_c}{t_c^2} + \dfrac{N_b}{t_b^2}}$	$\dfrac{\text{counts}}{\text{time}}$	(15)
16.	Coefficient of variation of observed sample (net) counting rate	$V_s = 100 \, \dfrac{\sqrt{N_c t_b^2 + N_b t_c^2}}{N_c t_b - N_b t_c}$	%	(34)

IV. Correction for counting losses due to resolving time

No.	Purpose	Formula	Units	Equation # in text
17.	Corrected counting rate	$R_t = \dfrac{R_o}{1 - R_o \tau}$	$\dfrac{\text{counts}}{\text{time}}$	(43)
18.	Corrected counting rate	$R_t = R_o \left(1 + \dfrac{C}{100} \right)$	$\dfrac{\text{counts}}{\text{time}}$	(47)
19.	Percent counting loss	$C = 100 \, \dfrac{R_o \tau}{1 - R_o \tau}$	%	(45)
20.	Condition for validity of 17,18,19	$R_o < \dfrac{0.2}{\tau}$	$\dfrac{\text{counts}}{\text{time}}$	(50)

V. Rate meter fluctuations
two thirds of the fluctuations will be within a range of 2 standard deviations ($2\sigma_d$)

No.	Purpose	Formula	Units	Equation # in text
21.	Standard deviation of counting rate	$\sigma_d = \dfrac{1}{S} \sqrt{\dfrac{R}{2 t_r}}$	divisions	(40)

VI. Measures of counter sensitivity

No.	Purpose	Formula	Units	Equation # in text
22.	Precision; smallest detectable activity	$= \dfrac{0.24 \, \sqrt{R_b}}{\text{calibration factor}}$	μc	(57)
23.	Background equivalent activity	$= \dfrac{R_b}{\text{calibration factor}}$	μc	(58)

Explanation of symbols and of some terms used in Table 18.

Note: When a symbol has the sign $'$, as for instance in N'_c, it indicates that the value has been determined approximately only in a preliminary experiment.

N — accumulated counts in an observation over some time interval.

N_b — counts accumulated during time t_b in the measurement of background.

N_c — counts accumulated during time t_c in the measurement of background and sample combined.

N_s — counts accumulated during time t_s in the measurement of a sample (background neglected).

P — acceptable per cent error in a measurement.

R_b — background counting rate.

R_c — Combined or gross counting rate observed when sample and background are measured together.

R_o — observed counting rate, which may be equal to or smaller than R_t, the true counting rate, due to counting losses.

R_s — counting rate due to sample alone (background subtracted from R_c or neglected): net counting rate.

R_t — true counting rate: the counting rate which would be observed if no counting losses due to the effect of dead time (resolving time) had occurred.

t_b — counting time when background is measured.

t_c — counting time when sample and background together are measured.

t_s — counting time when sample alone is measured (background neglected).

V — coefficient of variation (standard deviation in percent). Determined on the basis of required P and required reliability (confidence limit)

V_s — coefficient of variation of a sample counting rate R_s, when R_c and R_b are determined experimentally by measuring N_c, N_b, t_c and t_b, or when it is determined by observing N_s and t_s by neglecting the background.

σ_N — standard deviation of the number of counts accumulated in preset time counting.

σ_s — standard deviation of a sample counting rate R_s when this counting rate is determined as described for V_s

σ_t — standard deviation of time in preset count counting.

τ — dead time or resolving time determined for the assembly of a counter and the associated scaling circuit.

Background equivalent activity — activity in μc or nano c which would give a net counting rate equal to the background ($R_s = R_b$).

Calibration factor (sensitivity, response) — sample counting rate R_s with a sample of unit activity: net counts per second obtained with a sample of 1 μc. The dimension is $\sec^{-1} \mu c^{-1}$ which is sometimes written as "counts/sec/μc".

Precision, smallest detectable amount, minimum detectable activity — The activity of such a sample, the presence or absence of which will be almost always detected by counting when a set time is spent in counting sample and background (usually 10 minutes). It is calculated as three times the standard deviation for a vanishingly small sample, which is approximately equal to the standard deviation of the background.

15

Quantitative Measurements *in Vitro*

STANDARDIZATION OF ISOTOPES

At the present time, most of the clinically useful radioactive isotopes are available from responsible processing laboratories in a calibrated form, that is, under a label which not only identifies the isotope, but also states how many millicuries the container held at a specified date. Isotopes are usually supplied in a solution, and the label states also the total volume, or millicuries per ml. Only rarely will the isotope be available as the pure element. Usually it will be supplied either as an inorganic or organic compound, as for instance I^{131} as sodium iodide, or C^{14} as dextrose. If the particular compound contains only atoms of the radioactive isotope, it is said to be carrier free. If it contains in addition identical chemical molecules with the stable isotope of the element, it is said to have a (stable) carrier. When a solid sample of a radioactive compound is considered, the amount of radioactive isotope, expressed in millicuries per gram of the total weight of the element in question, is called specific activity. This specific activity has then the dimension of mc/gm. When the radioactive sample is obtained as a solution, specific activity is sometimes expressed also in terms of millicuries contained in a milliliter, and it has then the dimension of mc/ml. A better word to describe this second meaning of the term "specific activity" would be *specific concentration*, but this has not found acceptance in the literature. This ambiguity of the term "specific activity," however, rarely leads to misunderstandings. The total amount of radioactivity in a given bottle or sample is called "absolute activity."

A few years ago, isotopes were not available in reliably precalibrated form and the determination of the radioactivity in a given shipment was the first step in its use. This absolute measurement or "standardization," sometimes called "assay," of the available sample is not a simple procedure, and in only a few laboratories is such standardization carried out at present. The methods involved, however, are still useful and their discussion is the best introduction to the measurement of samples *in vitro*, which embraces perhaps half of the work load of an isotope laboratory.

Handling of Radioactive Samples.—A few preliminary remarks should be made at this point about the handling of radioactive samples. The first one refers to health protection. In a later chapter the physical measures to insure optimal health protection will be discussed (see also Chapters 10 and 11). The first encounter with maximal amounts of radioactive materials will occur when the shipment is received and opened, and when aliquots of this shipment are removed for assay and for use with patients or for preparation of dilutions. The monograph on *Safe Handling of Radioactive Isotopes,** should be consulted before this work is attempted, with particular attention to the precautions against ingestion, inhalation and absorption of radioactive materials. External exposure of the body can be measured by instruments described in the appropriate chapter, but the material absorbed cannot be easily determined in the small amounts which are biologically effective over many years of possible exposure.

The next remarks refer to the precision in the quantitative techniques of weighing, pipetting and preparing dilutions. Careless working habits can introduce errors of 5 to 10 per cent at this point, and familiarity with the rudiments of techniques in preparing dilutions is essential (difference between blow-out and delivery pipettes for instance, etc.). There are also some specific pitfalls when handling carrier-free isotopes. Since the gravimetric amounts are vanishingly small (minute fractions of a microgram), difficulties occur which are practically unknown in chemistry. Radioactive phosphorus will be adsorbed on the clean walls of glassware, unless this has been presoaked in a solution of stable phosphate. Salts of radioactive iodine may oxidize in solution, free iodine will be formed, which can volatilize. Sodium bisulfite should be added to the solution to prevent oxidation, and the solution should be kept alkaline by addition of sodium bicarbonate to give a pH of about 8, this will prevent volatilization of free iodine should it be present. The amounts of these chemicals are not critical. Fifty to 200 mg per liter solutions are about the required range. It must be remembered to add them also to water used in the preparation of the solution; otherwise they will be diluted beyond the effective concentration.

Such precautions are important because they affect the precision and reliability of measurements. Any radioactive contamination will increase the background in working areas and of counting equipment; the effect of background on sensitivity and precision has already been discussed at length. It is a matter of actual experience that the handling of a scintillation counter with hands only slightly contaminated with I^{131} may put this counter out of commission for weeks.

Ionization Chambers.—Ionization chambers are among the least sensitive but most reliable radiation measurement devices. In standardizing radioactive samples, sensitivity is of secondary and reliability of primary importance. In specialized laboratories, ionization chambers may be used with highly sensitive current measuring devices, but a clinical laboratory will usually have to limit itself to instruments using electrometer type string voltmeters, as discussed under dose measurement.

Safe Handling of Radioactive Isotopes, National Bureau of Standards, Handbook 42, 1949. Available from the Government Printing Office, Washington 25, D. C., price 20 cents.

One ionization chamber of this sort which was designed by Carl Braestrup* is illustrated in Figure 63. The chamber is first charged like a pocket electrometer chamber (see Fig. 48) to a string deflection corresponding to "0" (no radiation exposure). The chamber is then removed, its stem covered with a protective cap, and the radioactive sample, in a volume not exceeding a few ml, contained in a test tube, is inserted into the central opening. The sample is left in the chamber for about five to fifteen minutes, then it is removed and the chamber again inserted into the electrometer

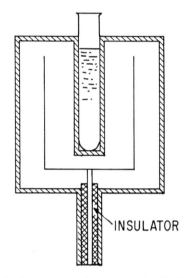

INSULATOR

Fig. 63.—Braestrup ionization chamber for the standardization of radioactive isotopes.

for reading. If the reading is D divisions and the time the sample was in the chamber M minutes, D/M (divisions per minute) is a measure of the activity in the radioactive sample. The calibration of the chamber, that is the number of divisions per minute observed for 1 mc, depends on the isotope and the radiations it emits. Table 19 gives an example of these data for several isotopes, as obtained with one such chamber.

If we have in this particular instrument, for instance, an I^{131} sample, which gives in fifteen minutes a deflection of thirty divisions, $D/M = 2$ divisions per minute and the activity is then $\dfrac{2}{2.4} = 0.83$ mc. If the total volume was 5 ml, the specific activity in the sample is 166 $\mu c/ml$. It will be noted from the table that the sensitivity for P^{32} is very small compared to the other isotopes; the reason is that P^{32} is a pure beta emitter and practically only the Bremsstrahlung contributes to the ionization of the gas in the chamber.

*Manufactured by Victoreen Instrument Co., Cleveland, Ohio.

The great advantage of the ionization chamber is that it can be checked reliably against a radium standard. Ionization due to 1 mc of radium is of course not equal to that due to 1 mc of another radioactive material, but any changes in the chamber, air density and electrometer will remain proportional within practically relevant limits, unless the ionization chamber is severely, and usually obviously, damaged. When using an ionization chamber, the background has to be determined and taken into account if it has significant value.

Table 19.—Calibration of the Braestrup-Victoreen Isotope Assay Ionization Chamber, Model 503

Isotope	Calibration factor Divisions per minute for 1 mc
Iodine-131	2.4
Gold-198	2.8
Phosphorus-32	0.038
Radium (filtered by 0.5 mm Pt)	6.8

The ionization chamber described and illustrated in Figure 63 requires samples of high activity, particularly when used with beta emitters, which is inconvenient since elaborate precautions are needed. There are ionization chambers which permit the entrance of beta particles into the sensitive volume, and which are therefore more sensitive, but they are less readily available and somewhat more complicated in use.*

Proportional, Geiger-Mueller and Scintillation Counters. — There are two basic differences between a counting device and an ionization chamber. Counters have much higher sensitivity (a determination can be done within the same time and precision on a sample of considerably smaller activity) but their performance is less stable during use (changes in the plateau for instance). This lower stability makes it practically impossible to obtain a counter or a counting set-up which has been "precalibrated" for various isotopes. Every counting device has to be calibrated by the user himself, and this calibration rechecked at every standardization.

In order to do this, it is necessary to have available standardized samples of the isotopes to be used. Such samples have been distributed by the National Bureau of Standards. At present, commercial laboratories are taking over this service   Standardized samples of radioactive isotopes of most nuclides in clinical use are available from such sources with a guaranteed accuracy of about 3 per cent. When such a sample is obtained, an aliquot of it is counted in the given set-up with a Geiger-Mueller counter and a calibration factor (net counts per second or per minute for one microcurie) is obtained. A calibration sample of each isotope used in the labora-

*One such chamber is described by H. H. Seliger and A. Schwebel, *Standardization of Beta Emitting Nuclides*, Nucleonics, *12*, Issue 7, page 58, 1954.

tory has to be obtained and the counter calibrated for each separately: *the calibration factors will be different for every isotope.*[*]

Calibration standards (standardized samples) are distributed 2 to 4 times a year. Most isotopes have a short half-life, and a standard decays below useful activity before a new one is available. For several months at a time, every laboratory is without a useful calibration standard. This problem can be solved in two ways.

A stronger reference sample is prepared, which is calibrated against the original standard sample, and when the original standard begins to become too weak by decay, the reference standard is used. This can be done repeatedly, but the errors in each preparation will add up; it is to be expected that a fifth derived reference standard will be out by at least 25 per cent, and probably more.

The second solution is to use a sample of some long-lived radioactive material such as radium, Co^{60} or Cs^{137} as a *performance standard*. Such a standard is not as reliable as a *calibration standard* of the particular short-lived isotope, but it will permit detection of gross changes in the performance of a counter. Let us assume that a given P^{32} calibration standard gave 107 counts per second for 1 μc, and that a performance standard of a few μc of radium sealed in some container gave 155 counts per second; as long as the same radium standard continues to give the same 155 counts per second, there is *some* assurance that $1\mu c$ of P^{32} will continue to give 107 counts per second. This assurance is not very great however, since it is possible that sensitivity to P^{32} beta radiation may change without a change in the sensitivity to the gamma radiation of the radium standard. For this reason every standardization set-up should be recalibrated with standard samples as frequently as such standards can be obtained, at least twice a year. This applies to every radiation detector when absolute accuracy is important. Between the times when recalibration is possible, a performance standard should be used daily.

For use with I^{131}, a performance standard has recently been developed which has a gamma ray spectrum so closely approximating the spectrum of I^{131} that it may be used also as a calibration standard, provided that all beta radiation of the I^{131} sample to be measured is filtered out (this can be achieved with an aluminum filter about 1 mm thick). This "mock-iodine" standard is a mixture of Ba^{133} and Cs^{137}. The two isotopes have different half-lives and their relative proportion changes with decay; the similarity of the spectrum of the mixture to I^{131} remains adequate for about ten years; the half-life is also approximately ten years.[†] It must be empha-

---

[*] W. B. Mann and H. H. Seliger. Preparation, Maintenance and Application of Standards of Radioactivity. NBS Circular 594, June 11, 1958. U. S. Government Printing Office, 35¢. Also Handbook 80 (see footnote page 205).

[†] For decay chart, see page 93 in M. Brucer, T. H. Oddie, J. S. Eldridge: *Thyroid Uptake Calibration. I. Mock-Iodine, A Radioactive Iodine Gamma-Ray Standard.* Oak Ridge Institute of Nuclear Studies, Inc., July 25, 1956, ORINS-14. Available from the Office of Technical Services, Department of Commerce, Washington 25, D. C., price 50 cents.

sized that "mock-iodine" is useful as a calibration standard only for gamma ray measurements; when a counting set-up is used which is sensitive to I^{131} betas, it is no better than any other performance standard.

An intermediary position between a "mock-iodine" calibration standard and a radium or cobalt[60] performance standard is the use of a Cs^{137} reference source, which emits a gamma ray of 662 kv, as compared to the main I^{131} gamma rays of 364 kv. In a scintillation counter, the difference between Cs^{137} and I^{131} is not very great, and in a Geiger-Mueller counter, used for γ counting this difference is also practically negligible.

The specific counting techniques in standardization work are basically the same as for any sample counting *in vitro*, which will be treated in the next section. The only special requirement is a high order of reliability. An error of 5 per cent should not be exceeded, which means the use of equation (7); for a 5 per cent error, a minimum of 3600 counts must be collected, when counting rate is high relative to background. Until recently, Geiger-Mueller counters were preferred to scintillation counters for standardization, but at present there seems to be a shift to scintillation counters as their reliability has been improving. Both will give good results, and the accuracy depends more on the care of sample preparations and the calibration than on the choice of one particular instrument.

SAMPLE MEASUREMENTS IN VITRO

Gamma Ray Counting.—Because of the high penetrating power of gamma radiation, there is a considerable freedom in arranging a counting set-up.

When a sample is at some distance from the counter, as illustrated in Figure 64a, only a small fraction of the total rays emitted by the sample impinges on the counter. In Figure 64b, the sample is very close and a much larger share of the emitted rays will reach the detector. The sensitivity will be even higher if the sample surrounds the counter as in Figure 64c. The highest sensitivity is achieved in an arrangement as in Figure 64d, where the counter surrounds the sample and practically all radiation from the sample goes through the detector.

This relative arrangement of counter and sample is called the "geometry" of a set-up. The differences in calibration factor, etc. are listed in Table 20, to be discussed in detail presently. When sample and counter are close to each other, no exact rules about the expected change of the calibration factor with change in position can be given; when the distance between the two is greater than about 10 times the physical size of either (height or length, whichever is greater), the inverse square rule gives a good approximation.

The inverse square rule can be formulated as follows: If at a distance d_1 of the sample from the counter a counting rate R_1 is observed, and the counting rate R_2 at a new distance d_2 is to be estimated, we have the relationship

$$\frac{R_1}{R_2} = \frac{d_2^2}{d_1^2} \tag{59}$$

or

$$R_2 = R_1 \left(\frac{d_1}{d_2}\right)^2. \tag{59a}$$

The use of increased distance is sometimes useful when samples have too high activity and resolving time correction becomes excessive, or when a sample has large volume, as for instance in counting of stool specimens, and where the use of an aliquot fraction is inadvisable because of the inhomogeneity, or for some other reasons. In increasing the distance it is necessary to guard against two sources of error. (1) When the sample is at a

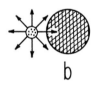

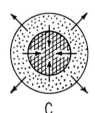

Fig. 64.—Four typical counting geometries: (*a*) sample at a distance from detector, (*b*) sample in close proximity to the detector, (*c*) sample surrounding the detector, (*d*) detector surrounding the sample.

distance from the counter, shielding of the sample-counter assembly becomes difficult and the background may increase and become variable. (2) The sample may come close to some objects which contribute to scatter; this does not interfere with counting, provided calibration was done with the same objects (tabletop, sample support, shielding materials) in the same position as when the samples are counted. One such scattering object is easily overlooked, and that is the observer himself, who can contribute 10 to 20 per cent to the counting rate if he is accessible to the radiation emitted by the sample and is "visible" to the counter.

Biological samples are usually in the form of liquids (blood, urine), semi-solids (stool), or tissues of comparable density, approximately equal to water. The differences in absorption of gamma radiation by such samples can therefore be neglected, particularly if the calibration standard is homogeneously mixed with similar material. The radioactivity in the samples is practically always due to the administration of a tracer or a therapeutic amount of the particular isotope previous to the withdrawal of the sample. This simplifies considerably the calibration of the counter, since an aliquot of the original dose can be retained, dissolved in a volume of water similar to that of the samples to be measured and used as a comparison standard. Frequently the sample activity is only a small fraction of the original dose; the comparison sample should then be suitably diluted. This procedure does not insure absolute accuracy in the determination of the activity in the sample in terms of microcuries, but it permits the reliable and comparatively simple determination of the *ratio* between the activity in the sample and the administered amount. A long-lived performance standard should still be used, since the reliability, even in the determination of ratios, may suffer when a counter begins to fail; this can frequently be detected in time if the use of a performance standard is a part of daily laboratory routine.

In any given sample there is, as a rule, a given specific activity, that is, an activity per unit of volume. The total activity presented to a counter depends, therefore, on the volume. The smallest amount of specific activity which can be measured can therefore be decreased by using a larger sample volume. This is limited only by the amount of sample available and by the counting geometry.

Limitations of available sample volume are determined by the biological condition, for it is rarely possible to obtain more than a few ml of blood, while urine may be available in liters.

Limitations of sample volume which can be used in a given counting geometry depend on the physical size and type of counter. In the case of Figure 64a and b, there is practically no limitation in this respect, but distance of sample from counter reduces the sensitivity. A better arrangement in this respect is offered by Figure 64c. This is called the Marinelli set-up. A beaker as shown in Figure 65 is generally used as sample container. The radiation detector is usually a Geiger-Mueller

Table 20.—Approximate Sensitivity in Gamma Counting of Liquid Samples for Some Selected Isotopes and Counting Methods

Description of Counter	Isotope	Sample volume ml	Background c/s	Data for absolute activity		Data for specific activity	
				Calibration factor c/s for 1 μc	Precision* nanocuries	Calibration factor c/s for 1 μc/ml	Precision* nanocuries/ml
Large Marinelli Beaker† Geiger-Mueller Counter	I^{131}	150	0.25	4.5	27	675	0.2
Small Marinelli Beaker† Bismuth-coated Geiger-Mueller Counter	I^{131}	10	0.4	165	1	1,650	0.1
Well Type Scintillation Counter‡ Thallium activated Na I crystal, 1¾″ diameter, 1½″ high	Au^{198}	4	3.5	15,000	0.03	60,000	0.0075
	Cr^{51}	4	3.5	1,800	0.24	7,200	0.06
	Co^{60}	4	3.5	16,000	0.1	64,000	0.0075
	Fe^{59}	4	3.5	9,600	0.045	38,000	0.01
	I^{131}	4	3.5	15,000	0.03	60,000	0.0075
	Na^{24}	4	3.5	11,000	0.045	44,000	0.01
Same counter as above, but 500 ml bottle placed on top of crystal	Co^{60}	500	3.3	820	0.45	400,000	0.001
Well Type Scintillation Counter** plastic phosphor, 5″ diameter, 6″ high	Co^{60}	100	7	9,000	0.06	900,000	0.0006

*"Precision" indicates the smallest detectable amount; see page 234 and equation (57)

†Data from The Thyroid, edited by Sydney C. Werner. Hoeber-Harper, New York, 1955, page 188

‡Personal communication, Warren K. Sinclair, Physics Department, M. D. Anderson Hospital, University of Texas

**See footnote *, page 252.

counter and the beaker is put over the counter. Table 20 lists the data for the Marinelli type counter and the other counter arrangements to be discussed in the following pages.

In this and in other tables with data on counters, the column labelled "precision" is calculated from equation (57) on page 235, where this term is defined.

The Marinelli beaker arrangement is one of the best devices for urine counting, since a large beaker can hold several hundred ml, so that errors in pipetting small volumes are reduced. A small volume Marinelli beaker with a suitably smaller Geiger-Mueller counter has also been used successfully. but better sensitivity can be obtained for smaller sample volumes by using the arrangement of Figure 64d.

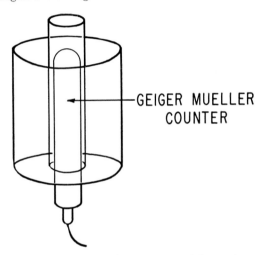

GEIGER MUELLER COUNTER

FIG. 65.—Marinelli beaker counting arrangement (geometry *c* of Fig. 64).

This arrangement with the counter surrounding the sample, had been used with some special purpose Geiger-Mueller counters, which were not easily available. It came into general use with the introduction of thallium activated sodium iodide crystals, which can be grown in sufficiently large size and in which a hole can be drilled. Such *well-type* counters of NaI are mostly $1\frac{3}{4}$ inches in diameter, 2 inches high and have a half-inch well drilled axially, which holds a standard size test tube. The crystals are usually encased in a plastic and put into an aluminum container with a glass bottom, to permit the transmission of light pulses to the phototube and to keep out extraneous light. As an optical coupling medium to the phototube, mineral oil, special cements or silicon grease are used (Fig. 66).

When the test tube contains a liquid volume up to 5 ml, the whole of the liquid is within the crystal well and there is little difference in sensitivity with volume. In Table 20 are listed the data for a typical NaI well-type crystal.

When comparing the sensitivity and calibration factors for the crystal counters given in the table with the discussion of scintillation counters (page 224), a discrepancy will be noted at first sight. It was there stated that the higher the gamma ray energy, the higher the light pulses which occur when a photon is absorbed. This makes the detection of higher energy photons easier, provided they are absorbed in the crystal. On the other hand, the higher the photon energy, the smaller the probability of their being ab-

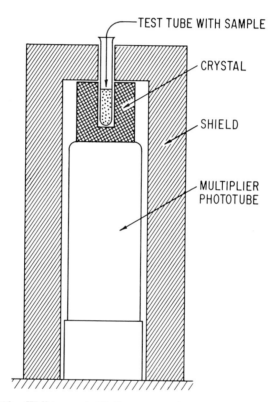

TEST TUBE WITH SAMPLE

CRYSTAL

SHIELD

MULTIPLIER PHOTOTUBE

FIG. 66.—Well type scintillation counter (geometry of Fig. 64*d*).

sorbed, the more of them will pass through the crystal without interacting with it: the efficiency becomes smaller. The table, however, seems to contradict this since it shows almost equal sensitivity for high energy Co^{60} and Na^{24} and for the lower energy I^{131}. The explanation lies in the difference in the decay schemes. I^{131} has only 80 per cent effective gamma rays of 364 kev per disintegration, whereas both Co^{60} and Na^{24} have two gamma rays (Co^{60}, about 1.2 mev; Na^{24}, 1.4 + 2.8 mev) so that here the probability of interaction is doubled and the loss due to high energy is compensated.

The test tube may be filled with a sample of larger volume than 5 ml; the liquid column is then partly outside the counter, the well geometry of Figure 64*d* is combined with the geometry of Figure 64*b* and the sensitivity drops. Still a gain in the determination of a given specific activity may be achieved by using volumes greater than 5 ml within certain limits (see Fig. 67). For the particular crystal and shielding, the optimal volume is 7 ml; there is negligible gain with a larger sample.

When large sample volumes must be used, a larger well and a larger counter are needed. This may be of advantage when only very low specific activity is present, or where it is difficult or undesirable to use a portion of the sample, as in counting stool specimens. Large crystals are prohibitive in cost for most routine uses; large well-type Geiger-Mueller counters have been made, but are not generally available. On occasion an attempt has been made to imitate a well-type geometry by arranging several

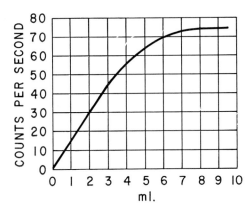

FIG. 67.—Increase of counting rate with increasing sample volume of constant specific activity in a well type scintillation counter with a well capacity of 5 ml.

Geiger-Mueller counters on the periphery of a circle; the sample is positioned in the middle and a scaling circuit is adapted in such a way that the counts of all counters are registered and counted together. A more practical solution is to change over from well-type geometry to the arrangement of Figure 64*b*, by using a large crystal (the well crystal can be easily adapted for this) and positioning a large sample *over* the crystal. An example of such a use with Co^{60} is listed in table 20. It can be seen that the calibration factor for total sample activity and for specific activity becomes very small, but that due to the large sample, a much smaller activity per ml can be detected (calibration factor reduced to about one-tenth, volume increased by one hundred, gain in counting rate of about ten!). Similar results will be obtained with most other gamma-emitting isotopes.

Large well scintillation counters of reasonable cost have been made of plastic phosphors.* For these materials the atomic number is too low to

*G. J. Hine and A. Miller: Large Plastic Well Makes Efficient Gamma Counter. Nucleonics, 1956, *10*, No. 10, page 78.

give easily detectable light pulses for gamma-ray energies of I^{131}, but they can be used conveniently for energies above 1 mev (the isotopes of Co^{60}, Fe^{59}, K^{42}, Na^{24}). The data for such a crystal of 5 inches diameter, 6 inches high and a well holding a 100 ml sample are also listed in table 20.

It is perhaps of interest to mention the largest well counter built so far and designed to accept a whole human body. The scintillating material is a liquid phosphor. This counter is in Los Alamos, but it is being reproduced in a few other institutions.

The geometry in which a sample is at some distance from the radiation detector (Fig. 64a) is used generally for *in vivo* counting, but it is useful in some *in vitro* counting problems, when the activity of the sample is too great for use with another arrangement or when the sample is too bulky and at the same time has sufficient activity for measurement in this set-up.

When the specific activity in a liquid sample is too small for counting with any of the mentioned set-ups, it is frequently possible to concentrate it by evaporation. Whenever this procedure is used, it is necessary to guard against loss of activity during evaporation; when this evaporation is carried out to dryness, a correction for self-absorption may have to be done. This will be discussed in the next section on beta counting.

Beta Particle Counting.—While one of the problems of optimal sensitivity in gamma counting is to achieve maximum absorption of this penetrating radiation within the radiation detector, the difficulty with beta counting is the opposite. Beta rays are easily absorbed; once they reach the sensitive volume of the counter (gas in a Geiger-Mueller counter, crystal in the scintillation counter) their efficiency is very high, close to 100 per cent. But because of this ease of absorption, they are as readily absorbed in the walls of a counter and may not reach the sensitive volume at all. Counter walls must be made as thin as possible.

Geiger-Mueller counters have been made of rather thin aluminum which permits the penetration of higher energy beta particles; such counters are quite fragile, since the thin walls have to withstand the difference between atmospheric pressure and the reduced pressure in the counter. For the same reason, thin-walled counters of glass are not in general use. In order to compromise between strength and need for thinness, counters for beta radiation are usually made of a strong material (glass, metal) except for a thin window at one end: *end-window counters*. The preferred material for the window is a natural mineral, mica, which can be split into very thin but strong sheets. Mica windows are available in thicknesses down to about 1.5 mg per square centimeter. Very thin window counters are both expensive and fragile; they are used for the measurement of soft beta-emitters such as C^{14} and S^{35}. For higher energy betas, as with P^{32} for instance, thicker and stronger windows of about 3 to 4 mg/cm^2 are preferred. Table 21 lists the reduction of counts with increasing window thickness for several typical isotopes, after deduction of the counting rates due to gamma radiation of those isotopes which have both gamma

and beta rays.* It will be seen that a window thickness of a few mg/cm²
causes a negligible reduction of counting rate for P^{32}, Au^{198}, I^{131} and Co^{60}; this
rate is halved by 5 mg/cm² for Ca^{45}, by 3 mg for S^{35} and by only 2.5 mg
for C^{14}.

Table 21

Window thickness in mg/cm²	Relative Counting Rate						
	P^{32}	Au^{198}	I^{131}	Co^{60}	Ca^{45}	S^{35}	C^{14}
0	100	100	100	100	100	100	100
1	99	98	96	92	89	81	78
2	99	96	92	84	78	66	60
3	98	94	88	77	69	53	46
4	97	92	84	70	62	43	35
5	96	90	81	65	54	35	27
6	96	89	78	60	48	28	21
7	95	87	75	54	43	23	16

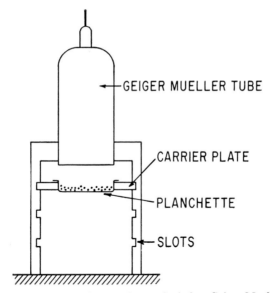

Fig. 68.—An example for the use of an end window Geiger-Mueller counter
(geometry *b* of Fig. 64).

There is less variation possible in the position of the sample and counter
for beta than for gamma counting. The counting geometry is in practice
always of the type illustrated in Figure 64*a* and 64*b*. Large distances are
neither necessary nor practical, since bulky samples of large volume are
useless for beta counting due to self-absorption. This will be discussed
in detail presently.

*A. I. Gleason, J. D. Taylor and D. L. Tabern: Absolute Beta Counting at Defined
Geometries. Nucleonics, 1951, *8*, No. 5, page 18.

The typical set-up is illustrated in Figure 68. The sample is contained on a metal planchette; the planchette fits into a plate which can be inserted; and removed by sliding it in and out of slots in a stand; the stand has sometimes several slots in order to change the distance of the sample from the counter (the purpose is to vary the sensitivity by changing sample distance).

The efficiency of a counter for beta radiation is close to 100 per cent, that is, most beta particles once they get inside will produce a count. The actual sensitivity is considerably smaller. It depends on the window absorption, and it is also reduced by the distance of the sample from the counter, and by the fact that only half of the beta rays leave the surface of the sample and go towards the counter, while the other half impinges on the planchette supporting the sample where they are either absorbed or scattered back towards the counter. Absorption of beta rays by the sample itself can be disregarded in most standardization measurements when the sample contains nothing but the radioactive isotope and a negligible amount of carrier and impurities, and when dry samples are used.

For beta counting, dry samples are used almost exclusively; solvents increase absorption and reduce sensitivity and also introduce an erratic error due to slow evaporation.

A fraction of the beta radiation which is scattered from the planchette may reach the counter. Not all beta particles, therefore, which go in a direction away from the counter, are lost as a source of counting events. The same occurs with beta rays hitting the supporting structures.

Assuming no absorption in the window and an inherent 100% efficiency of the counter it might be expected that the counting efficiency with a sample on a planchette would be never greater than 50%. Due to backscatter, however, it may exceed this figure significantly. It is important to realize that the amount and energy of this backscatter depends on the atomic number of the scattering material. It is essential, therefore, to use identical planchettes for a series of measurements and the associated calibration. A recalibration is always necessary when planchette types are switched (steel to plated iron or to aluminum) or when the support or enclosure is replaced, even when the identical counter is used and the dimensions are exactly reproduced.

When beta counters are used for the purpose of standardization, it is advisable to use a standardized sample of the identical isotope. P^{32} can be standardized by Bremsstrahlung counting in a scintillation counter, as described under the heading of "Specialized Methods" page 266f. Long lived, low energy, pure beta emitters such as Ca^{45}, S^{35} and C^{14}, are of prime interest, and for these standardized samples are useful over long periods after they have been obtained. Performance standards are therefore of secondary interest with beta counters. Radium D + E, deposited on a metal planchette, may be used for general checking, but even a gamma-emitter (radium, Co^{60}) might be used; it must be realized in this case that the position of the gamma-ray standard is quite critical and provision must be made so that it can be easily and securely placed in the same position for every check (a holder which is screwed to the counter housing and into which the standard container fits snugly is the simplest solution).

Self-absorption.—When biological samples are prepared for beta counting, they usually contain, even when dried, a significant amount of material (inorganic salts in urine, proteins in blood, etc.) which will absorb a fraction of the beta radiation. The fraction absorbed will depend on the sample thickness which is expressed best in mg/cm. As long as this thickness does not exceed the beta range of the isotopes used, a gain in sensitivity can be

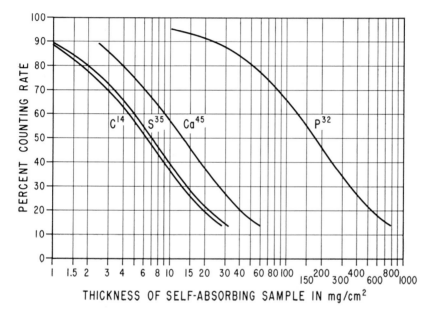

Fig. 69.—Decrease of counting rate due to self-absorption, when the counting rate of the *total* activity in the sample without absorption (weightless samples) is 100. (When the absorbing material has intermediate or high atomic number there is some initial increase of counting rate in thin samples due to selfscattering; this effect is disregarded in the illustration).

achieved by using larger and thicker samples. The graph in Figure 69 permits estimation of the expected counting rate for several isotopes if the calibration factor for a "weightless" sample, expected activity in the given sample, and its mg/cm² are known.

This graph, however, can be used only for a rough evaluation. For reliable measurements it is essential to determine the correction for self absorption for any particular experiment. This can be done by preparing a duplicate sample; a known amount of the carrier free isotope, q µc, is added to the second sample. Both samples are processed (dried, etc.) in the identical fashion, and counted. Let the two observed counting rates be R_1 and R_2. The calibration factor f for the given sample is then given

17

by the increased counts for the sample with the added activity $R_2 - R_1$, divided by the added activity:

$$f = \frac{R_2 - R_1}{q} \tag{60}$$

and this factor can be used to calculate the unknown activity a:

$$a = \frac{R_1}{f} \tag{61}$$

Although no improvement in sensitivity is possible by increasing sample size beyond the thickness corresponding to the range, an advantage of a different type is gained. When such "thick" samples are used, the counting rate becomes independent of sample thickness, since no beta particles reach the counter from material behind the range layer (this applies for pure beta-emitters only and when Bremsstrahlung is disregarded). A calibration of the counting set-up under these conditions can be made in terms of specific activity (counts per second for 1 μc per mg). The sample preparation, particularly the amount of material used, becomes then less critical. The expected calibration factor can be evaluated from Figure 69.

As an example, the estimated calibration factor in a given counter for P^{32} will be calculated. Let us assume that a calibration without self-absorption gives 20 c/s for 1 nonocurie total activity. The planchette area (1″ diameter) is 5 cm². A blood sample of a given volume is estimated to contain 7 nonocuries and to weigh, when dried on the planchette, 0.62 gm. The thickness is then 125 mg/cm². The counting rate without self-absorption would be 140 counts per second. This will be reduced for this sample thickness (curve for P^{32} in Figure 69) to 60 per cent; the estimated counting rate will be, therefore, about 80 counts per second. Now let us consider a "thick" sample (exceeding the beta range); the same sensitivity will be assumed as before without self-absorption (20 counts per second for 1 nonocurie). It will be further assumed that 0.02 nonocuries per mg dry residue are present on the planchette. The thickness of the layer corresponding to P^{32} beta range is 900 mg/cm². The total weight of this layer on the planchette is $900 \times 5 = 4500$ mg. This will contain altogether $4500 \times 0.02 = 90$ nonocuries. Figure 69 indicates that the counting rate drops to 14 per cent for distribution in beta-range-layer thickness. A weightless sample of 90 nonocuries will give a counting rate of $90 \times 20 = 1800$ counts per second. With self-absorption, 14 per cent of this counting rate will be observed or 250 counts per second. To generalize for this case: 0.02 nonocuries/mg will give 250 counts per second; 1 nonocurie/mg therefore will give 12,500 counts per second. This calibration factor for specific activity (per unit weight of sample) is now independent of the sample thickness, provided of course this thickness exceeds the beta range.

A few specific suggestions on problems in the preparation of dry samples should be given. Weightless samples (carrier-free) may dry unevenly, cause erratic geometry and produce, therefore, errors in calibration and counting. This unevenness can be reduced by cleaning the planchettes well, to make sure that no oily film is present, by adding some wetting agent to the sample before drying, or by using a piece of thin filter paper (dripolator coffee filters are the only source of really thin filter paper known to the writer!) in the planchette. A check for self-absorption is necessary, if the latter device is used. When samples with significant dry residue are prepared, the deposit may lack uniformity; this can be reduced by slow drying (heater lamps at sufficient distance). Such samples are sometimes powdery and flaky, and some of the material may be lost and even contaminate the counter. A thin film of collodion solution (a fraction of 1 per cent concentration) or a carefully placed disc of thin plastic foil may reduce this. In this case, the absorption by the protective layers has to be checked in addition to the self-absorption.

Most beta measurements need not be absolute in reference to a standard precisely known in terms of mc, but only relative with reference to an administered tracer dose. Calibrations may be done therefore by using a suitable portion of the tracer dose used. This method can be used also for calibration with self-absorption as discussed in connection with equation (60).

Shielding of Counting Set-Ups.—Every nuclear counting set-up must be shielded to reduce the amount and variability of the background. The shielding requirements depend on the sensitivity of the counter to gamma and beta radiation.

A scintillation counter requires considerable shielding because of its relatively high efficiency to penetrating cosmic radiation. A well crystal for instance needs an enclosure of at least 2 inches of lead. Suitable lead shields are supplied by the counter manufacturers, but they can be easily assembled by the user with "lead bricks" which usually measure $2 \times 4 \times 8$ inches. Lead bricks can be either bought from suppliers of nuclear equipment, or can be cast by a local lead foundry, sometimes at a considerable saving.

Geiger-Mueller counters need less shielding and 1 inch of lead is frequently sufficient.

The sensitivity of beta counters to external background radiation may be equal to that of Geiger-Mueller counters used for gamma counting, but it is frequently smaller and therefore less shielding may be needed. One potential difficulty with beta-counter shielding should be pointed out: lead occasionally contains natural radioactive elements, usually alpha and beta emitters. In such cases the lead enclosure has to be lined with a suitable material (brass, steel or plastic), to shield the counter from this soft radiation.

Effective shielding is heavy and expensive, particularly when it is thick enough to reduce significantly the background due to very energetic cosmic radiation. An arrangement illustrated in Figure 70 reduces this background for β counting without excessive shielding. The main counter and sample are surrounded by a second bell-shaped counter. This second counter is shielded from β radiation of the sample by the sample holder and the housing of the main counter. The two counters are connected to an anticoincidence circuit of Figure 51, the main counter as Detector A and the shielding counter as Detector B. When a β ray from the sample causes the main counter to operate, a count will be registered in the counting circuit. When,

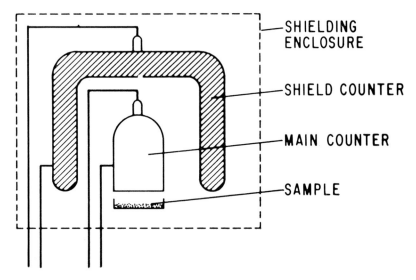

SHIELDING ENCLOSURE

SHIELD COUNTER

MAIN COUNTER

SAMPLE

FIG. 70.—Assembly for use of a shielding counter for reducing background by anti-coincidence counting.

however, a photon penetrates the shield in such a way that both counters operate, no counts will be registered, due to the operation of the anticoincidence mechanism. Should the photon operate only the shielding counter, also no counts will be registered since the circuit B is only passive: it can only close a contact, but cannot pass any pulses. Therefore such photons will not be counted at all. Some background, however, will remain. It will be due to ionizing events which bypass the shielding counter, either because they did not interact or because they came through the opening of this counter. An assembly of this sort can reduce the background by a factor of 10. Sensitivity as expressed by the smallest detectable amount is proportional to $\sqrt{R_b}$, according to equation (57). A background reduction to one-tenth will, therefore, reduce the smallest detectable amount to about one-third.

Identification of Isotopes in a Sample.—There are many occasions in the work with isotopes when it becomes necessary to identify the unknown radioactive material in a sample.

The range of possibilities is usually small, since only a few of the available isotopes are handled in a given laboratory.

If the possibilities are limited to a pure beta emitter and a gamma emitter, the decision is easily made by using over the sample an absorber exceeding the beta range (see Table 22). If the counting rate drops close to background, the sample contains the beta emitter. It must be remembered that, due to Bremsstrahlung, some net counting rate will be observed even with a beta counter; a strong sample of a high energy beta emitter (P^{32}) will show a considerable counting rate with a gamma counter even when its walls exceed the beta range.

A more positive identification can be made by plotting the absorption curves for the isotopes which are being handled. Plastic films and sheets are a suitable material for low energy beta emitters; aluminum is more convenient for higher energies, and lead or steel for gamma emitters.

Such absorption curves must be plotted for every counting set-up used, since window thickness and geometry may cause changes from the theoretical curve. From such plots the absorber which reduces the counting rate to half ("half value layer") may be selected for a quick check of an isotope for a decision between several possible materials. *Approximate values of such absorber thicknesses for several common pure beta emitters are listed in Table 22.*

Table 22.—Range and Half Value Layers for Several Isotopes with Pure Beta Emission

	mg/cm^2	
	---	---
	Range	*Half Value Absorber*
C^{14}	29	4
Ca^{45}	59	8
P^{32}	790	100
S^{35}	32	4.5

The same technique can be used for identification of gamma emitters, except that they do not have a limited range, but a continued exponential absorption. In order to avoid confusion by the faster absorption of beta radiation present in some gamma emitters, one should be sure that all betas are filtered out before the gamma absorption is plotted; usually the counter walls of a gamma counter are thick enough to accomplish this. The half value layers in lead are listed for some isotopes in Table 10, page 147. Here again this is only a general guide and actual measurements with available counters must be performed. As with beta emitters, it is convenient to select a filter corresponding to the half value layer of every isotope in use for ease in routine identification.

With gamma emitters it is possible to make a rather sophisticated identification by *gamma-ray spectrometry*; this is practical when a spectrometer is available in connection with work in double isotope tracer technique or some scanning device which will be described later.

Gamma ray spectroscopy with a scintillation counter is based on the fact that the intensity of light pulses produced in a scintillating phosphor during the absorption of ionizing radiation is proportional to the energy of this radiation.

The electrical circuit of a γ ray spectrometer is based on the anticoincidence circuit of Figure 51. The scintillation counter is connected to 2 circuits A and B in which the discriminators can be adjusted in several ways to be described presently and which are part of the anticoincidence circuit.

Let us adjust the 2 discriminators in such a way that the discriminator A passes pulses of V volts and the discriminator B operates only on larger pulses, $V + \Delta V$ volts.

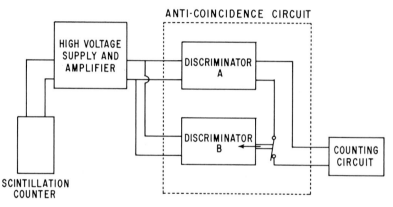

Fig. 71.—A single channel spectrometer using two discriminators in anticoincidence circuit. The threshold of discriminator A is set to V volt that of discriminator B to $V + \Delta V$ volt. The counting circuit registers only pulses which have a voltage between V and $V + \Delta V$.

Three types of event can now occur.
1. Pulse is less than V. None of the circuits operates, no counts are registered.
2. Pulse is larger than V but smaller than $V + \Delta V$. Circuit A passes a pulse, circuit B remains inoperative; a count is registered.
3. Pulse is larger than $V + \Delta V$. Circuit A operates, circuit B also operates and blocks the pulse of circuit A: no counts are registered.

In short, only pulses which are between V and $V + \Delta V$ are counted and we obtain the number of pulses within this range. We have an equivalent of an electrical sieve.

By changing the settings of the discriminators A and B, it is possible to determine the distribution of pulses according to their height. Hence the name of this circuit arrangement: "Pulse-Height Analyser."

Figure 72 illustrates diagrammatically the function of this analyser.

For convenience, the discriminator controls of A and B are coupled in such a way that the level V can be adjusted simultaneously in both, while keeping Δ V, the difference of threshold between the two discriminators, constant. A separate control permits changing this difference.

Since the voltage pulse height depends on the absorbed energy of radiation and since the maximum absorbed energy depends on the photon or particle energy, the pulse-height distribution represents the energy distribution of the radiation observed.

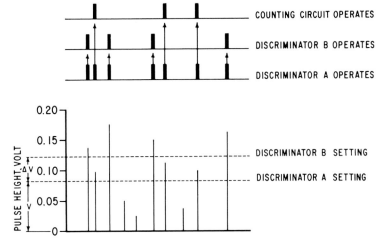

Fig. 72.—The lower diagram illustrates the pulse heights as they come from the scintillation counter. The upper diagram indicates how the Discriminator A and B operate in the anticoincidence circuit for different pulse heights. Note that when discriminator B operates, it blocks the pulses passed by discriminator A from reaching the counting circuit.

If we plot the number of counts observed for each voltage setting V we obtain a scintillation spectrum of the isotope under investigation. The voltage setting V of the discriminators corresponds to the energy absorbed. By observing an isotope of known energy the discriminator level setting can be calibrated in kev or Mev. Such γ-ray spectra with proper calibration are illustrated in Figure 73.

The γ-ray spectrum as obtained with a scintillation-counter spectrometer is not an exact representation of γ-ray energies emitted, since the scintillation pulse is proportional to the energy absorbed, which may be less than the whole photon energy. In a Compton interaction for instance the scattered photon may escape the crystal, in pair formation one or both annihilation rays may escape.*

* For a detailed discussion see: C. C. Harris, D. P. Hamblen, J. E. Francis, "Basic Principles of Scintillation Counting", Oak Ridge National Laboratory. Available from Office of Technical Services, Department of Commerce, Washington 25, D.C. Price $2.00.

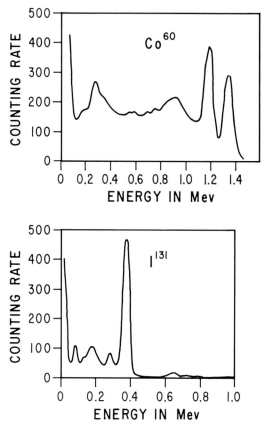

Fig. 73.—Gamma ray spectra of Co[60] and I[131] as obtained
with a scintillation counter spectrometer.

A change of Δ V, the difference between the discriminator levels, will
determine the sharpness of the peaks on the observed spectrum and the
counting rate with a given sample. This difference corresponds to the slit
or window of an optical spectrometer. The counting rate increases when it is
made wider; the peaks become narrower when it is reduced.

Using the image of a window when describing the level difference of the
two discriminators, the setting V for the discriminator level is called
"window sill".

In order to determine and to plot a γ-ray spectrum, a large number of
determinations have to be made. Usually, but not invariably, the window sill will be raised by one window width for each successive measurement. For high precision this may become a very long experiment. To
reduce this time a large number of anticoincidence circuits as in Figure 71
operate simultaneously, each having a different window sill setting. If

we express the window width and window sill again in terms of voltage, we can describe the circuits as follows:

Anticoincidence circuit #	Window sill	Window width	Pulse heights counted are between
1	V	ΔV	V and V $+ \Delta V$
2	V $+ \Delta V$	ΔV	V $+ \Delta V$ and V $+ 2\Delta V$
3	V $+ 2\Delta V$	ΔV	V $+ 2\Delta V$ and V $+ 3\Delta V$
.	.	.	.
n	V $+$ (n-1) ΔV	ΔV	V $+$ (n-1) ΔV and V$+$ nΔV

and obtain the whole spectrum in the time needed for a single count. Each anticoincidence circuit in such an arrangement is called a "channel" and the whole assembly a "Multi-channel Analyser" (sometimes more colloquially a "Kick-Sorter," with reference to the electrical pulses, or "kicks"). Multi-channel analysers are available with several hundred (usually about 250) channels. Since the most expensive part in such an instrument is the component which registers the counts, the observed counting events are usually stored in an electrical memory circuit and either displayed as a graph or printed out later on tape.

Specialized Methods.—Several methods of high sensitivity beta counting will be briefly described in the following. Some of them are of more interest for research work than in clinical applications, but since they may come into wider use in the near future, some acquaintance with them is indicated.

With the development of counting gas mixtures which can be used at atmospheric pressure, it becomes possible to use windowless counters where the dry sample is introduced directly inside of the counter. Whenever a sample is changed, the counting gas becomes contaminated by air which has to be flushed out. These *"Flow-Gas Counters"* are, therefore, always connected to a pressure cylinder containing the counter gas, which must flow through the counter for a definite short period after each sample change. The gain in sensitivity is due not only to the absence of window absorption, but also to improved geometry (the sample is directly adjacent to the counting gas). For samples without self-absorption, the efficiency is close to 50 per cent. A disadvantage of windowless counters is the ease with which they are contaminated by dry sample material which dusts off the planchettes. Some flow-gas counters have been built, therefore, with exceedingly thin windows (0.1 mg/cm²), which is possible since the counting gas is at atmospheric pressure. Such counters need no flushing between the insertions of samples; only a small gas flow needs to be maintained, to replace gas which decomposes during the counting process.

Scintillation counters can also be used for beta counting; special provisions for sample positioning are needed to exclude extraneous light. The crystal housing must be very thin so as not to absorb too large a fraction of beta rays. There is no need to have large crystals, thin wafers of thickness corresponding to the largest used beta range are adequate; this reduces considerably background due to ambient gamma radiation.

The limitation of useful sample size due to self-absorption can be overcome to some extent by the following methods.

1. *Chemical purification* can eliminate a considerable portion of inert material which contributes to self-absorption. The suitable methods will depend on the chemical compounds involved and no general directions are therefore possible. When the isotope can be removed from a solution by electroplating, as with iron for instance, relatively simple techniques can be worked out.

2. *Gas Counting.* The radioactive compound can be converted into a gas, as for instance into CO_2 with C^{14} and this is added to the counting gas with which a Geiger-Mueller counter is filled. This method means of course that the counter has to be filled every time a new sample is counted, and that the samples must be prepared and handled as a gas. The advantage is, however, complete absence of self-absorption and efficiency approaching 100 per cent namely 37,000 counts per μc! This method can be used for tritium which has such soft beta energy (18 kev) that few other methods give useful sensitivity.

3. *Liquid Scintillation Counters.* Scintillating solutions can be prepared with suitable phosphors and solvents, in which the sample can be dissolved. As with gas counting there is then no self-absorption. The difficulties with this method are again sample preparation, since the sample must be in such chemical form that it does not interfere with the scintillating properties of the phosphor, although recently samples in the forms of solid powder have been used successfully. The light pulses are extremely weak. To achieve suitable sensitivity of the phototube, therefore, such a high voltage must be used that tube noise becomes high. To reduce the noise, the counter assembly is placed in a refrigerator and two phototubes are used in a coincidence circuit. A coincidence circuit is an electronic device added to the scaler which lets light pulses come through to the counting circuit only when both phototubes produce a pulse *simultaneously* (in coincidence), but no counts are registered when a pulse occurs in one of the tubes only. When a scintillation takes place in the liquid scintillator, it is seen by both phototubes simultaneously and a count is registered. Tube noise, on the other hand, occurs in the two tubes at random instants, independently of each other, and most of the noise pulses are rejected by the coincidence circuit.

The sensitivity of liquid scintillation counters is very high. With C^{14} it approaches 20,000 counts per second for 1 μc, and with tritium 6,000 counts per second for 1 μc.

4. *Bremsstrahlung Counting.* Self-absorption can be practically eliminated also by counting higher energy β-emitting isotopes like P^{32}, not by observing interaction of β particles with the radiation detector directly, but by count-

ing x-ray quanta produced by Bremsstrahlung, when β radiation is absorbed in the sample itself and in surrounding matter. The high efficiency in a well-type scintillation counter makes this practical, and the increased sample size which can be used makes the sensitivity of this method approach the sensitivity of direct β-counting. The liquid sample is used in a test tube as in γ-counting, so that sample preparation is simplified.

An example for such counting in a well type crystal for P^{32} in blood samples gives a calibration factor of 0.3 counts per second for 1 nanocurie sample. Background is 4 c/s. The smallest detectable amount in absolute activity measurement is 1.6 nanocuries and for specific activity 0.3 nanocuries per ml (5 ml well capacity). (See page 235.)

This method is useful also for other isotopes. With Y^{90} the efficiency will be greater than for P^{32} and for Sr^{90} it will be considerably smaller.

Radiochromatography. It is frequently of interest to examine to which particular protein fraction some tagged material belongs or becomes associated with during metabolic processes. This can be done by chromatographic or electrophoretic separation of protein fractions and by determining in which fraction or fractions the radioactive material is located.

After the paper strip with separated proteins is obtained, there are several methods available to determine the location of the radioactive tracer.

The simplest method is to cut up the strip of paper in narrow pieces normal to the migration direction and to count each piece like a sample with any suitable detector. The disadvantage is that the original strip is cut up and that the correlation of the observed activity with the migration pattern becomes difficult.

The other method uses a radiation detector equipped with a cap of a material which will absorb most of the radiations emitted by the radioactive isotope used for tagging. A slit is made in this cap, and the paper strip is moved across it at a constant speed by means of a mechanical drive. The radiation detector is connected to a counting-rate recorder. As the paper strip moves in front of the slit, the counting-rate record plots the activity distribution over the strip.

If the speed of the recorder chart is the same as the travel speed of the paper strip, a simple and direct comparison between the chromatogram and the radioactivity distribution can be made, as illustrated in Figure 74. Tracing B indicates that the radioactive tracer migrated with β globulin and albumen.

In addition to the location of the activity on the strip it is sometimes required to know the total activity in various protein fractions. This can be obtained by integrating the areas under the rate record, for instance with a planimeter. This integrated counting rate can be, however, rather simply recorded directly, since the total activity is simply proportional to the accumulated counts. An electrical output is provided from the ratemeter, in such a way that the current is proportional to the total counts and a second pen records this current on the recorder chart.

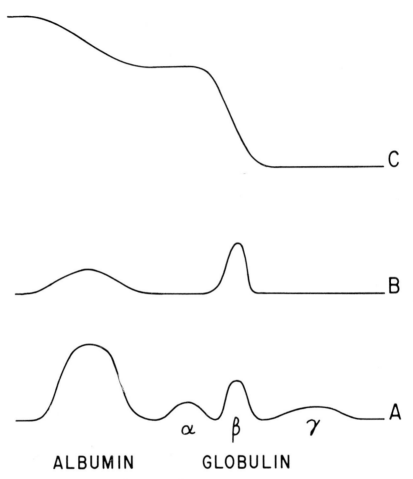

Fɪɢ. 74.—Chromatographic Strip with Tagged Proteins. Curve A: optical density of the strip with protein fractions stained by a chemical reaction. Curve B: record of scanning with a rate-meter (radioactivity is present in β globulin and in albumen). Curve C: integrated record of curve B (the first plateau from the right represents the total activity in β globulin; the second plateau represents the total activity present in the strip; the difference between the two represents the activity in albumen).

Such a paperstrip scanning device will have the following controls: 1, speed control for the motion of the chromatographic paper strip, 2, response time control for the rate meter, 3, calibration adjustment for the rate-recorder pen, and perhaps 4, calibration adjustment for the integrating recorder pen.

In selecting the speed of the chromatographic strip movement it should be considered that the counting rate will be independent of the speed with which a given spot on the paper passes under the counter slit, but that if it moves too quickly, the response time of the recording circuit may be too slow and the meter will not respond. The paper travel speed must be, therefore, matched to response time: the optimal setting is that for which the time it takes a point on the paper to pass under the slit of the counter is about equal to twice the response time. If faster scanning is desired, a shorter response time should be selected. The limitations for the response time are of course due to statistical fluctuations, so that weak samples require long response time and slow paper travel.

The deflection on the integrating record is inversely proportional to the paper travel speed. After this speed and the corresponding response time of the rate-recorder have been selected, the calibration adjustment for the integrating recorder must be set in such a way that the pen does not deflect off scale. This has to be usually done in a preliminary test run.

Double Isotope Technique.—When two different isotopes are present in the sample, it is not possible to determine their activities by simple counting. This can be achieved in three ways, depending on the nature of the isotopes present.

1. *Gamma-Ray Spectrometer.* The principles of gamma-ray spectroscopy have been described in the section on identification of isotopes. If the two isotopes present in the sample have two gamma-ray energy peaks of sufficiently different energy, as for instance Cr^{51} and Fe^{59}, they can be determined by this method. The technique is not quite as simple as it may appear at first, since the lower energy isotope will contribute to the counting rate at the peak of the high energy isotope and vice versa. Calibration factors for the two isotopes have to be determined, therefore, for both regions of the spectrum.

Let us assume that the calibration factors for the two regions of the spectrum of one isotope are c_1 and c_2, and of the other isotope f_1 and f_2. The counting rates for the sample, observed for the two regions, are R_1 and R_2. The unknown activities are A_c and A_f. We have then two equations: The observed counting rate R_1 in the first spectral region, due to the activities of both isotopes A_c and A_f is

$$R_1 = c_1 A_c + f_1 A_f \qquad (62)$$

and for the other spectral region

$$R_2 = c_2 A_c + f_2 A_f \qquad (63)$$

These equations are solved for the unknown activities A_c and A_f:

$$A_c = \frac{f_2 R_1 - f_1 R_2}{c_1 f_2 - c_2 f_1} \qquad (64)$$

and

$$A_f = - \frac{c_2 R_1 - c_1 R_2}{c_1 f_2 - c_2 f_1} \qquad (65)$$

The simultaneous determination of the two isotopes will be impossible if the ratios of calibration factors in the two regions are the same. Let us call this ratio for one isotope Q_c and for the other isotope Q_f, so that:

$$Q_c = \frac{c_1}{c_2} \tag{66}$$

and

$$Q_f = \frac{f_1}{f_2} \tag{67}$$

No determination is possible if

$$Q_c = Q_f$$

Equations (64) and (65) can be expressed by substituting (66) and (67) after some transformation as:

$$A_c = \frac{1}{c_2} \times \frac{R_1 - Q_f R_2}{Q_c - Q_f} \tag{68}$$

$$A_f = \frac{1}{f_2} \times \frac{Q_c R_2 - R_1}{Q_c - Q_f} \tag{69}$$

For $Q_c = Q_f$ both the denominator and numerator become zero and A_c and A_f are indeterminate*.

The condition for the ability to separate the two isotopes is therefore that Q_c is different from Q_f; the larger the difference the better the method.

The spectrometer settings for regions 1 and 2 must therefore be selected so as to give the greatest difference between Q_f and Q_c. It also must be considered that if the counting rates are low, counting times for acceptable errors will be high. This means that narrow windows are undesirable; the windows must be selected as wide as it is possible to make them, provided the difference between Q_f and Q_c remains sufficiently high. A guide to such

---

* It is not easy to see why the numerator becomes zero. It is equal to $R_1 - Q_f R_2$ From (62) and (63) it follows that

$$\frac{R_1}{R_2} = \frac{c_1 A_c + f_1 A_f}{c_2 A_c + f_2 A_f} = \frac{f_1}{f_2} \times \frac{\frac{c_1}{f_1} A_c + A_f}{\frac{c_2}{f_2} A_c + A_f}$$

Since $Q_c = Q_f$ it follows that $\dfrac{c_1}{c_2} = \dfrac{f_1}{f_2}$ and also $\dfrac{f_1}{c_1} = \dfrac{f_2}{c_2}$ so that the second fraction be-

comes unity and $\dfrac{R_1}{R_2} = \dfrac{f_1}{f_2} = Q_f$ and $R_1 = Q_f R_2$. By substituting this value for R_1 in

the expression for the numerator $R_1 - Q_f R_2$, this numerator becomes zero.

a selection of suitable window setting is usually found by inspection of the scintillation spectra of the two isotopes of interest.

2. *Isotopes of Different Half-life.* If one isotope has a much shorter half-life than the other, the sample is first counted while there is significant activity of both isotopes present and again later, when the short-lived isotope has decayed. The second count will measure the activity of the long-lived isotope; after correcting for decay, the counting rate corresponding to this isotope is subtracted from the first count. The difference is then due to the first isotope and its activity can be calculated from the appropriate calibration factor (these factors will be different for the two isotopes).

When the two half-lives are too long it is possible to determine both isotopes before one is completely decayed, by using equations (64) and (65) and considering that the mathematical situation is identical if we say "at different times" instead of "at different spectrometer settings". If the time elapsed between the two measurements is t, then what we called efficiencies of the two isotopes c_2 and f_2 will become

$$c_2 = c_1 2^{-t/T_c}$$

and

$$f_2 = f_1 2^{-t/T_f}$$

where T_c and T_f are the two half-lives, and c_1, and f_1, are the calibration factors. We have then by substituting in (64) and (65)

$$A_c = \frac{f_1 R_1 2^{-t/T_f} - f_1 R_2}{c_1 f_1 2^{-t/T_f} - c_1 f_1 2^{-t/T_c}} = \frac{1}{c_1} \times \frac{R_1 2^{-t/T_f} - R_2}{2^{-t/T_f} - 2^{-t/T_c}} \tag{70}$$

and similarly:

$$A_f = \frac{1}{f_1} \times \frac{R_1 - R_2 2^{-t/T_c}}{2^{-t/T_f} - 2^{-t/T_c}} \tag{71}$$

3. *One of the Two Isotopes is a Pure Beta-Emitter.* The calibration factors are determined for the second isotope, which is also a gamma-emitter, in the usual way and also with an absorbing filter over the sample, in an end-window counter. The filter must be thick enough to absorb all beta radiation from the first isotope. The sample is counted with this filter and without. The calibration factor with filter and the associated counting rate permit calculation of the activity of the second isotope. The counting rate due to this isotope is then calculated from the no-filter calibration

factor of this isotope and subtracted from the counting rate of the sample observed without filter. The difference is the counting rate due to the first, beta-emitting, isotope.

This method can be extended to two pure β-emitters or pure γ-emitters by measuring them first without and then with some suitable filter, which reduces the calibration factors for the two isotopes by a different factor. To do this, the calibration factors for the two isotopes will have to be determined first without the filter (c_1 and f_1) and then with the filter (c_2 and f_2). From the counting rates of the unknown mixture without the filter (R_1) and with the filter (R_2), the activities of the two components can be determined from (64) and (65). This method will be found useful on rare occasions only, but it is a way to use double isotope techniques when no spectrometer is available.

16

Quantitative Measurements *in Vivo*

THERE are no basic differences in the determination of the activity of a radioactive deposit within the body of a patient and of the activity in a sample *in vitro*. The practical differences, however, are considerable. They are due to the circumstance that it is not possible to manipulate the deposit of radioactive material at will with reference to the counter as is possible with a separate isolated sample. Distance of the counter from the radioactive source, size of the source, absorption and backscatter vary with the anatomical variation of the organ of interest. The conditions discussed for reliable measurements *in vitro* cannot be rigidly maintained, therefore, and the influence of their variability on the measurements has to be considered and minimized by suitable design of the experimental arrangements.

A representative example of the quantitative determination of a radioactive deposit in the body is the measurement of radioactive iodine uptake by the thyroid gland. This will be discussed, therefore, at first and in detail, both as a guide for this particular procedure and as a typical example of the difficulties involved and of the methods available to overcome them.

Measurement of Thyroidal Uptake.—The determination of the fraction of an administered tracer dose of radioactive iodine taken up by the thyroid gland is one of the most frequent nuclear measurements encountered in clinical use. This determination is performed on a "sample" which cannot be removed from the body; the measurement has to be done on the gland which is in the patient's neck, with a variety of uncertainties from patient to patient, due to differences in size, location and background. Different techniques proposed and in use have the common aim of minimizing the dependence of the results on these variations.

The requirements for the reproducibility of the measurements are determined by the physiological range of uptake variations between euthyroid and hyperthyroid patients. If it is assumed for the purpose of discussion that the overlap between the two conditions ranges from 55 per cent to 65 per cent uptake of the total administered test dose by the thyroid gland, it is only necessary to be able to determine whether the uptake is less than 55 per cent or more than 65 per cent. Should we accept an error of 10 per cent in the uptake, the practical requirements would be met.

The requirements in counting precision can be illustrated by an example. With a tracer dose of 10 μc a diagnostically equivocal uptake would be between 5.5 and 6.5 μc, a range of 1 μc. 1μc in 6 μc (mean of the range) corresponds to a variation of 17 per cent, which determines the minimum precision needed in counting. This seems to be a very modest requirement, and a smaller error should be easily attainable. A recently conducted survey on measurements with a mannequin-type phantom in a number of laboratories in this country has shown, however, that actual errors frequently exceed either of the above criteria by a considerable margin.

Although some of the difficulties in uptake measurements are interrelated, it is best to discuss the uncertainty factors involved, and the methods of minimizing their effects separately, and later to summarize this in the form of some recommended procedures.

The *size of the thyroid* gland is an uncertainty which is easily handled. The only problem in this connection is created by the necessity of shielding the radiation detector from the general body background, which is due to the fraction of the tracer dose in tissues and circulating blood. Shielding for this purpose will have to restrict the field of view of the counter. The size of this field is determined by the shield construction and by the working distance. The smaller this field, the less is the measured body background, but if the field is made too small, the counter may fail to "see," that is to detect, the radiation from parts of the thyroid outside of this field. The result would be a false low reading. The field of view therefore must be large enough to contain the largest thyroid gland which may be encountered, taking also into account possible errors in "aiming" the detector in the right direction, preferably toward the center of the gland. Such a shielding is illustrated in Figure 75. The necessary condition is usually satisfied when the field of view is about 8 inches in diameter or a 8 $\times$ 8 inch square. This can be checked by using a small source of I^{131}, placing it on a flat surface at the working distance from the counter and counting it in various locations on the surface. The area in which the counts are constant within say 5 to 10 per cent represents the field of view; outside of this field of view the counting rate will drop, depending on the effectiveness of the shield. A sharp drop is desirable, but a practical compromise between weight of the shield and degree of shielding has to be made. Such a compromise results in lead wall thickness of about 1 inch. The suggested field of 8 inches diameter may not include a substernal extension of the thyroid gland. Clinical examination and scanning methods will indicate this condition; a larger than normal working distance will solve the problem after suitable recalibration.

The *variations in the location of the thyroid gland within the neck* are perhaps the greatest obstacle to precise uptake measurements. The effect of location and size of the gland cannot be separated completely, since a large gland not only occupies more space than a small gland in the field of view of a counter, but has also different dimensions in depth and therefore a different average or effective distance. The thyroid gland is imbedded in the neck; this affects the radiation intensity reaching the counter in several ways: 1. Distance of radioactive material from the counter; 2. Absorption by the gland itself (corresponding to self-absorption in a sample) and by the overlying tissues, and 3. Scatter by the tissues of the neck. It is a simple matter to adjust the counter to a given distance from the skin of the neck, but the average depth of the gland below the skin may vary by as much as 2 to 3 centimeters. This uncertainty in distance can be minimized by using such a long working distance that a few centimeters error would be negligible even within the range of inverse square relationship between counting rate and distance. Such a working distance necessary to achieve the desired effect would have to be a meter or more; this is impracticable for several reasons. The sensitivity of the counter would be reduced by more than 10 times compared to conventional distances, the collimation requirement for the shield to keep the

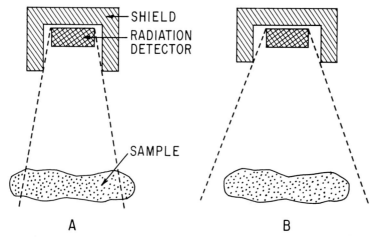

Fig. 75.—Shielding of an uptake counter. A: excessive collimation, observed counting rate will be too low; B: suitable shielding, all of the organ contributes to the observed counting rate.

field of view to 8 inches becomes excessive, and the aiming of such a collimator is critical and difficult. Short working distances increase the errors due to the variations of gland position so that it is impractical to increase sensitivity in this way. The working distance selected in practice is a compromise between sensitivity and the error due to the uncertainty of the gland location. There appears to be general agreement that this compromise leads to a working distance of between 20 and 30 cm. The effects of absorption of radiation by the overlying tissues of the neck are normally more or less obscured by scatter. The effect of absorption alone can be studied if the scatter contribution to the counting rate is eliminated by a gamma-ray spectrometer or by suitable adjustment of the discriminator setting in a scintillation counter. This makes the radiation detector selectively sensitive to essentially only the primary I^{131} energies. A similar effect can be achieved by the use of a lead filter of a few millimeters thickness, which filters out more of the soft backscattered radiation than of the harder primary wavelengths. When measuring in suitable phantoms under these conditions, it is found that the counting rate decreases by about 10 per cent for each centimeter increase of thyroid depth below the skin. If the range of thyroid location below skin is assumed to be within 2 cm only, the overall error due to absorption will amount to about 20 per cent.

The scatter by the neck increases the observed counting rate, since some of the primary radiant energy, which diverges from the field will be seen by the counter when its sensitivity to the lower energy of scattered radiation is not reduced by a lead filter or a spectrometer. When the counter is sensitive to the scatter, the observed counting rate is about 25 per cent* greater for an I^{131} source 1 cm below the surface of a water phantom than for the same source suspended in air. This indicates that the increase of counting rate by scatter more than compensates for the loss due to absorption at this depth. This increase is cancelled by absorption only when the iodine source is about 5 cm below the phantom surface. It is therefore to be expected that scatter has considerable effect on the change in counting rate with change in thyroid depth. It should be realized that the scatter is proportional to the amount of radiation impinging on scattering material, so that when the thyroid gland is at the surface, only about half of all the radiation emitted within the gland impinges on neck tissues and produces backscatter, and that when the thyroid gland is deep within the neck, all radiation from the source hits neck tissues and contributes to scatter (backscatter *and* forward-scatter). The overall radiation intensity from the neck due to radioactivity in the gland is influenced therefore by two opposing factors: (1) absorption is increased with greater thyroid depth, which reduces the observed counting rate, (this is also reduced by the increased distance from the counter); (2) scatter is increased with increased depth (this effect is particularly pronounced within the first few centimeters under the skin), which increases the counting rate, if the sensitivity of the radiation detector is reasonably wave-length independent. These two effects tend to cancel each other, so that the dependence of the uptake measurement on the thyroid depth in the neck is minimized. Under these conditions, the change of counting rate due to change of thyroid depth by 2 cm is reduced from 20 per cent when scatter effect is eliminated, to about 10 per cent when the counter is sensitive to scattered radiation.

The next problem to be considered is the calibration of an uptake counter. This may appear to be quite simple at first. The most convenient source for such calibration is a duplicate of a tracer dose, identical to the tracer given to the patient. This has several advantages: the aliquot solution is readily available, the decay of the reference source and of the tracer material in the patient is the same, so that checking against such a reference source at the time of uptake measurement corrects automatically for decay.

---

* The actual value will depend on the counter and, with a scintillation counter, on the discrimination setting.

There are some disadvantages, however: this reference source may be a liquid requiring precautions against spillage, and errors of pipetting may occur in its preparation. This disadvantage does not exist when doses in individual capsules are used. In many laboratories "mock-iodine" sources have been found useful. They have been described under performance and reference standards.

The reasons for the difficulties in the calibration of a thyroid uptake counter become apparent with the consideration of scatter, absorption and uncertainty of thyroid location.

When a counter which is sensitive to scatter is used, the calibration must be performed with the reference source in a suitable phantom. It will be recalled that an error of about 25 per cent is introduced if the reference source is measured in air and compared to the counting rate of the source in a phantom and hence in the neck. A suitable phantom, however, is easily made. A cylindrical water container made of plastic, not less than 6 inches in diameter and about 10 inches high can be used, with the reference source positioned about 1 cm behind the front surface (the source can be a 20 to 50 cc volumetric flask or some other container of similar dimensions). The disadvantage of a water phantom is that it can be usually employed only in a vertical position. A plastic phantom, or a phantom made of masonite, can be handled more conveniently. There are only a few critical considerations: the phantom should not be too small; no significant errors are introduced if it is made larger than the neck; the reference source should be under the surface facing the counter, and between $\frac{1}{2}$ and $1\frac{1}{2}$ cm deep in the phantom material. While the use of a phantom for calibration is a simple device which increases the reliability of uptake measurements under all circumstances, many laboratories still work without a phantom (calibrating with the reference source in air) or with an inadequate phantom. Under these circumstances the errors of calibration can be reduced by reducing the sensitivity of the counter to scattered radiation. This can be achieved by adding a lead filter of a few millimeters ($\frac{1}{32}$ to $\frac{1}{16}$ inch) thickness in front of the counter or by using a gamma-ray spectrometer. The price of the simplification of the calibration set-up is: 1, the reduction of sensitivity by a factor of two or more, due to absorption of radiation by the filter, and 2, an increase of errors due to the uncertainty in the location of the thyroid gland.

The measurement of the patient takes usually two to ten minutes, and it is of course essential that the patient does not change position during this interval. Perhaps the easiest way to achieve this is to have the uptake set-up arranged so that the patient lies down; in a sitting patient, suitable immobilization of head and neck has to be provided.

One specific counter arrangement should be mentioned in this connection, since it potentially not only eliminates the dependence of uptake measurements on the position of the patient, but also reduces to some degree the influence of the thyroid gland location within the neck: this is a ring counter set-up where four counters are arranged around the neck of the patient so that he sits approximately in the middle of the counter array. The four counters are connected to a scaling circuit so that all counts are added and registered. The purpose of this arrangement is that if the source (or patient) moves and goes farther away from one or two of the counters, it comes closer to one or two of the other ones. In this way, the effects of changes in position on the observed counting rate tend to cancel out. This arrangement is rather expensive, and it appears that with some care, equally reliable uptake measurements are obtained with the simpler set-up using a single counter.

The sensitivity of an uptake set-up determines the tracer dose required for the measurement. A bismuth-coated Geiger-Mueller counter works satisfactorily down to about 10 microcuries. A scintillation counter can be used with doses smaller than 1 microcurie. For the measurement of blood iodine levels, which is finding widespread use, tracer doses of about 20 microcuries have to be used; with these doses the lower sensitivity of a Geiger-Mueller counter presents no disadvantage and it is frequently preferred to the scintillation counter because of lower cost and greater reliability. When radioiodine diagnostic procedures are required with children, the smallest dose possible with a scintillation counter is of significant advantage. However, even with a Geiger-Mueller counter it is possible to measure uptake with a 1 μc tracer dose, when the standard working distance is reduced. Table 23 illustrates calibration factors, background and precision of two representative instruments.

Table 23.—Methods of Measuring I[131] Uptake in the Thyroid Gland

Radiation Detector	Working Distance cm	Background c/s	Calibration Factor c/s for 1 μc	Precision* μc
Bismuth-coated Geiger-Mueller Counter	23	1	1.8	0.15
Thallium activated NaI Crystal, 1 inch diameter, 1 inch high	20	12	39	0.02

*See explanation to table 20, page 250.

A problem closely related to the determination of the radioactive iodine uptake by the thyroid gland is the measurement of the uptake in a functioning metastasis of thyroid cancer. The difference is only the location of the deposit. The uncertainty about the size and location can be greater than with the thyroid gland. When x-ray films offer a guide in this respect, it is sometimes possible to construct a phantom (water or masonite) to obtain an approximate value for the combined absorption and scatter. As a rule, a lower reliability is acceptable for this purpose, and a simple correction for distance of the lesion from the skin is found satisfactory.

However complex the discussed uptake measurements may appear, one complicating factor has still been neglected, the radiation due to the presence of radioactive material in the other parts of the body and particularly in the circulating blood. This complication may be ignored when uptake measurements are done twenty-four hours after the administration of the tracer dose, since after that time, no significant activity is present outside of the gland. When measurements have to be done earlier, it may be necessary to use additional shielding of the counter from the rest of the body and to take into account the activity in the blood within the field of view of the counter.

A quite effective device to account for the contribution to the observed counting rate by the radioactivity from the body is to measure this contribution by shielding the organ under investigation with a few inches of lead. This will cut out most of the radiation from the organ itself, and the remaining counting rate is total background (conventional background plus contribution from the rest of the body). When this total background is subtracted from the observed gross counts without the added shield, a more nearly correct net counting rate is obtained.

It is more difficult to establish the contribution of the radioactivity in the circulating blood in the tissues surrounding the observed organ and also within the organ itself. The solution can be found by observing the activity in another part of the body which itself has no biochemical uptake of the particular element or compound used. This measurement gives a counting rate which is proportional to the blood level of the radioactive material, and if the ratio between blood volume in this part of the body (the thigh for instance) and the region under investigation (the thyroid gland and the neck for instance) is known, the contribution due to blood can be calculated and deducted from the measurement over the organ. This ratio can be established by using a compound which is not taken up by the examined organ (for the thyroid gland, iodinated serum protein may be used, or the uptake of iodine in the gland can be blocked by Lugol's solution). An average value for the ratio can be obtained by studying a few individuals in the manner described.

The need for the quantitative determination of deposit of other radioactive isotopes within other organs in the body is not frequent. When it is, the approach is similar to the measurement of iodine uptake in the thyroid gland.

A special problem is the uptake of P^{32} in eye tumors. Due to the short range of the beta radiation and the small size of the organ, small thin-window or thin-wall counters can be used without additional shielding. The quantitiative reliability of the results is low, but the information required is actually only presence or absence of a significant increase in counting rate over the tumor, as compared to normal areas, so that the relatively crude results are of sufficient diagnostic value.

High energy β-emitting isotopes, like P^{32} and Y^{90} can be counted also *in vivo* by Bremsstrahlung with a Geiger Mueller or preferably a scintillation counter. Since the photon energy of Bremsstrahlung has a very wide range, and depends on the atomic number of the absorbing material, it is not easy to calibrate reliably a counting arrangement for this purpose. Careful construction of suitable phantoms is essential.

In vivo counting is basically identical to *in vitro* counting, when the amount of activity in the whole body ("body burden") has to be measured. The only difference is the size of the sample, which presents two distinct specific problems.

1. The counting assembly becomes large. This has the consequence that a simple well-type counter cannot be constructed from a solid crystal. Liquid scintillators have been used in a hollow metal cylinder large enough for a human subject to be placed in the center. A large number of photo-tubes must be used with such a cylinder in a complex mixing circuit. A single detector at a distance from the body can also be used. In order to reduce the effect of varying distance of different parts of the body, such crystal has to be placed fairly far away from the body and the body must be given a curved position to approximate its shape to the segment of a circle with the detector as center. Since counting efficiency becomes smaller with increased distance, a large crystal with a correspondingly large photo-multiplier tube must be used to compensate for this. The shielding must enclose patient and detector, so that the necessary shield has the size of a small room. All these factors combined make a whole-body counter a very expensive instrument.

2. Self-absorption was neglected in γ-counting for *in vitro* samples. Due to the large sample size in whole-body counting, self-absorption is significant. It can amount to a 25% correction in a large dog and will be even higher in man.

Whole-body counters can be made sufficiently sensitive to measure the activity of naturally occurring radioactive isotopes. In order to utilize such high sensitivity in tracer work, γ-ray spectrometers must be used to separate the tracer from radioactive materials not normally present in the human body (whether naturally occurring or from fall-out). In such use the solid crystals are preferable to liquid scintillators, since they have a better spectrometric resolution.

17

Observation of the Time Factor in Physiological Processes by Radioactive Tracers

THE measurements discussed so far were concerned with the determination of radioactivity at a certain instant. The samples were obtained in some way and at a given time, and the deposits within the body were observed under the tacit assumption that they did not change during the period of observation. Physiological processes, however, are not static but are subject to change with time, and this change is frequently a significant parameter in their understanding and in the evaluation of whether they are normal or disturbed by disease.

As a rule the biochemical processes are in a state of dynamic equilibrium; metabolic utilization and breakdown of any given compound, however simple or complex, is continuously counteracted by reconstruction from materials taken into the body, so that whatever is eliminated is replenished to insure the *status quo*. When a compound which plays a role in this metabolic equilibrium is tagged by a radioactive tracer, its passage through the phases of the dynamic equilibrium becomes detectable and the continuous changes which constitute the complex metabolic equilibrium become accessible to observation.

This possibility of observing the time sequence in metabolic processes is one of the valuable potentialities of radioactive tracers, and therefore the techniques in the observation of radioactivity within the body, as it changes with time, are of great importance.

In addition to metabolic and biochemical processes, there are other processes within the body which are characterized by their dynamic parameters; some are quite complex, as for instance formation of blood cells; some are relatively simple, as for instance cardiac action and blood circulation, or resorptive processes in and from various tissues and organs.

The particular techniques which are most suitable for a given problem are best classified by the speed of the physiological changes to be observed; a practical division for the purpose of discussion is, (1) Slow changes occurring over periods of days, (2) Changes of intermediate speed, occurring over a period of hours, and (3) Rapid changes reaching an equilibrium value in seconds and minutes.

1. *Slow Changes.* When the changes under observation occur over a period of days, the techniques are for practical purposes identical with the quantitative *in vitro* or *in vivo* measurements. Let us take as an example

the determination of the effective half-life of P^{32} in the body. If the administered dose is known, the easiest method is the daily collection of excreta and their measurement by a suitable *in vitro* method. When the daily value for the total dose administered minus total excretion up to that day is plotted, enough points will be obtained to evaluate the curve quantitatively. If correction for physical decay is made, a curve for biological decay will be obtained. If the collections and measurements were made each in weekly intervals, some significant characteristics of the phosphorus behavior would have been lost, since the excretion is faster during the first few days than later; this initial phase could have been overlooked in weekly measurements. This points up the necessity of determining the required frequency of measurements by the physiological characteristics of the phenomenon under observation.

Another example may illustrate this. Let us consider the determination of the effective half-life of I^{131} in the thyroid gland. The uptake phase is over about twenty-four hours after the administration of a dose. The elimination has an effective half-life which varies between three and six days. Daily measurements are adequate and they will give the necessary number of points. The required technique will be, therefore, simply daily "uptake" measurements. When the problem is not only the determination of elimination of iodine by the thyroid gland, but also the speed of uptake or build-up, measurements will have to be done more frequently, at least every hour. More frequent observations would be also necessary, if instead of I^{131} an iodine isotope of shorter half-life such as I^{132} were used. If the problem is limited only to the question of when the maximum uptake occurs, the measurements will have to be repeated every few hours or oftener. If the question is the shape of the initial rapid phase of the uptake curve (a problem relevant in some clinical diagnostic tests), the measurements have to be done every few minutes, and different techniques than simple uptake measurements become necessary. Figure 76 illustrates graphically the differences in handling these questions in our example.

The build-up of protein bound iodine in the blood is a slow process, occurring over a period of days. Simple collection of samples once or twice daily and their assay by a suitable *in vitro* method gives enough data for a complete evaluation of the time sequence.

2. *Intermediate Speeds.* For the observation of the build-up of iodine in the thyroid gland it is necessary to make measurements at least several times during the first hour. While this is possible by ordinary uptake measurements with a scaling circuit, it becomes quite a laborious procedure when it is necessary to start the scaler, watch for it to finish the counting for the preset number of counts or the preset time, take down the reading and restart the scaler again without loss of time. The same situation obtains in a variety of tests, as for instance in liver function studies with iodine-tagged Rose Bengal. The use of an ordinary scaler with conventional reading methods is too arduous if such work is done frequently.

A good and reasonably inexpensive solution of this problem is a printing counter or a printing timer connected to an available scaling circuit, as described on page 194.

The speed of printing devices is limited, and the numerals do not follow the counts faster than about 10 per second. Electronic scaling stages of the circuit can be used to slow down the operation of the counter, but the intermediary counts are lost: if for instance a scaling factor of 100 is used, the numerals of the printer will jump every 100 counts and it can respond to counting rates up to 1000 per second. But if the printed result is in-

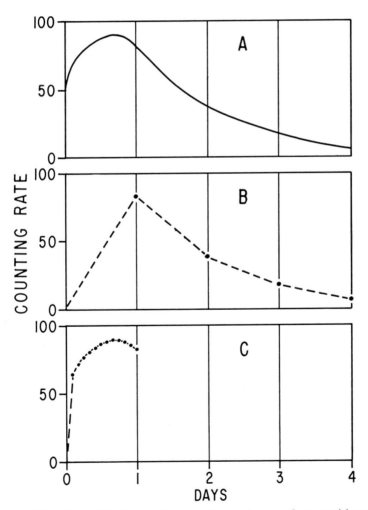

Fig. 76.—The effect of the interval between observations on the recognition of the shape of uptake and clearance curves. A: actual curve; B: daily observation represents well the elimination, but the uptake curve is distorted and the maximum seems to occur later than it actually does; C: hourly observations show correctly the time of maximum uptake, but the rapid initial rise appears to be slower than it is actually.

spected and is for instance 72, it is not known whether this means that a total of 7,200 or say 7,292 counts have accrued (92 counts will have appeared on the read-out lights, which do not enter the printer, since the mechanical printer was set to a scaling factor 100). It may seem therefore at first that no gain in statistical accuracy is achieved by using scaling factors in the counting circuit preceding the printer. This is not quite true, however, since circuit scaling "regularizes" the counts. What is meant will become clearer by an example. Let us assume a counting rate of 100 counts per second and a scaling factor of 64. We shall use a printing interval of one minute ("preset time"). The total counts accumulated for each "print" after each minute will be around 6,000 within statistical variations, and the statistical per cent error V will be according to equation (3) (p. 201) V = 1.3%. The printer will show probably one of the three numbers: 93, 94, or 95. The "correct" number which corresponds to 6000 counts is 94 (94 × 64 = 6016). The uncertainty here is ± 64 counts, or an error in printing of about 1 per cent This will combine with the statistical error to an overall error of about 1.6 per cent. We could have used the printing counter also without the counting rate reduction in the scaling circuit by reducing the sensitivity of the detector (for instance by using a longer distance from the body or by a lead filter). If we reduce the rate by these means to 10 counts per second and even neglect the resolving time of the printer at this speed, we shall accumulate 600 total counts each minute with a per cent error V = 4%, or a considerably higher error than was obtained by using scaling factors. Still the speed of printers is a limiting factor, and measurements at intervals shorter than a minute lose reliability regardless of the actual counting rate.

Time printers, which print continuously the elapsed time for a preset number of accumulated counts, are potentially somewhat faster. Their printing speed is also about one-tenth of a second, which means that in a ten-second interval, a timing error of 1 per cent is reached. This is usually satisfactory and the actual limits of accuracy will be set more frequently by the statistical errors in counts observed in this interval than by timing errors.

In spite of the advantage of the shorter time intervals which can be used with time printers and the constant statistical error inherent in the preset count methods, count printers with preset time intervals are generally preferred in observations of changes in time. This has to do with the necessity of plotting the results obtained by any print method on graph paper. With preset time, say one minute, the observed counts can be plotted easily as ordinates against one-minute divisions on the abscissa. For time printers with preset counts it is not only necessary to calculate the counting rate for each printed reading, but the abscissa for each point must be obtained by adding the total time elapsed since the beginning of the experiment; this procedure may become extremely tedious.

3. *Rapid Changes.* Some of the limitations of the printing methods have

been pointed out above. They can be summarized as, (a) Manual plotting of the data is required to obtain a graph; (b) The response speed is limited, and not more than a few readings per minute can be obtained. Both limitations are overcome when a recording rate-meter is used; this consists of a rate-meter (see page 195) which is connected to a strip chart recorder, on which the observed counting rates are plotted automatically as a curve.

The accuracy of a counting-rate recorder depends on counting statistics. It will be recalled that a rate-meter is basically a "preset time" device, where the preset time equivalent is twice the response time. The accuracy is therefore determined by the selected response time and the observed counting rate.

Although the recorded curve may appear smooth, it does not contain inherently more "points" than those corresponding to the response time. The response time must therefore be selected with reference to the speed of the changes in the physiological phenomenon. If the whole change occurs within say ten seconds, and at least 20 points must be available for interpretation, a response time of one-half second is required. As the next step, it has to be ascertained whether during this half-second enough counts will be observed to assure the required precision; this is a straightforward problem using equation (3). Let us assume that during the relevant period the counting rate is 200 counts per second; then 100 counts will be accumulated during each half-second interval and the error will be $V = 10\%$. This statistical error usually determines the shortest possible response time and therefore the fastest changes which can be recorded. The practical limitation in speed with rate recorders is not in the instrument itself but in counting statistics. This can be generally summarized by the statement that for the observation of rapid changes, high counting rates are needed which can be achieved by using high sensitivity detectors or large tracer doses, or both.

The convenience of having an instrument which performs by itself the plotting of the required curve brings up the question of why rate-meters and recorders are not used for observation of changes of activity of intermediate speeds. The answer to this lies partly in the technical characteristics of rate-meters and partly in counting statistics. Rate-meters have a response time which is limited in duration. Beyond a response time of a few minutes, electronic components become less reliable, so that in practical instruments response times much longer than that cannot be achieved. If the counting rate is high enough so that sufficient counts can be observed within the maximum available response time, this limitation is of no significance. But for observing slow changes, isotopes of relatively longer half-life have to be used, the total dose is more limited, counting rates usually become much lower and statistical fluctuation during the available response time too great. When this condition occurs, larger counting intervals are needed and printing timers or counters have to be used.

The decision between the selection of a printing device or of a rate recorder depends therefore on the expected counting rate and the needed frequency of readings (points on the curve). When more than a few readings per minute are required, a counting-rate recorder must be used. For the required frequency of readings, a sufficient counting rate is needed to keep the statistical errors within the required value. The counting-rate recorder can be used also for observation of slowly changing processes, if the counting rate is high enough so that a significant number of counts are accumulated within the longest response time available in the rate meter. If the counting rate for this interval is not high enough, printing devices have to be used which do not have this limitation.

A technical property of recording devices must be considered in the evaluation of the records obtained. The majority of recording instruments have a pen which deflects over an arc on the chart paper. This makes it sometimes very difficult to evaluate the slopes of the obtained curves. For this purpose, a rectilinear recording device is preferable, in which the deflection is perpendicular to the chart edge and linearly proportional to the observed magnitude. Such rectilinear recorders are available. When the physiological problem is less exacting, particularly if the essential information is simply at what time a maximum activity has occurred, as for instance in the determination of circulation time, the simpler non-rectilinear recorders are satisfactory.

Quite frequently the physiological changes observed by a tracer technique have an exponential build-up or clearance (decay) phase. In such cases the curves have to be replotted on semilogarithmic paper. This replotting can be eliminated if special amplifiers are used between the rate-meter and recorder which have a "logarithmic" response, and which therefore produce a deflection on the recorder not directly proportional to the counting rate but to its logarithm. In this way a curve is directly obtained which corresponds to a plot on semilogarithmic paper and "half-lives" or their biological equivalents can be obtained by simply using a straight-edge.

Shielding in Radiation Measurements for the Observation of Changes With Time.—One of the examples discussed in this section was the build-up of iodine in thyroid uptake and its clearance or elimination. It was mentioned that any uptake set-up can be used for this purpose with suitable counting apparatus. In some procedures for build-up and clearance measurements, it is neither necessary nor even desirable to have a radiation detector which "sees" the whole organ under examination, but it is sufficient when it sees only a sample or some fractional volume of this organ. This may have considerable advantages from the point of view of shielding. The field of view of the detector can be made narrower, so that the background is reduced and the measurements made more reliable and less dependent on the activity present in the circulating blood of surrounding tissues. The advantages of this arrangement become clear if, as an example, liver function tests with radioactive tracers are considered. A shielded enclosure seeing the whole of the liver would be not only extremely heavy, but also of such dimensions that the heart itself could not be wholly excluded. Valid rate observations can be performed better without sacrificing any physiologically relevant factors, when the detector sees only a small part of the liver and excludes other organs in the vicinity. The necessary narrowing of the field of view of the detector can be achieved by a collimating shield, which will be discussed in detail in the next chapter. The suitability of a particular collimator is determined by the physiological conditions of the experiment. In the case of liver tests just mentioned, a narrow collimator, provided it has adequate sensitivity, is desirable. When observing the clearance rate of a deposit of radioactive sodium from the tissues, it must be made sure that the collimator sees all of this original deposit and is not so directional that small movements of the patient take the deposit outside the field of view of the counter and so simulate a misleadingly fast clearance rate.

18

Determination of Isotope Distribution within the Body

BIOCHEMICAL affinity of some organs and tumors for some specific elements or their compounds leads to the concentration and deposition of these materials within such tissues. When radioactive elements are used for tagging these compounds, a deposit of higher concentration is found at such sites than elsewhere in the body. The ratio between the specific activity found in the organ or tissues under investigation and the specific activity elsewhere is called differential uptake. In preceding chapters, the determination of the amount of radioactivity in the body or the time sequence of its accumulation was discussed. In this chapter a different use of the radioactivity detectable in these deposits will be presented, namely the determination of their location and shape, since this anatomical information is of as great potential use as the functional information discussed so far.

A radioactive deposit can be compared to a luminous body within a semitransparent, absorbing and diffusing medium; ionizing radiation is partially absorbed and scattered, but it also penetrates body tissues. Its presence cannot be detected by the eye, but it can be observed by radiation detectors.

In using such a detector to find a discrete source of radioactive material inside the body or in any accessible position, the first step is a direct application of the inverse square rule. That is, the closer a detector is to a source of radiation, the greater is the radiation intensity impinging on the detector and the higher the counting rate. This permits the location of lost or misplaced radium, for instance in a room or even in a building, and is one of the basic methods in prospecting for radioactive minerals. The detector must have two properties: it must be easily movable and the change of counting rate must be made conveniently and rapidly detectable. Precision requirements are low (presence or absence of a change is all the information needed), but sensitivity requirements are high.

When a large area (room or building) has to be explored, it is necessary that the whole detector and accessory circuits be portable; battery-powered instruments are extensively used for this purpose When the task is the exploration of radioactivity in the human body or in an organ, only the detector proper has to be mobile, and a detector "probe," connected to the stationary circuit by a flexible cable is a convenient instrument.

Ease of observing an increase or decrease of the radiation level as the detector is moved can be achieved in several ways. A rate-meter shows changes on a scale; a neon bulb which flashes at every count gives a rough but frequently adequate indication of counting-rate changes. Visual indicators have a disadvantage; the eye must shift from watching the position of the detector probe to the indicating instrument and back. An audible signal, such as clicks in a loudspeaker or a headphone, overcomes this disadvantage. Audible signals are preferable to visual ones also because the ear can follow a higher rate of clicks than the eye can of flashes. For occasional use, an ordinary scaling circuit which contains an electromagnetic digital counter can be adapted to auditory indication, since the electromagnetic counters give audible clicks when they operate. All that is necessary is to select a scaling factor in such a way that the highest counting rate encountered does not exceed the resolving time of the register and block it. This improvised arrangement does not take advantage of the great frequency range of the human ear, since the speed of the mechanical register is a limiting factor. It can also lead to mistakes in localization; if the detector comes suddenly close to a radioactive source, the counting rate may exceed the resolving time of the register so quickly that it becomes blocked before the transition to the higher counting rate can be noticed; when this occurs, the radioactive deposit will be missed. When this arrangement is used, the detector must be moved slowly while exploring an area, so that blocking can be anticipated.

Probe detectors of this type have been made and are used during surgical exploration for brain tumors and occasionally to check completeness of a thyroidectomy. Geiger-Mueller counters about $\frac{1}{8}$ inch in diameter and a few inches long, with thin stainless steel walls, have been constructed, which are sensitive to P^{32} beta radiation. Scintillation counters are also constructed as probe detectors, by using a small crystal connected optically to a phototube by a plastic light-pipe; this permits having the crystal several inches away from the phototube with a sufficiently thin and long probe.

Localization by "inverse square" has serious limitations. It is restricted practically to the rough localization of a single deposit. If there are two sources of radiation not far apart, within the body, it is usually impossible to distinguish them, and a more refined technique is needed.

The ideal solution is to obtain a complete image of the "luminescent" radioactive deposit, as is possible in photography with visible light by using an optical system. The only optical system useful with gamma rays is the pinhole camera. It will be briefly discussed later in this chapter.

A practical solution is to enclose a radiation detector in a tube with thick and heavy walls. Radiation emitted by a radioactive source can reach such a shielded detector only when it is located in the axis of the tube; when the source is sufficiently far off this axis, the shielding walls will absorb the radiation and no counts will be observed. Figure 77 illus-

19

trates this.   Such a collimated detector sees radiation sources only when
they are within a limited field of view, which is determined by the geometry
of the counter and collimator and the absorption by the shield material of
the particular energy of radiation.   Source A will be seen *in toto* by the
detector in the illustration.   Source B will be seen only so far as its radiation
penetrates the collimating shield.

A collimated counter of this construction therefore has directional properties, and can be used to localize a single radioactive deposit even if there

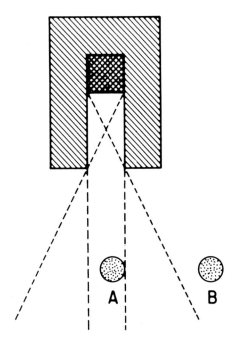

Fig. 77.—Directional sensitivity of a collimated radiation detector.   Source B is
shielded from the detector and the counting rate is small compared to that due to source
A, assuming they have the same activity.

are several in a region, provided that they are sufficiently far apart so as
not to appear together within the viewing angle of the detector.

When a collimated detector is used to search out a relatively small
radioactive deposit in the body, collimation and the inverse square rule
have important functions: that is, it is sensitive predominantly within its
viewing angle and the counting rate increases with decreasing distance
from the source.   A small detector of this sort, for instance a bismuth
coated Geiger-Mueller tube with a lead shield and an opening of $\frac{1}{2}$ to 1 inch,
can be made weighing a few pounds.   It can be used freehand, without a
stand, to search for thyroid metastases after a tracer dose of a few hundred
microcuries of radioactive iodine has been given, and it is a valuable tool for

preliminary orientation.   Its precision in the localization of a deposit and
in the determination of its shape is low because of its poor resolving power.

The resolving power of a collimated detector may be defined as the
distance at which two small sources of radiation can be separated from
each other, that is, detected as distinct deposits. When their distance apart
is less than this "resolving power," they will be seen as a single source.

In Figure 77, let us investigate whether or not the sources A and B will
be distinguished separately with the illustrated arrangement. To discuss
this question, the viewing angle of the detector must be examined in more
detail.

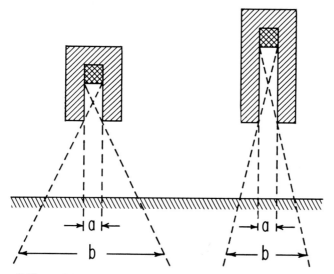

Fig. 78.—Collimated detector.   Maximum sensitivity is in the region b; reduced sensitivity in the region b; minimum sensitivity outside of region b. Region a is determined
by the size of the collimating hole; it is the same on the left and right diagram. Region b
is smaller on the right than on the left and is determined by the depth of the hole.

In Figure 78 a collimated detector "looks" at a plane surface. By examin-
ing the area designated as "a" in this figure in relation to the detector
itself, it will be realized that any small source of radiation within this area
will be seen by any point within the detector, so that movement of a source
within this field will not change the counting rate. If the source is positioned somewhere outside "a," but within the area "b," only part of the
detector will see it, and other parts will be shielded from the source by the
collimating shield. The farther the source is from the area "a," the greater
will this effect be, and the smaller the counting rate. When finally the
source is moved beyond the area "b," no radiation will reach the detector
except that which actually passes through the collimating shield.

If the right and left diagrams of Figure 78 are compared, it can be seen
that the extent of the area "a" is determined only by the diameter of the

collimating hole, and that the area "b" depends not only on the diameter of the collimating hole but also on the depth of the detector within the collimator, and the distance from the source. If the collimator comes closer to the surface of the source, the extent of area "a" will remain unchanged, but the area "b" will be reduced: the overall angle of view of the collimator will become smaller and the resolving power better.

We can say now generally that the resolving power will be the better, the smaller the collimating hole is, the deeper the detector is positioned

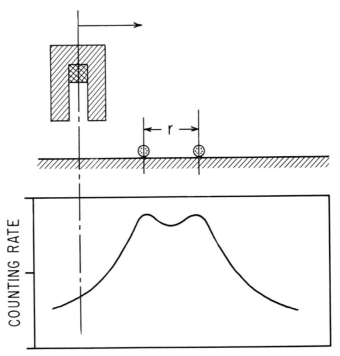

Fig. 79.—Linear scan with a collimated detector of two sources spaced 2 cm from each other, at a given distance between the plane of the sources and the collimator.

within the collimator, the thicker the walls of the collimator are, and the closer the collimator is to the source. It is quite difficult to determine for a given collimator the areas "a" and "b," and the effect of given wall thickness by calculation, and an empirical test is advisable in order to find the overall resolving power of any individual assembly. The experimental arrangement is illustrated in Figure 79. Two small radioactive sources are placed on a surface at a distance r from each other, and a collimating counter suspended at a fixed distance over them in such a manner that it can be moved by desired amounts along the line defined by the two sources. The distance by which the counter is moved at each step should be of the same order of magnitude as the diameter of the collimating hole (a practical

figure is half the hole diameter for each step). The counting rate is determined for each position of the counter as it scans step by step along the line
through the two sources, and these counting rates are plotted as ordinates,
against the counter positions as abscissa.

Figure 80 gives three such plots for different distances r of the sources
from each other. At first inspection the conclusion will be that when the
sources are 2 cm apart they are detectable as separate, and that at 1 cm

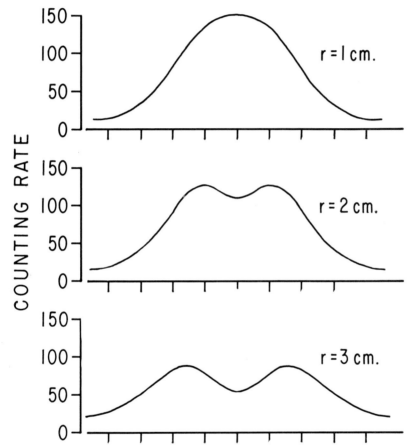

Fig. 80.—Linear scan of two sources spaced 1, 2, and 3 cm. apart. Resolving power
of the collimated detector appears to be about 2 cm.

they seem to fuse into a single source, hence the resolving power is 2 cm.
This conclusion may be misleading, however, since we have to consider
whether the observed dip in the curve is statistically significant or not;
if it is not, its occurrence may be accidental and it may not appear when
the experiment is repeated. The standard deviation of the counting rate
at the adjoining peaks has to be evaluated, therefore, and the dip in the
curve can be accepted as valid only if it exceeds the standard deviation.

This consideration is of considerable practical consequence. The per cent standard deviation decreases with the total number of counts accumulated; this number is greater, the longer the time used for counting and the higher the observed counting rate. The smaller the per cent error, the greater is the significance of a relatively small dip in the curve when two sources are being studied, hence the greater the resolution of the counter. The resolution of a given collimating counter thus depends not only on its construction, but also on the time used for counting, or the tracer dose used, and on the sensitivity of the counter. These three factors are closely interrelated.

To add the final complication to the discussion of this problem, let us consider what happens when the attempt is made to increase the resolving power by using smaller and deeper holes in the collimator. As a rule, we do not have within the body deposits of radioactive materials of very small dimensions. A collimator with a large hole sees a larger volume and therefore a larger fraction of the total radioactivity than when the angle of view is restricted by the size and depth of the hole. With smaller holes, low counting rates and larger statistical errors result; the effective resolving power is reduced, so that the geometrical gain may be lost, unless high tracer doses or long counting times are used.

Since consideration of radiation damage to the patient as a rule limits the tracer dose which can be used, a practical compromise in the construction of a collimating detector and in the counting statistics has to be reached.

For collimated Geiger-Mueller counters the hole size ranges between $\frac{1}{2}$ and 1 inch. For scintillation counters, because of their higher sensitivity, the hole size can be made smaller, and it ranges usually between $\frac{1}{4}$ and $\frac{1}{2}$ inch. The resulting practical resolving powers range between 2 and 4 cm. Maximal resolution is not always a desirable property. In a preliminary manual survey for radioactive deposits, particularly for thyroid metastases, it is easy to miss a small lesion when collimation is too good: the rise in counting rate may occur and disappear too quickly to be noticed under these conditions. It is advisable therefore to use moderate collimation ($\frac{3}{4}$ to 1 inch hole) for a preliminary survey, and maximal collimation for a careful examination of the active deposit, which has been roughly localized by the coarser method. If two different counters with suitable collimation are not available, it is possible to have a counter with different collimating adapters which can be readily interchanged. The assembly will be too heavy to be moved by hand, but flexible stands are available which support the detector and shield and permit moving the assembly with sufficient ease.

Manual Scanning.—The detailed examination of radioactive deposits consists basically in determing the counting rate over the surface of the body at as many points on the body surface as possible using a collimated counter that is, by some method of scanning. Although at present automatic scanning is gradually replacing the manual method, the latter will be discussed at first in some detail. It requires much less expensive

instrumentation and will therefore continue to be useful in smaller laboratories, also it is easier to understand, so that the transition to the automatic techniques becomes simpler.

Let us start with the example of a thyroid gland and an adjoining nodule,
which appears by palpation to be about $\frac{3}{4}$ of an inch away from the body
of the gland, and which may be a lymph node or aberrant thyroid tissue. Is
or is not this nodule functioning in the sense that it takes up iodine? The
locations of the gland and of the nodule are known. A line is drawn which
goes through the nodule and the gland, and a collimated counter, with a
$\frac{1}{4}$ inch resolving power, for instance, is now positioned over the thyroid
gland. It should be as close to the skin as possible; it will be recalled by
inspecting Figure 78 that the closer the counter, the better the resolution.
Some provision must be made to note and fix the position of the counter
over the neck (this may be achieved simply by affixing a ruler to the patient's
neck, or by having the counter suspension provided with distance marks).
The counting rate is determined in this position. The counter is then
moved by $\frac{1}{4}$ inch or less (resolving power is $\frac{1}{4}$ of an inch) in the direction
of the line pointing to the nodule, and another count is made. This is
continued until the counter has passed the nodule. The counting rates
are plotted against the corresponding distances. The curve will then indicate
by inspection the correlation between clinical findings and radioactive
uptake. If the counting rate dropped close to background when the counter
was moved beyond the margin of the thyroid gland and did not increase
again when the counter was over the nodule, there is no detectable activity
in this nodule. But if the counts went up over the nodule, particularly
if a drop in counting rate occurred in an intermediate position of the counter,
the nodule takes up iodine and behaves metabolically like active thyroid
tissue.

The limitation in determining this plot of counting rates along a line,
which has been called a "profile," is that it gives information along this
line only, and relevant information may be missed if an unsuitable line was
selected.

This becomes clearer if we consider a different problem, not the differentiation of two distinct anatomical locations, but the determination of
the extent and shape of a single organ with a radioactive deposit. There is
no particular line along which the information should be collected. We deal
with an area, all points of which, particularly along the borders, are relevant.
Linear manual scanning can still be used, but it has to be done along a
series of parallel lines, so that the whole organ is explored. A profile for
each line can be plotted, this procedure is sometimes useful. A better
evaluation of the results is obtained if the counting rates are noted down on
graph paper at each point at which counts were obtained, and if then all
the points with the same counting rates are connected by lines. Such
isocount lines will then represent the shape and distribution of radioactivity, in the way that altitude lines on a geographical map represent

hills or mountains. This procedure is quite laborious, and for this purpose automatic scanning is unquestionably superior in routine work.

In any method using collimated counters, the resolving power is lowered to some extent by scattered radiation, since secondary radiation is emitted not only from the site of the radioactive deposit, but also from surrounding tissues which are traversed by the primary radiation from the deposit. If a border of a deposit is considered, the effect of the scattered radiation as seen by the counter is to simulate the presence of radioactive material beyond this border. The organ therefore appears larger to the counter, and its borders more diffuse. This effect of scattered radiation can be eliminated by using a gamma ray spectrometer, which was mentioned on page 277, since scattered radiation has longer wavelengths, that is lower energy, than the original gamma rays emitted by the isotope. The purpose of the spectrometer is to eliminate the diffuse scattered radiation only; the window or slit width can therefore be quite wide; actually it can be made "open" towards the higher energy end of the spectrum, so that in effect only the low-energy discriminator setting is used and adjusted to eliminate scattered radiation. This technique improves the resolution of a directional counter significantly and has the additional advantage of reducing the background.

While scattered radiation and its deleterious influence on resolution can be eliminated by the use of a spectrometer, there is another interfering effect which cannot be reduced by instrumental devices; this is the presence of the radioactive tracer material in the circulating blood or surrounding tissues. An extreme case of such interference is readily understood, when there is a very small differential uptake by the organ of interest. Under such conditions, it is obvious that no spatial information can be obtained. The higher the preferential uptake by the organ under investigation, as compared to circulating blood and surrounding tissues, the better will be its delineation. Increase of differential uptake is not a problem to be solved by physical instrumentation, but by physiological and biochemical methods. To give an example: when a tracer dose is administered, which is taken up by the organ or tissues to be investigated, it will frequently be found that at some specific time a maximum uptake is found in this organ, while a minimum concentration exists in the surrounding tissues. In the case of the thyroid gland it is simple to select the optimal working time; after twenty-four hours there is a minimum of radioactive iodine left in the circulating blood, so that there is optimum difference between the activity in the gland and elsewhere in the body. This difference remains unchanged for several days. In such a situation the suitable period for scanning is long and not critical. In the case of brain tumor localization with I[131] tagged diiodofluorescein, the situation is different; the optimal differential uptake, which occurs a short time after the tracer dose administration, is rather rapidly reduced (the radioactive material, concentrated at first significantly in the tumor tissues, diffuses into the other parts of the brain). Observations have to be made during this interval of maximum concentration. To do this, the time sequence of concentration has to be known, and the experiment arranged accordingly. With iodinated serum protein the concentration in brain tumors is maintained much longer. Selection of a suitable isotopic material, and the chemical compound which is used, depend not only on suitable physical qualities of radiation emitted by the isotope, but also on the physiological and biochemical behavior. It is desirable to have maximal differential uptake by the tissues to be examined, and sufficiently long maintenance of such uptake to allow enough time to do the measurements.

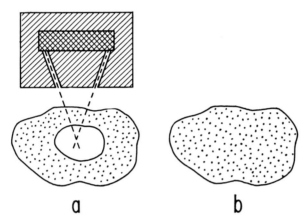

a   b

Fig. 81.—Depth sensitive collimated detector. Organ *a* will give a lower counting rate in the illustrated position than would be obtained with organ *b*: the filling defect in organ *a* is detectable.

The straight collimators which have been discussed so far have one basic shortcoming, they have directional sense, but no sense of depth; they are not able to supply information on how deep a radioactive deposit is within the body. This limitation may be important if we consider for instance a radioactive deposit which has a "filling defect," as occurs in the thyroid gland when a non-functioning cyst or tumor is located within normal tissues. Figure 81a illustrates this schematically. If the two bodies are scanned in the usual manner, the profiles will be similar except that the one for 81a will be somewhat flatter than for 81b.

More complex collimators have been designed to handle this problem, with a series of holes which are angled towards a point of convergence outside of the counter. A simplified diagram of such a collimator is given in Figure 81. Two collimating holes only are drawn; they converge at the level of the filling defect. If this deposit is now scanned with such a counter, the filling defect will be detectable, since radiation emitted by the radioactivity above and below the defect will be shielded from the detector proper by the slant of the collimating holes. A collimator of this type can effectively

scan a layer of tissues and different layers can be explored by changing the
height of the collimator over the body.

The angulated holes have to be quite narrow in order to be effective;
this reduces the sensitivity considerably. In order to overcome the excessive
loss of sensitivity, a honeycomb system of such holes is used, all converging
towards the same point. Figure 82 shows the variations of sensitivity due
to change in distance between detector and source for a straight bore and a
conical collimator. It will be noted that even with a 61 hole collimator the
discrimination with depth is not impressive: maximum sensitivity is at

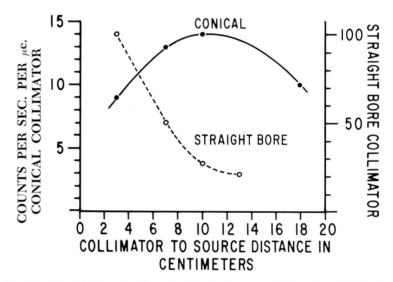

Fig. 82.—Sensitivity as function of collimator to source distance for a 61 hole focusing
collimator, 5 cm long (solid line), and for a collimator with a straight bore of 3 inch diameter, 5 cm long (dotted line). Plotted from data on page 104 of Handbook 80 (see
footnote page 205). Ordinate scale markings in counts per second for 1 μc.

10 cm; a change in distance of 2 cm results in less than 10% change in counting rate. The main result of the conical collimation is a reduction of the
inverse square effect, which is clearly seen in the curve for the straight bore
collimator. Considerable improvement is possible by using for the collimator materials which have very high absorption coefficients, such as tungsten
or gold. Machining of tungsten is difficult, so that tungsten as well as gold
conical collimators are too expensive for general use.

Automatic Scanning.—A complete image of a radioactive deposit, that
is of an organ showing differential uptake, can be achieved by manual
scanning and plotting of isocount lines. In order to obtain such an image
more directly, instruments have been designed which perform the scanning
and plotting automatically. Besides a collimated detector and a
scaling circuit, a scanning apparatus has two essential components: (1)

the scanning device proper, that is an arrangement to move the detector in a plane over the patient's body in such a way that the whole surface is explored with sufficient detail, and (2) an image-forming device which presents the results of counting in a visually meaningful way.

1. Most *scanning devices* are designed basically on the same principle. The collimated detector is moved in a straight line, for a selected distance; after it has reached the end of the preset motion, the whole carriage is shifted parallel to itself by a selected distance and the counter starts to move in the opposite direction along this new line, until it has reached the set limit. The carriage then shifts again by the same amount, the counter reverses its direction of travel again and this process is continued until all of the area to be examined has been scanned. The more slowly the counter moves along its carriage, and the smaller the shifts of the carriage, the more detailed will be the information obtained on the shape of the radioactive deposit. This is limited of course by the resolution inherent in the collimator itself. Speed of travel and carriage shift have to be adjusted, therefore, to the resolution. If this resolution is for instance $\frac{1}{4}$ inch, the carriage shift will be adjusted to a similar distance; much smaller shifts will not add to the reliability of the result, but will only increase the time to complete the scanning operation. The speed of counter travel will also depend on the resolution of the counter and on the counting rate. The relevant time during which a counter collects counts with reference to a given point over the organ is determined by resolution and travel speed. Let us assume that the resolution is $\frac{1}{2}$ inch, and travel speed 10 inches per minute; this means that the counter will traverse $\frac{1}{2}$ inch, corresponding to its field of view or resolution, in three seconds. This three-second interval will correspond functionally to a preset time. If the average counting rate is 10 per second, the counting circuit will accumulate 30 counts, and the information, visual or otherwise, will be of low reliability.

It appears therefore that for highest reliability slow travel speeds of counters on a scanning device are essential. If the speeds are made too slow, the scanning operation may take a long time and a new factor may counteract the sharpness of the ultimate image, namely patient motion. This is the same situation as in diagnostic radiology where longer exposure times result in blurred x-ray images because of such motion. In practice, the time during which the patient can be reasonably well immobilized is limited. The requirements for immobilization are less stringent than in radiography, since the resolving power of an x-ray image is about $\frac{1}{3}$ of a millimeter, whereas the resolving power of a collimated counter is a few millimeters at best. The practical limit of scanning time, therefore, is perhaps about twenty to thirty minutes. Counting statistics can be improved of course by higher tracer doses; this has the usual limitations due to potential radiation damage involved.

For the same travel speed of the counter, the overall scanning time depends on the total area explored. This area should therefore be limited to the actually relevant extent. Adjustable stops are provided on scanning devices for this purpose. By limiting the scanning field, it is sometimes possible to reduce the travel speed of the counter and to improve the resulting image.

2. *Image Forming Devices.* When the collimated detector scans a body area for radioactivity, the observed counting rate is characteristic for the spot which it is traversing. The simplest way to obtain an image is to connect the detector rigidly to a marking device so that this traverses a sheet of paper in the same manner that the detector traverses the body area.

Most marking devices in use at present employ an electromagnetic dot printer which makes a dot or a short line on the paper whenever an electrical impulse is applied to the electromagnet. This impulse is produced in a scaling circuit in the same way that the circuit operates an electromagnetic digital counter; after a preset number of counts have been accumulated in the electronic scaling stages, a relay is closed and an electrical pulse is produced which is strong enough to actuate the electromagnet, either of the digital counter of or the dot printer over the paper.

This arrangement is therefore essentially a preset count procedure. Instead of indicating the elapsed time in seconds, the elapsed time is represented by the distance between two adjoining dots made on paper, since the counter travels at a constant speed. The higher the counting rate, the shorter is the elapsed time and the closer will the dots be on the paper. The visual result is similar to a halftone print; the apparent density of a line will be inversely proportional to the spacing between the dots and proportional to the observed counting rate. When the counter carriage is shifted after the completion of a traverse along one line, a second line is printed in a similar way and an overall image is formed by the grid pattern of lines with varying densities. (For illustrations of such patterns see Silver, *Radioactive Isotopes in Medicine and Biology*, pages 77ff and 160.)

In the use of scanning devices, the question frequently arises, what scaling factor in the circuit should be selected. The first consideration is of course the resolving time, that is the speed of the dot printing electromagnet, which is limited to between 10 and 20 impulses per second. If the scaling factor in the circuit is so low that output pulses are more frequent than this, the printer will jam and instead of a line of maximal density, a blank will appear. There is, however, a second limiting factor, and that is the dot size and counter travel speed. Let us assume that the counter speed is 3 mm per second and the dot size is $\frac{1}{2}$ mm. If the counting rate and scaling factors are such that a printing impulse occurs 6 times per second, the printed dots will be adjacent to each other and a maximal density line will be obtained. A higher impulse rate will not give them a denser line, and in order to have optimal information on the image, it is recommended that the scaling factor be made sufficiently large so that at areas of maximum activity the dots are sufficiently spaced to appear as separate marks.

A significant improvement in image formation by scanning has been achieved recently by replacing the electromechanical dot-marking device with a photographic dot-printer. Instead of a dot-marking electromagnet, a small neon bulb is activated by the scaler impulses. The light of the bulb, after passing through a limiting diaphragm, falls on a photographic film and appears after development as a dark dot. The lamp, the mechanism which couples it, the counter and the photographic film, must be of course in a lightproof housing.

The advantage of this photographic technique becomes apparent if the limitations of dot spacing in dot-marking devices are considered. With dot-marking, a maximum density is reached when the dots are adjacent; an increase of line density does not occur when counting rate increases and the dots become superimposed; a higher scaling factor must be used, at some expense of image quality over the areas of lower activity. This limitation does not hold for photographic dot recording, since the film density is doubled when a light pulse strikes the same spot of the emulsion twice. This type of image formation becomes identical to the image on a television tube, where the image is formed also by parallel line grid scanning, and where the light intensity (corresponding to the densities in the film) depends on the intensity in the corresponding object points. With photographic recording, the scaling factor is not limited by the area of maximum activity and it can be selected to best suit the overall levels.

The problems of resolution, collimation, depth sensitivity and scattered radiation in automatic scanning are identical to those encountered in manual scanning, with perhaps one exception. It has been mentioned that in manual scanning with counters of high resolution, that is maximal collimation, there is danger that a small radioactive concentration will be passed over too quickly for the counter to give a perceptible indication, so that this deposit may be missed. This risk is less with automatic scanning, which does not use judgment but explores every point with equal thoroughness. For this reason it is possible to use better collimators and obtain higher resolution with automatic scanning devices than by manual methods, considering the limitations of the reduced sensitivity and higher tracer doses required with better collimators.

Whole Body Scanning.—Given a sufficiently large travel area for the scanning detector, any automatic scanning device can explore and record the activity distribution in the whole body. With conventional tracer doses, however, it will take several hours to do this, and it is rarely possible to immobilize a patient long enough. By using multiple scanning heads with associated marking devices, the overall time is reduced. A whole body scanner with ten such counters scanning simultaneously will do the recording in one tenth of the time needed with a conventional one counter scanner.

Direct Image-Forming Devices.—There is one optical image-forming device which will work with γ radiation: a pinhole, as it was used in the classic camera obscura. In order to be effective for γ radiation, this hole must be made in material which will absorb a large fraction of impinging radiation; the sheet must be thick. The hole cannot be made too small, otherwise not enough radiation will go through. The resolution of this pinhole camera will be therefore quite limited. When film is used to record the image, exposure times are long, of the order of one hour, even when therapeutic doses of an isotope like I^{131} are used. Exposure time can be reduced by using a flat plate of a scintillating crystal as an intensifying screen in front of the film or by electronic intensifying systems.

Brain Tumor Localization.—The spherical shape of the head and the brain does not present a preferential plane for scanning. Localization in depth, that is three-dimensional localization of a tumor in the brain, is also of greater clinical importance than it is for instance in the localization of a

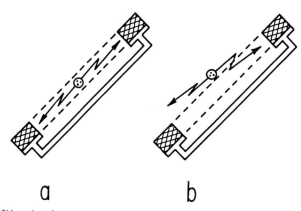

a   b

Fig. 83.—Directional property of two radiation detectors to a positron emitting source, when they are connected to a coincidence circuit; coincidence counts are observed only when a pulse occurs in both detectors simultaneously; this can take place only when the positron source is on the line connecting the two detectors (*a*) and not when the source is outside (*b*).

metastatic lesion of a thyroid gland. The attempts to obtain a more precise localization of an area with differential uptake in the brain have taken several directions.

Ordinary collimated counters and depth-sensitive counters with honeycomb collimating cones are used with a variety of scanning plans and mapping methods. Some are based on moving the directional counter not over a plane but over a spherical surface, concentric to the skull. Other methods scan the head in two parallel planes or in a frontal and a saggital plane, in order better to pinpoint the site of maximal activity in the brain. The scanning plans require considerable time and precise positioning of the collimators; automatic scanning is gradually replacing manual techniques.

The lower differential uptake of the brain tumors and the need for more precise localization have led to the introduction of a technique which has not been used in thyroid scanning. This technique is based on the physical properties of positron radiation, as it is emitted for instance by some radioactive isotopes of copper and arsenic. A positron combines with an electron practically immediately after being emitted and their mass is converted into annihilation radiation of 2 half-mev photons which go in opposite directions along a straight line (see page 76). If we consider a point source of a positron emitter and arrange two counters opposed to each other with the source between them, these counters can see the annihilation radiation simultaneously only when the source is on the line connecting them, as illustrated in Figure 83a. When the source is outside of this line (Fig. 83b), the two annihilation rays of the *same* positron will never impinge on both counters. It is possible of course for both counters to be activated simultaneously by annihilation rays originating from two different positrons emitted at the same time; this requires two accidental coincidences, and will not occur frequently. The counting circuit is arranged in such a way that a count is registered only when both counters produce a pulse simultaneously. Such a coincidence circuit has been described on page 196. Two counters, connected to a coincidence circuit and coupled rigidly by a mechanical device in a fixed relation to each other, are sensitive almost exclusively to positron emitters which are located on the line connecting them. This directional sensitivity can be even further improved by using a spectrometer with a channel covering the annihilation band only. If such a double coincidence counter arrangement is moved in the plane in which the source is located, a precise line of position for the source can be obtained. If the scanning is repeated in another such plane, a second line of position is obtained, and the intersection of the two lines will give quite a precise "fix" for the location of the source. This method has some additional and less obvious advantages besides the precise localization: the directional properties are not due to shielding collimators, the assembly can therefore be made lighter than a collimating counter; the coincidence circuit reduces the influence of radiation background and tube noise. The limitations with this technique are of a biological nature; the differential uptake by brain tumors is not very high and considerable radioactivity is present in normal surrounding tissues. Furthermore, most positron-emitters have quite short half-lives, which limits their usefulness essentially to the vicinity of installations where they can be produced.

19

Autoradiography

THE methods of obtaining information on the distribution of a radioactive isotope in the body described in the preceding chapter have the advantage of high sensitivity and of the speed with which the result becomes available. They have, however, two disadvantages, complex instrumentation and a resolving power which is limited at best to a fraction of an inch. The limited resolving power makes scanning methods useless when information about isotope distribution at the histological level is needed. This can be obtained by using photographic emulsions as radiation detectors. An image is formed on a photographic emulsion when it is placed in contact with the material containing a radioactive isotope. This technique is called *autoradiography*. The low sensitivity of films, as compared to nuclear counters, can be offset by long exposure times which are limited only by the half life of the isotope. Most of the radiation energy is emitted by radioactive disintegrations during the first and second half-lives (after 2 half-lives 75% of all disintegrations will have occurred). Longer exposures are, therefore of no practical value. For isotopes with long half-lives it may appear at first that the sensitivity of autoradiographic method is limited only by the available time. This is not true for two reasons.

1. Photographic emulsions do not keep indefinitely, they gradually develop fogging which is due to chemical changes and to radiation background. Chemical fogging can be delayed by storage at low temperature and low humidity, but even at ideal conditions 2 years is about the longest time an emulsion remains useful. 2. The latent image in the emulsion fades with time exponentially like the decay of a radioactive substance. In prolonged exposure to a radioactive material this latent image grows and decays like a radioactive daughter in a radioactive parent. In such growth the activity of a daughter product reaches a maximum value after a definite time. If we call this time (at which the latent image also will reach a maximum) t, the half-lives of the isotope used T_r and of the latent image T_e, the optimal exposure time can be calculated from the equation

$$t = 3.3 \frac{T_e T_r}{T_r - T_e} \log_{10} \left(\frac{T_r}{T_e}\right) \qquad (72)*$$

* From equation (4.2) on page 479 in Robley D. Evans, The Atomic Nucleus, McGraw-Hill Book Co., Inc., New York, 1955, by substituting half-life for average life and $\log_{10}$ for $\log_e$.

(304)

When the two half-lives are nearly equal that is $T_e \simeq T_r \simeq T$ an approximation to (72) is more convenient for the calculation of t:

$$t \simeq 1.44\sqrt{T_e T_r} \simeq 1.44T \tag{73}*$$

It will be recalled that 1.44T is called the average life (see page 34).

The fading of the latent image depends on the photographic emulsion, and the storage conditions; it is quite variable. Ordinary photographic films have a half-life of many months. The Kodak nuclear materials have as a rule a half-life of 30 days and there are some emulsions with a half-life of only 10 days. This information is usually available from the manufacturer.

As an example we shall determine optimal exposure time for P^{32} (half-life 14 days) with an emulsion of a half-life of 30 days. From (72):

$$t = 3.3 \times \frac{14 \times 30}{-16} \times \log \left(\frac{14}{30}\right) = 3.3\,(-26)\,(-0.33) = 29 \text{ days}$$

For I^{131} with $T_r = 8$ days we get in the same way optimal exposure at $t = 20$ days.

In these examples the optimal exposure time is about twice the half-life of the isotope, which is shorter than the half-life of the latent image.

For critical work, when maximum sensitivity is required, equations (72) and (73) should be used. For most practical work a simplified rule will suffice, which follows from these equations and from the consideration that most radiation (75%) will have been delivered in 2 half-lives of the radioactive material[†]: *expose for 1½ to 2 times the half-life of the radioactive material or of the half-life of the latent image, whichever is shorter.*

Frequently the radioactivity will be so high that overexposure will result when optimal time is used. Under such conditions shorter times will have to be used which can be estimated from the Tables 24 and 25, or by a preliminary experiment. An alternate method is to prepare several autoradiographs of the same specimen and to develop them at short intervals one after the other.

The basic elements of the photographic process were discussed on page 180f. It must now be considered how the distribution of the radioactive material becomes represented by the silver grains in the emulsion. If we examine a microscopically small deposit in a histological section (a point source) and consider the radiation emitted by this deposit impinging on an emulsion which is close to it, we shall expect to see an agglomeration of sliver grains. The density of these grains will be highest over the deposit, decreasing outward from this center. The image of the point source will be not a point, but a diffused disk. The smaller this disk, the truer will

*From equation (4.3) of Evans' reference, (p. 304).

† This applies approximately also for the build-up of an exponentially fading latent image.

20

be the image and the greater the resolution of a more complex source distribution, which can be considered as a multiplicity of point sources of varying intensity. The size of the diffusion disk will depend on several factors: 1, proximity of the film image to the histological section; 2, nature and range of the radiations emitted by the isotope; 3, grain structure and thickness of the photographic emulsion; 4, the method of development.

A point source emits radiation in all directions. The photographic emulsion will be exposed to this radiation with an intensity inversely proportional to the square of the distance from this point. The better the contact between the emulsion and the section, the greater will be the gradient of radiation intensity between the silver halide molecules directly above the radiation source and those at increasing distances away from it.

With a radioactive source, a second factor will contribute to the sharpness of the image. Most radioactive materials used in autoradiography are beta-emitters, or emit beta together with gamma radiation. Beta and alpha

Table 24.—Estimated Mean Range of Electrons in Nuclear Emulsions*

Nuclide	$\bar{E}(Mev)$	Range (Microns)
P32	0.69	800
I131	0.187	100
C14	0.049	10
H3	0.006	1

* Based on curves given by R. H. Herz, Nucleonics, 9:24–39 (1951).

radiations lose intensity not only because of increased distance between source and detector, but also because of their high absorption and limited range. On the other hand gamma radiation has no limited range, and its absorption in photographic emulsion is small. Beta rays show a much greater photographic effect than gamma rays. Both phenomena combine to help in improving the resolution in autoradiograms.

With soft beta radiation and good contact between film and section, the limits of resolving power in autoradiography are set by the range of the beta radiation and by the graininess of the photographic emulsion.

The ranges of some beta radiations are listed in Table 24, which indicates the limits of the resolution obtainable with the isotopes mentioned, even with the best possible photographic technique.

The graininess of the photographic image can be reduced to microscopic levels, but only at the expense of film sensitivity. It is a general property of emulsions that increased sensitivity is accompanied by a coarser grain structure. Most films have some natural fog level, which is in part inherent in the emulsion and in part due to background radiation, and increases with storage time. This fog interferes somewhat with the final resolution.

Photographic processing (type of developer, developing time and temperature) also affect graininess and sensitivity. More rigorous development increases sensitivity, graininess and fog at the same time.

Consequently there are two ways of achieving optimal resolution in autoradiography with a given isotope: optimal contact between section and emulsion and the use of highest resolution film with suitable processing. The first approach presents some technical difficulties, which however can be overcome, but the second has inherent limitations, since low sensitivity requires higher tracer doses which cannot always be used; a compromise has to be made. In the following, some typical methods used in autoradiography with a few frequently used photographic materials will be presented. Table 25 lists some of the typical data with I^{131} for the techniques which will be discussed.

The simplest method of assuring contact between a photographic emulsion and a histological section is to press together mechanically by some clamping device a piece of dental x-ray film and the section mounted on a glass microscope slide; a cover glass should not be used. The film and slide are left together for a suitable exposure time; the film is then removed and processed; ordinary x-ray developing solutions, or a formula similar to the Kodak D 19 developer, are satisfactory. Fixation and drying are not critical. This simple technique is limited to macroscopic localization, since it is impossible to replace the film in original alignment over the section with precision. It is useful, however, when a particular area on the slide is large enough so that it can be identified visually after microscopic examination; this is frequently the case in thyroid lesions. The coarse grain of x-ray films is not objectionable in contact autoradiography.

Contact autoradiography is useful not only with tissue sections but also in paper chromatography. The paper strip with separated protein fractions is left in contact with a photographic film in the same manner as a tissue section. After exposure and development, the blackening of the film indicates the location of the radioactivity on the paper. This method is particularly useful with two dimensional separation on paper.

Autoradiography is not limited to visual inspection, it can be used also as a quantitative method, when the density of the photographic image is measured by a densitometer and compared to the densities obtained with the same photographic material exposed to different concentrations of the radioactive material for the same time as the autoradiograph and processed in the same way. Constant exposure time for the reference films and autoradiograph is essential, due to fading of the latent image. Such a quantitative use of autoradiography is the only method for estimating not only the average dose but the true dose to small tissue areas when the uptake of a radioactive isotope is not uniform, as for instance the uptake of iodine in the thyroid gland.

In order to overcome the difficulty of correlating the photographic image with the slide, several methods have been worked out for maintaining

Table 25.—*Autoradiographic Techniques*

Method	Material	Resolution	Background fog	Sensitivity* μc/gm.
Contact autoradiography	Dental x-ray film	Low	High, visible	0.2–0.4
Emulsion painting	Ansco autoradiographic emulsion "A"	Low	High, visible	0.02–0.04
Emulsion painting and dipping	Kodak nuclear track pellicles NTB 2 and NTB 3	Medium	Medium, visible only under microscope	2
Emulsion flotation	Kodak scientific plates Code autoradiography Kodak Ltd (England) AR-10 stripping film	High	Negligible, even under microscope	20

*Lowest concentration of I^{131} per gram of tissue which will produce a satisfactory autoradiogram after about 2 half-lives, when 5μ thick sections are used (thicker section will require proportionally less exposure).

the photographic emulsion in undisturbed alignment with the section throughout the whole sequence of exposure and processing.

1. *Emulsion painting* makes use of photographic emulsions which have not been hardened and can be liquefied by warming. They are available in the form of globules, pellicles, or they may be melted off from film. The liquid emulsion is applied over the histological section by a fine brush. It solidifies again on cooling and is developed after suitable exposure, without removing it from the slide. If no shrinkage has occurred, the autoradiographic image will have remained in alignment with the histological section, and a microscopic comparison and correlation between the two is possible. While there are fine-grain emulsions available for emulsion painting, the main use of this technique is for low resolution purposes, since it is quite difficult to prepare uniform thin films by this method. When relatively coarse-grain emulsions are used, the requirements for thin films are less critical and adequate resolution is easily obtained with high sensitivity materials to distinguish, for instance, functioning and nonfunctioning follicles in the thyroid gland, which are visible only with magnification under a microscope.

2. *Section Dipping.* A modification of emulsion painting is to dip the section mounted on a glass slide into the liquified emulsion (the emulsion deposited on the back of the slide is scraped off after processing). This modification is superior to the painting technique, it results in a thin and uniform emulsion layer and has been used successfully for high resolution work with Kodak NTB bulk emulsions.

3. *Section flotation* consists of picking up the histological section, floating on the surface of water, on a photographic plate or film. It has the advantage that practically any photographic film can be used. The best resolution is obtained with specially prepared nuclear emulsions. The disadvantage is that the photographic processing solutions have to penetrate the histological section and may damage it.

4. *Emulsion flotation* is the reverse of section flotation: a thin emulsion film is obtained by stripping the emulsion from specially prepared plates and floated on the surface of a water bath; this film is picked up by the glass slide on which the already stained histological section is mounted. The section can be covered first by a thin (about 1 micron) layer of collodion applied to it in a diluted solution (1 per cent, in a mixture of equal parts of ether and alcohol). This collodion layer protects the section and its stains from the effect of photographic chemicals. Stripping films are thin (4 to 5 microns) and quite uniform. Alignment between emulsion and section is excellent and very high resolution can be obtained with slow films of fine grain. With I^{131} in the thyroid gland, it is possible to evaluate differences in the activity between single cells.

Table 25 contains some quantitative data on various techniques when used with I^{131}. It is useful to interpret the listed sensitivities in terms of the minimal required tracer dose. For contact autoradiography of a somewhat enlarged thyroid gland of 100 grams weight, 20 to 40 μc will be needed in the whole gland at the beginning of the exposure. If the uptake of this gland has been in the normal range, about 30 per cent, a tracer dose of 60 to 120 μc would have been required. Usually, it takes several days between a preoperative administration of a tracer dose and the availability of the sections; if this interval is about a week, the tracer dose must be doubled, a total of 120 to 140 μc will be needed. Similarly it will be found that for the emulsion painting technique, one-tenth that amount, or about an ordinary tracer dose as used for uptake studies would suffice. For the highest resolution obtainable with emulsion flotation material, on the other hand, 3 times the dose, 360 to 720 μc, is needed, which approaches a therapeutic dose; in cases of complete thyroidectomy with suspected malignancy this is not prohibitive. It has to be remembered that for shorter exposures, when the information is urgently needed for a clinical decision, the tracer dose has to be increased accordingly.

Table 26.—Approximate Specific Activity ($\mu c/gm$) Required for Several Isotopes, with an Exposure of One to Two Weeks, Relative to I^{131}. These Factors Are Applicable to Single Coated Films. For Double Coated X-ray Films, the Differences Are Less.

Isotope	Relative Sensitivity	For Equivalent Exposure—$\mu c/gm$
H_3*	0.3	3.3
C^{14}	0.3	3.3
S^{35}*	0.3	3.3
Ca^{45}	0.6†	1.6
I^{131}	1.0	1 0
P^{32}	2.7	0.37

* assumed to have the same efficiency as C^{14}
†The author has some doubts about this reported value, and estimates it to be closer to 0.4.

While the data in Table 25 refer to I^{131}, they can be used for rough estimates of the specific activities required with other isotopes for comparable exposure times (one to two weeks). The photographic effect decreases with the energy of beta radiation; Table 26* gives the specific activity needed for several isotopes relative to I^{131}.

Autoradiographic techniques are simple in principle, but, except for contact methods, they require familiarity and facility with a considerable mass of minute details in order to avoid a variety of pitfalls and artifacts. While the reference (see footnote below) attempts to give comprehensive instructions, it is recommended that reading be supplemented by some personal instruction and by practical supervised experience in the darkroom. While this remark applies to the whole section on instrumentation, it is particularly valid in connection with autoradiography.

* This table is based with some modifications on table 2 in *Autoradiography in Biology and Medicine* by George A. Boyd, page 49, Academic Press, Inc., New York, 1955. This book gives, in table 22 (pages 125–135) a comprehensive review of data on a variety of isotopes used with most available emulsions and techniques.

20

Use of Radiation Detectors for Health Protection

THE aims of health protection in connection with radiological hazards were discussed in Chapter 10. The techniques used to eliminate or to reduce these hazards were also presented. The purpose of the present chapter is to describe the means of evaluating their effectiveness.

The two basic types of instruments used in this work are total dose and dose rate measuring devices. They are used for three types of radiation measurements: personnel, area, and process monitoring.

Total dose measuring devices are condenser type ionization chambers (see page 186) and photographic film dosimeters. Chemical radiation detectors are not suitable for the dose ranges of interest for health monitoring.

Condenser-type ionization chambers are made as small fountain-pen-sized instruments which can be carried in the pocket. Their useful range is usually 50 to 250 mr. When they are used to measure the dose accumulated over days or weeks, they show some spontaneous discharge even when they are not exposed to man-made radiation; this discharge is due partly to background radiation and partly to electrical leakage. It varies in different makes and even in individual instruments of the same manufacturer, and it can change in the course of time. Its order of magnitude is $\frac{1}{2}$ to 5 mr per day, and it must be determined for each chamber and checked at frequent intervals. This leakage limits the time intervals over which these chambers can be used without recharging. Daily reading and charging offer optimal reliability; a week is about the practical maximum. Leakage tests must be made regularly (at least once a month, particularly in humid weather). Early pocket chambers of this type had to be kept in a dessicator when not in use; modern improved devices do not require this. The scales on the built-in electrometers or on the external reading devices are calibrated in milliroentgens; this calibration can be accepted as sufficiently reliable for monitoring purposes with most gamma-ray energies encountered with radioactive isotopes (a significant deviation occurs below 100 kev). Because of relatively thick walls, these chambers are not sensitive to beta radiation.

Photographic film offers in many respects the best means to measure the total dose accumulated over an extended interval. The blackening of the exposed film after development can be easily measured quantitatively with a densitometer, and the observed density is linearly proportional to the exposure, that is to the total dose, over a considerable range. This range depends on the characteristics of the film emulsion and on processing. The smallest dose which can be detected by a film of high sensitivity to gamma radiation is about 5 mr; the ratio between the maximum and minimum measurable exposure (the range) is between 30:1 and 400:1. This means that when a film of high sensitivity is used, exposures between 5 mr and about 0.5 r can be measured. When film is used for measurements of larger exposures, less sensitive emulsions are required. By using two films of different sensitivities packed together, any required dose range can be covered.

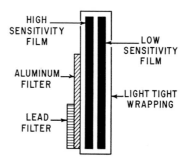

Fig. 84.—Schematic illustration of a film badge for monitoring personnel exposure. The filters permit the differentiation between exposure to beta, x-ray, and high energy gamma radiation. A film badge as illustrated will differentiate between radiation of different types only if the exposure occurs from the left. It is customary, therefore, to use identical filters on both sides of the film packet, which makes the badge bidirectional.

Since these films keep over one or two years without developing objectionable fogging, they can be used for measurements extending over a period of weeks and months.

Another advantage of photographic measurement of dose is that it is is easy to estimate the nature of radiation exposure. In Figure 84 parts of the film are covered by an aluminum and by a lead sheet, and a portion is left uncovered (except that it is wrapped, of course, in a lightproof material). If this film is exposed to beta radiation and the thickness of the aluminum sheet exceeds the range of this radiation, only the uncovered area of the film will show blackening. An exposure to gamma radiation of a few hundred kev will blacken not only the uncovered area, but also the area under the aluminum filter; the film behind the lead filter will show much lower density because of high absorption of the comparatively low-energy gamma radiation by lead. High-energy gamma radiation, of a few mev, will be less absorbed by the lead filter and the differences between film areas behind the different filters will be reduced. The total density is therefore a measure of dose, and the relative densities an indication of type and energy of radiation.

Below energies of 100 kev, the speed of film emulsions has strong energy dependence; it may increase 5 to 30 fold. In this region, therefore, films are useless for quantitative measurements. At higher energies this dependence is small, below 10 per cent up to several mev.

Films for this purpose are packed in the size of dental x-ray films and are carried in some sort of holder which usually contains filters for identification of the radiation. The holders have clips for attaching to clothing. The complete assembly is called a film badge.

The disadvantage of film dosimetry is that films have to be processed (developed and so forth) before readings can be made. Self-developing film badges of "picture in a minute" type have been made, but they are not yet available to the public. Film processing has to be done with great care to maintain reproducible results.* It is not advisable, therefore, to attempt to do these measurements in the individual laboratory; a commercial film-badge service is preferable. Periodic checks of the reliability of such services are advisable by exposing film badges to known amounts of radiation, calculated on the basis of the Γ of the isotope available.

Dose-rate meters are ionization chambers, used in connection with vacuum-tube or other types of amplifiers, particularly battery-powered portable instruments (see page 186ff). Portable Geiger-Mueller or scintillation counter rate meters are also used; they have a much higher sensitivity but lower precision and greater variation in response (calibration) for different energies.

The required sensitivity is determined by the permissible weekly exposure of 100 mr. For a week of forty working-hours, this means a maximum continuous dose rate of 2.5 mr per hour. For skin exposure the permissible dose is 15 times higher, and the corresponding dose rate here is 37 mr per hour. Portable rate-meters have a selector switch, which permits a choice of several sensitivity ranges. The highest sensitivity of ionization chamber dose-rate meters is usually 20 to 25 mr per hour full scale, so that a single division corresponds to between 0.5 and 1 mr per hour. The ranges of lower sensitivity may go to several r per hour full scale, which is useful in measuring high radiation levels of short duration.

Ionization chamber dose-rate meters usually have plastic walls of sufficient thickness to make them resistant to damage in handling. They have provisions to remove some section of this wall and to uncover a thin plastic window so as to make the instrument sensitive to beta radiation; the scale calibrations are not applicable for this type of use and the meter deflection can be interpreted only in a qualitative way.

The wave-length dependence of these ionization chambers is similar to that of pocket chambers; they are reliable for gamma-ray energies above 100 kev. The precision of these devices is not high, about 25 per cent; this is, however, adequate for monitoring purposes.

*Additional information can be found in the National Bureau of Standards Handbook 57: *Photographic Dosimetry of X and Gamma Rays.* For sale by the Superintendent of Documents, Washington 25, D.C. Price 15 cents.

Portable Geiger-Mueller counters have much higher inherent sensitivity than ionization chambers; however, their wave-length dependence is great. The meters are calibrated either in counts per minute or in milliroentgens. In the latter case this calibration is usually done with high-energy gamma radiation (Co^{60} or radium). When they are to be used with other radioactive isotopes for dose-rate determination, they must be recalibrated with a known source of the particular isotope. Portable Geiger-Mueller counters frequently have thin walls or windows, so that some sensitivity in beta detection is available; this is again of little value for quantitative measurements, but very useful in finding low-level contamination. Many of these instruments have a light signal to indicate visually the occurrence of a counting event. Some have provisions for connecting a headphone, to make the counts audible. Portable scintillation counters have maximum sensitivity and they can detect small changes in natural radioactive background. This extreme sensitivity is of limited use in health protection measurements; their main application is in prospecting for radioactive minerals.

Application to Monitoring Problems.—All measures of radiation protection have, of course, the final aim of limiting the radiation exposure of people to the permissible value. The final check of success or failure of these measures is *personnel monitoring*, that is the measurement of total dose received by individuals.

When daily information is required, pocket ionization chambers are the only practical device. Film badges are less expensive, and they can be worn over a period of a week to a month; further, they can give indication about the source of exposure (low or high energy gamma and x-rays, or beta radiation); the results are not available immediately.

A common sense rule is to have all personnel working with radioactive isotopes wear film badges during working hours. At the beginning, daily measurements of key people with pocket chambers are highly advisable, until the health safety of the laboratory working conditions has been established; after that, the pocket chambers should be worn when an unexplained rise in film-badge reading is reported, or when techniques are changed, new isotopes are introduced or increased quantities are used.

The hands can easily get more than 15 times the dose indicated on the film badge worn on a coat, since they frequently come close to radioactive materials which are inside of shielding enclosures. However, a higher exposure level is permitted for hands than for the whole body (see page 143). Pocket chambers and film badges can be, for occasional use, taped to the hand, but this is usually inconvenient. Special ring type film badges are available for these purposes. They consist of small waterproof film packs, attached to plastic rings which can be worn on a finger.

This external monitoring will not reveal internal radiation exposure due to accidental ingestion or inhalation of radioactive material. This danger is probably greatest with I^{131}. Such internal exposure is easily detected by standard uptake methods. It is advisable to do such uptake monitoring at regular intervals on everybody who handles this isotope. Other isotopes are less easily detected, but internal exposure can usually be established, if not by external counting, then by occasional measurements by *in vitro* methods of excreta or expired air, depending on the metabolic behavior of the particular element.

Area Monitoring.—In order to establish adequacy of shielding or, when radiation levels are high, to determine the permissible time for work in such areas, the dose rates at various working areas have to be established; this surveying is called area monitoring and can be done both by total dose and by dose-rate meters. Measurements are made at strategic points in workrooms; common sense will guide in their selection (sinks, desks, etc.) Records of such surveys by area monitoring should be kept. A convenient way to do this is to note the observed dose rates at the surveyed locations on a floor plan.

Dose rate meters are convenient for a quick survey; they should be used for preliminary work and for checking of unusual situations (occasional shipments of large amounts of a short-lived isotope, for instance). A better overall result is obtained by the slower method of total dose instruments, since they will average the possibly changing levels of radiation in a given room, for example, a hot laboratory, where shipments are unpacked, dilutions prepared and put behind storage shields.

Process monitoring is used for establishing the radiological safety of certain operations which are either part of routine or which have to be performed occasionally. If potential radiation levels are high, the actual dose rates must be known, in order to decide whether the operation is at all possible, or how much time can be allowed for its completion, and perhaps to organize work in relays, so that each person performs a share of the work within the permissible exposure time. An example of such a situation is the autopsy of a patient who received 100 millicuries of radioactive gold. For process monitoring, dose-rate meters only are useful; their reading permits a rapid estimate of time which can be spent by an individual at the particular job.

Waste disposal requires no special instruments. The amount of radioactivity to be disposed of can usually be determined by *in vitro* measurement of aliquot samples, or by improvising an adaptation of uptake measurement technique for the total bulk material. This is rarely feasible for the measurement of the radioactivity which is disposed of in the sink by washing of contaminated glassware. A rough, but practically adequate estimate is that less than 1 per cent of radioactive material used in a laboratory is washed out from glassware.

Finally, a special problem in health protection measurements should be mentioned briefly: checking for flaking or leaking of the radioactive material from an external radiation source (for instance a Co^{60} teletherapy unit or a Sr^{90} surface applicator). For a γ-emitter this test is performed by wiping the housing as near to the source as possible (usually the part where treatment cones are inserted) with a cotton swab on an applicator stick and counting the swab in a well-type scintillation counter. A β-emitter is tested by wiping the surface of the source on a piece of paper, which has been cut to fit a planchette, and counting with an end window counter. At present significant leakage is considered to exist if activities exceeding 5 nano-curies are found.

21

Laboratory Design

In starting an isotope program in a hospital or in a private office, the first question to be answered is how much space is required. The answer depends on the type of work planned, on the expected work-load, and on some general conditions set by the necessary measurement techniques.

A modest beginning will be to plan for diagnostic use of radioactive iodine only. This will require an uptake measuring apparatus and a well-type scintillation counter; both can be housed in a single room. But some other additional area will be needed for storage, handling and preparation of tracer doses and some processing of blood samples. If these auxiliary operations are done in the same room in which the measuring instruments are located, an erratic background will almost inevitably result, which will interfere with the accuracy of measurements. However good the shielding of isotopes in storage is, there will be some measurable contribution to background when storage containers are in the same room with counters; as the stored isotopes decay or are used up this background contribution will decrease, and it will rise again with the receipt of new shipments. In spite of the most careful handling, some minor spillage of radioactive material will occur; this may be negligible from the point of view of health hazards, but it may be detectable in the counting equipment. Glassware, bottles, and other materials which have been used for handling radioactive material, will create an addition to background counting rate which will change after washing and other disposal. These effects can be eliminated if the counting room proper is a separate unit and all operations except radioactivity measurements are carried out elsewhere and at some distance. The second area need not be large; it should contain a sink; it can be part of another laboratory, under the condition that sufficient bench space can be reserved for isotope work. In this case, the whole room may become a radiation area in the sense of requirements for personnel monitoring, and everybody working there will have to be provided with film badges.

The two room set-up is sufficient only when the patients seen for tracer studies and therapy can be scheduled for either morning or afternoon visits, or if waiting rooms are available which are far enough removed from the counting rooms; otherwise the presence of a patient who has received a tracer dose may interfere with measurements, particularly in a well counter; patients with therapeutic doses will certainly create an increased back- ground. When a separation of patients and counting equipment is not feasible by scheduling or by remote waiting areas, it will become necessary to separate the less sensitive uptake-counting equipment from the more sensitive sample-counting instruments. This becomes almost imperative when the patient load is so great that sample counting must frequently be done at the same time as uptake measurements.

Increasing the variety of isotopes used and widening of the scope of diagnostic and therapeutic applications will make further additions to the available space necessary, but these requirements must be met according to the specific needs and no general rules can be formulated.

To summarize: 1. Minimal requirements are two rooms, one for handling radioactive materials and the second for measurements; 2. Increased work load will make a third room necessary, so that *in vivo* and *in vitro* counting can be separated.

There are no special structural requirements for a room where only measurements on patients are made. When samples are handled, the surfaces are likely to become occasionally contaminated. Trays and waxed paper covering table tops will allow easy decontamination. In addition it is helpful to have the table-top material itself non-absorbent and washable (stainless steel, plastic laminates) or to have it made of some easily replaceable, inexpensive material (composition boards). In areas where high activities are handled, it is advisable to have floors covered in such a way that they also can be easily washed and replaced in sections; composition tiles appear to be the best way to achieve both.* It is not economical to build a storage room or closet with lead-lined walls; storage shielding is accomplished much more easily by shielding individual containers or by constructing a small lead enclosure or box to hold the available containers. Enclosures can be economically assembled out of lead bricks. The effectiveness of the shield should be checked by measuring the dose rate outside of the enclosure, when a known amount of every isotope to be stored is placed one at a time inside. This measurement will indicate the dose rate per millicurie of the isotopes stored, so that maximum amounts which may be kept in the enclosure can be easily calculated. When larger amounts must be stored, lead bricks can be added to increase the shielding or additional enclosures can be assembled.

Construction materials used in counting areas must be checked for natural radioactivity, since some paints, bricks and particularly tiles (with thorium-containing glaze) may significantly increase the background.

Since isotope laboratories are frequently operated by radiologists or by the staff of a radiological department in a hospital, there is a tendency to locate the isotope work in the vicinity of x-ray equipment. The possibility of interference of the x-radiation with nuclear measurements has to be evaluated under these circumstances.

The starting point is the assumption that a diagnostic and radiotherapy

---

*National Bureau of Standards Handbook 48: *Control and Removal of Radioactive Contamination in Laboratories*, pages 11 to 16. For sale by the Superintendent of Documents, Washington 25, D.C. Price 15 cents.

area has adequate radiation protection. This means a radiation level of not more than 100 mr per week. If a forty-hour working week is assumed, the average dose rate per minute will be about 0.05 mr. If it is further assumed that equipment is on half the time and off half the time, the dose rate will vary between 0 and 0.1 mr per minute. Counting equipment registers radiation bursts which accompany radioactive disintegration or, generally, high energy photons impinging on the detector (we are not concerned in this connection with beta radiation). We must know, therefore, to how many photons 0.1 mr per minute corresponds; this varies with x-ray energy. Some illustrative values are listed in Table 27, where the number of photons

*Table 27.—Number of X-ray Photons Per Minute Traversing an Area of 25 cm² (Cross Section of a Well Type Scintillation Counter), When the Dose Rate is 0.1 mr Per Minute**

X-ray energy kev	Number of photons per minute
80	2000 × 100,000
100	600 "
150	350 "
200	250 "
400	100 "
1,000	50 "
1,500	35 "
2,000	30 "
20,000	5 "

*Calculated from Figure 20 and table 88, pages 87 and 88, in *Radiation Dosimetry*, edited by G. J. Hine and G. L. Brownell, Academic Press, Inc., New York, 1956.

per minute impinging on a 2 × 2 inch scintillation counter has been calculated for 0.1 mr per minute. If we assume that the source of this radiation is for example a 400 kv constant potential machine and that the radiation detector is shielded with 2 inches of lead (attenuation factor about 10^{10}), there will be no significant increase of background counts, but if uptake is measured, scatter from the patient's neck into the detector may be appreciable. With an x-ray source of one million volts, the number of photons will be smaller, but the shielding effect of lead will be less, so that an appreciable counting rate may be observed. Precise quantitative evaluation of the effect on the counting rate is almost impossible because of the changes in radiation quality with absorption and scatter. In practice it appears that a distance of 100 feet between the counting room and a radiotherapy installation using conventional x-rays up to 400 kv is sufficient. When Co^{60} machines and betatrons are used, 300 feet or more may be required.

Equipment.—The equipment requirements are determined, as are space requirements, by the contemplated work. For diagnostic and therapeutic use of radioactive iodine, the minimum needs are a scaling circuit, radiation detectors for uptake and for sample measurements.

When isotopes are obtained from a manufacturer in prepared and standardized tracer and therapeutic doses, handling precautions are simple. Long forceps are usually all that is needed for administration to patients. Syringes with plastic shields are available for injection of β-emiting isotopes. Interstitial administration of larger activities calls for individual techniques (see for instance Silver: *Radioactive Isotopes in Medicine and Biology*, pages 256 and 257). If radioactive materials are obtained in bulk solution, the preparation of dilutions and the dispensing of individual doses requires some additional handling equipment. Depending on activity and the results of process monitoring (see Chapter 20) remote pipetting devices, shielding of solutions while pipetting and ventilated hoods may be needed.

Remote-pipetting devices may be long (about 2 feet) holders for the pipette, with a syringe at the handle of the holder, and a rubber tube connecting the pipette and the syringe. This permits filling and emptying a pipette by visual control without bringing the hands close to the solution or the pipette. Usually it will be found sufficient to use pipetting devices which are attached directly to the pipette. This keeps the hands away from the active bulk solution by the length of the pipette. A considerable variety of such devices are available commercially. They are either a type of syringe with the plunger controlled by a screw motion or rubber bulbs with finger-operated valves to draw up and to dispense the solution. Pipetting of radioactive solutions by mouth should never be done, even when a length of rubber tube is used between pipette and mouth.

Some compounds may undergo chemical changes, particularly when dilutions are made, which volatilize the radioactive material so that it can be inhaled. Such volatilization must be prevented by suitable chemical measures (maintenance of proper pH *etc.*) (see page 243).

Possibility of percutaneous absorption of many compounds makes the use of rubber or plastic gloves mandatory while handling glassware containing radioactive materials.

The body of the operator can be protected when necessary by keeping the bulk solutions in a lead shield (the shipping container or a shield assembled from lead bricks). If the activity in the pipette causes excessive body exposure, a vertical lead plate or a lead brick barrier must be used and inspection of the pipette done through a lead glass shield which forms the upper part of the vertical lead plate (the use of a mirror is rarely needed in biological work). The table on which pipetting is done must also be shielded with a horizontal lead plate. Suitable assemblies of horizontal and vertical lead shields with lead glass are usually available commercially, as designed for handling of radium.

The selection of a scaling circuit is complicated by the great variety of manufacturers and models. It is not possible to recommend specific makes,* but a visit to a few established laboratories, where work in this field has been carried out for some time, will give some guidance.

The beginner may be tempted to get the most elaborate scaling circuit

*A comprehensive list of manufacturers of nuclear equipment is published annually by "Nucleonics" in a special issue (Buyer's Guide) each November.

which he can afford. It must be considered, however, that all electronic equipment gets out of order occasionally; a good insurance against interruption of work, while apparatus is out for repair, is to buy two simple scaling circuits instead of a single elaborate one; the second scaler will permit continuity of work, when one becomes inoperative. In selecting a particular make, the local servicing facilities are an important factor. One manufacturer, who might have been recommended for superior engineering, may have no service facilities available in the vicinity and equipment will have to be shipped out of town for repair. If another manufacturer has a local service organization available on call without delay, his equipment may be found more satisfactory in the long run, although it might perhaps not be the best available, which could not be serviced promptly.

Transistorized equipment may simplify servicing problems in the future. Due to the miniaturization possible with transistor circuits, equipment can be built in modular plug-in units, many of which (counting stages for instance) will be identical. A complete set of replacement modules need not be expensive and could be kept on hand. In case of malfunction every module could be replaced one by one until the trouble disappears. This could easily be done by a technically untrained person. Should this potential of transistor engineering be realized in nuclear instrumentation, some of the recommendations made in the preceding paragraph will have to be revised.

An uptake measurement set-up, with a Geiger-Mueller counter or scintillation crystal as detector, and a well-type scintillation counter, will complete the basic instrumentation, and permit the handling not only of I^{131}, but also of P^{32}, and of other isotopes for blood volume determination and tests using Co^{60} or Co^{58} tagged vitamin B_{12}.

The equipment can be purchased for about three thousand dollars; about one thousand dollars will have to be expended in addition for lead bricks to make storage enclosures and to assemble a shield for handling dilutions of high activity, and for glassware (volumetric flasks, pipettes, pipetting devices and syringes).

The next step in expanding clinical instrumentation is either a collimated scintillation counter for manual scanning (about one thousand dollars with a suitable stand), which can also be used for liver function tests and other studies by exchanging collimating shields, or an automatic scanning device (three to five thousand dollars).

Measurements with low-energy beta emitters will require a Geiger-Mueller counter, with a thin end window, or a flow gas counter. With isotope applications of this nature, we approach the borderline between clinical use and research activity; the instrumentation has to be adapted to the particular problems and general rules are of little value.

For monitoring radiation exposure, film badges, worn by every person participating in work with radioactive materials, are the first requirement. They are supplemented by pocket ionization chambers, which should be used whenever new techniques are introduced or unusual situations are expected, which may be accompanied by higher radiation levels than normally prevail.

A portable ionization chamber, designed as a dose-rate meter, is desirable for area monitoring and is essential for process monitoring. Every location where exposure to personnel for full-time occupancy may exceed the weekly permissible levels, must be surveyed periodically and if dose rates exceeding 2 to 2.5 mr per hour are found, the locations should be posted with radiation signs indicating the radiation dose rate. Areas where radiation levels are below those permissible for occupational exposure but in excess of non-occupational levels should also be posted, but the dose rate need not be noted on them.

A portable Geiger-Mueller counter is not essential; it is, however, of great convenience in inspecting working areas and equipment for low-level contamination, which may be insignificant as a health hazard but will interfere with measurements.

The qualifications of professional personnel directing and participating in clinical isotope work are of fundamental importance, but it is much more difficult to formulate them without ambiguity than to describe specifications and requirements for instrumentation. One of the original conditions for authorization to obtain radioactive isotopes from the Atomic Energy Commission, was the establishing of a local isotope committe in an institution. This committee had to have at least one member experienced in the use of radioactive materials. As additional members were recommended a radiologist, an internist, a hematologist, a pathologist or another basic scientist, preferably a physicist. The internist represented frequently, in the beginning, the driving force in starting an isotope program; at present, the interest in this field appears to be shifting to radiologists. Whatever the primary specialized professional field of the worker may be, he should have some solid background in the specialities represented on the isotope committee, or be assisted by a team, representing such background. Formal training requirements for licensing by the Atomic Energy Commission are changing from time to time.* Various types of training courses are available in a number of medical institutions.†

When the patient load is small, the physician may be able to cope both with the medical and technical aspects, but at some stage, technical help will be required. Technicians trained in the field of nuclear measurements are very few; there are scarcely any training facilities available as yet on this level. Usually, therefore they have to be trained on the job; the time and effort needed for such training will depend on their background and intelligence. Technicians with experience in routine and particularly research laboratories, who have worked in physics, physiology and biochemistry, are perhaps the most promising material available.

*Information about current rules can be obtained from: Isotopes Branch, Division of Licensing and Regulation, U. S. Atomic Energy Commission, 1717 H Street N. W., Washington 25, D. C.

†Edith H. Quimby: Training Programs in Clinical Use of Radioactive Isotopes. Amer. Jour. Roentgenol., *79*, 138, 1958.

Appendix A

USEFUL PHYSICAL CONSTANTS

(J.W.M. DuMond and E.R. Cohen, Least Squares Adjustment of the Atomic Constants, 1952. Rev. Mod. Phys. *25*, 691, 1953.)

Avogadro's Number—$N = 6.025 \times 10^{23}$ molecules per gram-mole.

Planck's Constant—$h = 6.625 \times 10^{-27}$ erg-seconds.

Velocity of light—$c = 2.998 \times 10^{10}$ cm per second.

Quantum energy times wave length—$h \times \nu = 12.40$ kev Å.

Electron Charge—$e = 4.803 \times 10^{-10}$ esu of charge.

One Mass Unit—$mu = 1.6598 \times 10^{-24}$ grams.

Energy Equivalent of one Mass Unit $= 1.492 \times 10^{-3}$ ergs
$\qquad\qquad\qquad\qquad\qquad\quad = 931.16$ Mev.

Electron Rest Mass—$m_o = 9.108 \times 10^{-28}$ gm
$\qquad\qquad\qquad\qquad\; = 0.000549$ mu
$\qquad\qquad\qquad\qquad\; = 0.51098$ Mev.

Proton Rest Mass—$M_o = 1.6724 \times 10^{-24}$ gm
$\qquad\qquad\qquad\qquad\; = 1.00759$ mu
$\qquad\qquad\qquad\qquad\; = 938.23$ Mev.

Neutron Rest Mass—$M_n = 1.6747 \times 10^{-24}$ gm
$\qquad\qquad\qquad\qquad\quad = 1.00898$ mu
$\qquad\qquad\qquad\qquad\quad = 939.53$ Mev.

Appendix B

CONVENIENT CONVERSION FACTORS

1 ampere (amp) $= 3 \times 10^9$ esu of charge per second
$= 6.25 \times 10^{18}$ electrons per second.

1 calorie (cal) $= 4.184 \times 10^7$ ergs per gram.

1 curie (c) provides disintegrations at the rate of 3.70×10^{10} per second.
1 millicurie (mc)—3.70×10^7 disintegrations per second.
1 microcurie (μc)—3.70×10^4 disintegrations per second.
1 nanocurie (nano-c)-37 disintegrations per second.

1 day $= 1440$ minutes
$= 86400$ seconds.

1 electron volt (ev) $= 1.602 \times 10^{-12}$ ergs.
1 million electron volts (Mev) $= 1.602 \times 10^{-6}$ ergs.

1 electrostatic unit of charge (esu) $= 2.083 \times 10^9$ electrons.
1 erg $= 6.24 \times 10^5$ Mev.

1 gram $= 5.60999 \times 10^{26}$ Mev
$= 6.0242 \times 10^{23}$ mu.

1 rad $= 100$ ergs absorbed per gram of any absorber
$= 6.24 \times 10^7$ Mev absorbed per gram.

1 roentgen (r) produces ionization $= 1$ esu of charge per 0.001293 gm dry air
$= 1$ e.s.u. of charge per cu cm air (NTP)
$= 1.61 \times 10^{12}$ ion pairs per gram of dry air
$= 2.083 \times 10^9$ ion pairs per cu cm air (NTP)
$= 5.47 \times 10^7$ Mev per gram of dry air
$= 7.08 \times 10^4$ Mev per cu cm air (NTP)
$= 93$–98 ergs per gram of water (or soft tissue) for photon energies from 200 kvp (hvl 0.5 mm Cu) to 1 Mvp (hvl 3.3 mm Pb.)

W $= 34$ electron volts per ion pair, (average for radiations of interest in this book.)

(324)

Appendix C

PHYSICAL DATA FOR A NUMBER OF RADIOACTIVE NUCLIDES

In this table are listed a large number of the radioactive nuclides currently used in medical practice or in research. The data represent a collection from a number of published sources. Most of the radioactive decay data are from the Table of Isotopes by Strominger, Hollander, and Seaborg, in Reviews of Modern Physics, April, 1958. Values for average beta energies and for Γ have been either taken from Radiation Dosimetry, by, Hine and Brownell, Academic Press, 1956, National Bureau of Standards Handbook 78 (Report of International Commission on Radiological Units and Measurements, 1959), or computed by the present author from decay data. (Listing of the individual beta and gamma energies, which appeared in the previous edition of this book, has been omitted. If the complete decay scheme is desired it is to be found in the table mentioned above.)

Element	Atomic Number Z	Mass Number A	Half Period	Radiation	$\overline{E}_\beta$ Mev	Γ* r per mc-hr at 1 cm.
Antimony	51	122	67 hr	β^-, γ	0.566	2.7
		124	60 da	β^-, γ	0.35	9.8
Argon	18	37	35 da	EC	0.003	
Arsenic	33	74	17.5 da	β^+, β^-, γ	0.37	5.1
		76	26.8 hr	β^-, γ	1.14	3.1
Beryllium	3	7	53 da	EC, γ	0.00005	0.3
Bismuth	83	210	5 da	β^-	0.375	
Bromine	35	82	35.7 hr	β^-, γ	0.142	14.6
Cadmium	48	109	1.3 yr	EC	0.023	
Calcium	20	45	164 da	β^-	0.077	
(with Scandium 47)		47	4.7 da	β^-, γ	0.553	5.95
Carbon	6	11	20.4 min	β^+	0.380	6.2
		14	5570 yr	β^-	0.050	
Cerium	58	141	33 da	β^-, γ	0.150	0.5
Cesium	55	134	2.3 yr	β^-, γ	0.116	8.0
(with Barium 137-m)		137	30 yr	β^-, γ	0.242	3.0
Chlorine	17	38	37.3 min	β^-, γ	1.50	8.64
Chromium	24	51	27.8 da	EC, γ	0.005	0.18

*For positron emitters the energy of the annihilation radiation is included in Γ.

(325)

Appendix C (*Continued*)

Element	Atomic Number Z	Mass Number A	Half Period	Radiation	$\overline{E}\beta$ Mev	Γ r per mc-hr at 1 cm
Cobalt	27	57	270 da	EC	0.007	
		58	72 da	EC, β^+, γ	0.035	5.4
		60	5.2 yr	β^-, γ	0.093	12.9
Copper	29	64	12.8 hr	EC, β^+, β^-, γ	0.130	1.1
Gallium	31	72	14.3 hr	β^-, γ	0.475	13.6
Gold	79	198	2.69 da	β^-, γ	0.328	2.27
		199	3.15 da	β^-, γ	0.13	0.42
Hydrogen	1	3	12.26 yr	β^-	0.006	
Iodine	53	125	60 da	EC, γ	0.027	0.6
		130	12.6 hr	β^-, γ	0.285	12.1
		131	8.1 da	β^-, γ	0.188	2.20
		132	2.33 hr	β^-, γ	0.483	12.3
Iron	26	55	2.94 yr	EC	0.006	
		59	45 da	β^-, γ	0.118	6.8
Krypton	36	85	10.3 yr	β^-, γ	0.224	0.02
Lanthanum	57	140	40 hr	β^-, γ	0.54	12.0
Magnesium (with Aluminium 28)	12	28	21.2 hr	β^-, γ	1.38	10.2
Manganese	25	52	5.8 da	EC, β^+, γ	0.072	18.5
		54	320 da	EC, γ	0.006	4.7
Mercury	80	197	2.7 da	EC, γ	0.07	0.4
		203	47.9 da	β^-, γ	0.10	1.2
Molybdenum	42	99	66 hr	β^-, γ	0.400	1.29
Nickel	28	56	6.4 da	EC	0.007	
		63	125 yr	β^-	0.018	
Niobium	41	95	35 da	β^-, γ	0.043	4.5
Phosphorus	15	32	14.3 da	β^-	0.70	
Potassium	19	42	12.5 hr	β^-, γ	1.45	1.4
Praesodymium	59	142	19.3 hr	β^-, γ	0.79	0.64
		143	13.7 da	β^-	0.315	
Promethium	61	147	2.5 yr	β^-	0.062	
Radium (in equilibrium with Rn, Ra A, B, and C)	88	228	1620 yr	α, β^-, γ	No β with filter	8.25 with 0.5 mm Pt filter
Rubidium	37	86	18.6 da	β^-, γ	0.68	0.49
Scandium	21	46	85 da	β^-, γ	0.12	11.0
		47	3.4 da	β^-, γ	0.146	0.48
Selenium	34	75	127 da	EC, γ	0.011	1.84
Silver	47	111	7.5 da	β^-, γ	0.34	0.17

Appendix C (*Continued*)

Element	Atomic Number Z	Mass Number A	Half Period	Radiation	$\overline{E}_\beta$ Mev	Γ r per mc-hr at 1 cm
Sodium	11	22	2.6 yr	β^+, γ	0.193	13.2
		24	15 hr	β^-, γ	0.56	18.7
Strontium	38	85	65 da	EC, γ	0.014	3.2
		89	54 da	β^-	0.56	
(with Yttrium-90)		90	28 yr	β^-	0.20+0.93	
Sulfur	16	35	87 da	β^-	0.049	
Tellurium	52	121	17 da	EC, γ	0.027	3.4
Thallium	81	204	4.1 yr	β^-, EC	0.234	
Thulium	69	170	125 da	β^-, γ	0.32	0.01
Tin (with Indium-113m)	50	113	115 da	EC, γ	0.025	3.5
Tungsten	74	185	74 da	β^-	0.130	
Vanadium	23	48	16 da	β^+, EC, γ	0.14	10.0
Xenon	54	133	5.27 da	β^-, γ	0.110	0.44
Yttrium	39	90	64.6 hr	β^-	0.93	
		91	58 da	β^-, γ	0.585	0.21
Zinc	30	65	245 da	EC, β^+, γ	0.010	2.9
Zirconium (with Niobium-95)	40	95	65 da	β^-, γ	0.163	9.0

* Iridium-192 and Tantalum-182, which are being used in interstitial therapy, have not been included in this table because of uncertainties in the value of $\overline{E}_\beta$ and Γ. At present treatments are usually based on rather empirically determined "radium equivalents".

Appendix D

SOME CHARACTERISTICS OF THE STANDARD MAN

(From National Bureau of Standards Handbook 47, Recommendations of
the International Commission on Radiological Protection, 1950)

Weight Distribution in the Standard Man
(Total body weight, 70 kg)

Organ	Weight in Grams	Organ	Weight in Grams
Muscles	30,000	Heart	300
Skeleton		Lymphoid Tissue	700
Bones	7000	Brain	1500
Red Marrow	1500	Spinal Cord	30
Yellow Marrow	1500	Bladder	150
Blood	5000	Salivary Glands	50
Gastrointestinal Tract	2000	Eyes	30
Lungs	1000	Teeth	20
Liver	1700	Prostate	20
Kidney	300	Adrenals	20
Spleen	150	Thymus	10
Pancreas	70	Skin and Sub-	8500
Thyroid	20	cutaneous Tissues	
Testes	40	Other Tissues and Organs	8390

Chemical Composition of the Body

Element	Percentage of Total Body Weight	Total Weight Grams
Oxygen	65.0	45,000
Carbon	18.0	12,600
Hydrogen	10.0	7000
Nitrogen	3.0	2100
Calcium	1.5	1050
Phosphorus	1.0	700
Sulfur	0.25	175
Potassium	0.2	140
Sodium	0.15	105
Chlorine	0.15	105
Magnesium	0.05	35
Iron	0.006	4
Copper	0.0002	0.1
Manganese	0.00003	0.02
Iodine	0.00004	0.03

Appendix D (*Continued*)

Water Balance

Daily Water Intake	Ml		Daily Water Output	Ml
In food (including 300 ml water of oxidation)	1000		Sweat	500
			From Lungs	400
As fluids	1500		In feces	100
Total water intake	2500		Urine	1500
			Total water output	2500

Respiration

8 Hours at work	10×10^6 cm³ air
16 Hours not at work	10×10^6
Total in 24 Hours	2×10^7

Appendix E

FOUR PLACE LOGARITHMS

N	0	1	2	3	4	5	6	7	8	9
10	0000	0043	0086	0128	0170	0212	0253	0294	0334	0374
11	0414	0453	0492	0531	0569	0607	0645	0682	0719	0755
12	0792	0828	0864	0899	0934	0969	1004	1038	1072	1106
13	1139	1173	1206	1239	1271	1303	1335	1367	1399	1430
14	1461	1492	1523	1553	1584	1614	1644	1673	1703	1732
15	1761	1790	1818	1847	1875	1903	1931	1959	1987	2014
16	2041	2068	2095	2122	2148	2175	2201	2227	2253	2279
17	2304	2330	2355	2380	2405	2430	2455	2480	2504	2529
18	2553	2577	2601	2625	2648	2672	2695	2718	2742	2765
19	2788	2810	2833	2856	2878	2900	2923	2945	2967	2989
20	3010	3032	3054	3075	3096	3118	3139	3160	3181	3201
21	3222	3243	3263	3284	3304	3324	3345	3365	3385	3404
22	3424	3444	3464	3483	3502	3522	3541	3560	3579	3598
23	3617	3636	3655	3674	3692	3711	3729	3747	3766	3784
24	3802	3820	3838	3856	3874	3892	3909	3927	3945	3962
25	3979	3997	4014	4031	4048	4065	4082	4099	4116	4133
26	4150	4166	4183	4200	4216	4232	4249	4265	4281	4298
27	4314	4330	4346	4362	4378	4393	4409	4425	4440	4456
28	4472	4487	4502	4518	4533	4548	4564	4579	4594	4609
29	4624	4639	4654	4669	4683	4698	4713	4728	4742	4757
30	4771	4786	4800	4814	4829	4843	4857	4871	4886	4900
31	4914	4928	4942	4955	4969	4983	4907	5011	5024	5038
32	5051	5065	5079	5092	5105	5119	5132	5145	5159	5172
33	5185	5198	5211	5224	5237	5250	5263	5276	5289	5302
34	5315	5328	5340	5353	5366	5378	5391	5403	5416	5428
35	5441	5453	5465	5478	5490	5502	5514	5527	5539	5551
36	5563	5575	5587	5599	5611	5623	5635	5647	5658	5670
37	5682	5694	5705	5717	5729	5740	5752	5763	5775	5786
38	5798	5809	5821	5832	5843	5855	5866	5877	5888	5899
39	5911	5922	5933	5944	5955	5966	5977	5988	5999	6010
40	6021	6031	6042	6053	6064	6075	6085	6096	6107	6117
41	6128	6138	6149	6160	6170	6180	6191	6201	6212	6222
42	6232	6243	6253	6263	6274	6284	6294	6304	6314	6325
43	6335	6345	6355	6365	6375	6385	6395	6405	6415	6425
44	6435	6444	6454	6464	6474	6484	6493	6503	6513	6522
45	6532	6542	6551	6561	6571	6580	6590	6599	6609	6618
46	6628	6637	6646	6656	6665	6675	6684	6693	6702	6712
47	6721	6730	6739	6749	6758	6767	6776	6785	6794	6803
48	6812	6821	6830	6839	6848	6857	6866	6875	6884	6893
49	6902	6911	6920	6928	6937	6946	6955	6964	6972	6981
50	6990	6998	7007	7016	7024	7033	7042	7050	7059	7067
51	7076	7084	7093	7101	7110	7118	7126	7135	7143	7152
52	7160	7168	7177	7185	7193	7202	7210	7218	7226	7235
53	7243	7251	7259	7267	7275	7284	7292	7300	7308	7316
54	7324	7332	7340	7348	7356	7364	7372	7380	7388	7396
N	0	1	2	3	4	5	6	7	8	9

Appendix E

FOUR PLACE LOGARITHMS—Continued

N	0	1	2	3	4	5	6	7	8	9
55	7404	7412	7419	7427	7435	7443	7451	7459	7466	7474
56	7482	7490	7497	7505	7513	7520	7528	7536	7543	7551
57	7559	7566	7574	7582	7589	7597	7604	7612	7619	7627
58	7634	7642	7649	7657	7664	7672	7679	7686	7684	7701
59	7709	7716	7723	7731	7738	7745	7752	7760	7767	7774
60	7782	7789	7796	7803	7810	7818	7825	7832	7839	7846
61	7853	7860	7868	7875	7882	7889	7896	7903	7910	7917
62	7924	7931	7938	7945	7952	7959	7966	7973	7980	7987
63	7993	8000	8007	8014	8021	8028	8035	8041	8048	8055
64	8062	8069	8075	8082	8089	8096	8102	8109	8116	8122
65	8129	8136	8142	8149	8156	8162	8169	8176	8182	8189
66	8195	8202	8209	8215	8222	8228	8235	8241	8248	8254
67	8261	8267	8274	8280	8287	8293	8299	8306	8312	8319
68	8325	8331	8338	8344	8351	8357	8363	8370	8376	8382
69	8388	8395	8401	8407	8414	8420	8426	8432	8439	8455
70	8451	8457	8463	8470	8476	8482	8488	8494	8500	8506
71	8513	8519	8525	8531	8537	8543	8549	8555	8561	8567
72	8573	8579	8585	8591	8597	8603	8609	8615	8621	8627
73	8633	8639	8645	8651	8657	8663	8669	8675	8681	8686
74	8692	8698	8704	8710	8716	8722	8727	8733	8739	8745
75	8751	8756	8762	8768	8774	8779	8785	8791	8797	8802
76	8808	8814	8820	8825	8831	8837	8842	8848	8854	8859
77	8865	8871	8876	8882	8887	8893	8899	8904	8910	8915
78	8921	8927	8932	8938	8943	8949	8954	8960	8965	8971
79	8976	8982	8987	8993	8998	9004	9009	9015	9020	9025
80	9031	9036	9042	9047	9053	9058	9063	9069	9074	9079
81	9085	9090	9096	9101	9106	9112	9117	9122	9128	9133
82	9138	9143	9149	9154	9159	9165	9170	9175	9180	9186
83	9191	9196	9201	9206	9212	9217	9222	9227	9232	9238
84	9243	9248	9253	9258	9263	9269	9274	9279	9284	9289
85	9294	9299	9304	9309	9315	9320	9325	9330	9335	9340
86	9345	9350	9355	9360	9365	9370	9375	9380	9385	9390
87	9395	9400	9405	9410	9415	9420	9425	9430	9435	9440
88	9445	9450	9455	9460	9465	9469	9474	9479	9484	9489
89	9494	9499	9504	9509	9513	9518	9523	9528	9533	9538
90	9542	9547	9552	9557	9562	9566	9571	9576	9581	9586
91	9590	9595	9600	9605	9609	9614	9619	9624	9628	9633
92	9638	9643	9647	9652	9657	9661	9666	9671	9675	9680
93	9685	9689	9694	9699	9703	9708	9713	9717	9722	9727
94	9731	9736	9741	9745	9750	9754	9759	9763	9768	9773
95	9777	9782	9786	9791	9795	9800	9805	9809	9814	9818
96	9823	9827	9832	9836	9841	9845	9850	9854	9859	9863
97	9868	9872	9877	9881	9886	9890	9894	9899	9903	9908
98	9912	9917	9921	9926	9930	9934	9939	9943	9948	9952
99	9956	9961	9965	9969	9974	9978	9983	9987	9991	9996
N	0	1	2	3	4	5	6	7	8	9

Appendix F

EXPONENTIALS

x	e^{-x}	x	e^{-x}	x	e^{-x}
0.00	1.000	0.40	0.670	1.0	0.368
0.01	0.990	0.41	0.664	1.1	0.333
0.02	0.980	0.42	0.657	1.2	0.301
0.03	0.970	0.43	0.651	1.3	0.273
0.04	0.961	0.44	0.644	1.4	0.247
0.05	0.951	0.45	0.638	1.5	0.223
0.06	0.942	0.46	0.631	1.6	0.202
0.07	0.932	0.47	0.625	1.7	0.183
0.08	0.923	0.48	0.619	1.8	0.165
0.09	0.914	0.49	0.613	1.9	0.150
0.10	0.905	0.50	0.607	2.0	0.135
0.11	0.896	0.52	0.595	2.1	0.122
0.12	0.887	0.54	0.583	2.2	0.111
0.13	0.878	0.56	0.571	2.3	0.100
0.14	0.869	0.58	0.560	2.4	0.0907
0.15	0.861			2.5	0.0821
0.16	0.852	0.60	0.549	2.6	0.0743
0.17	0.844	0.62	0.538	2.7	0.0672
0.18	0.835	0.64	0.527	2.8	0.0608
0.19	0.827	0.66	0.517	2.9	0.0550
		0.68	0.507		
0.20	0.819			3.0	0.0498
0.21	0.811	0.70	0.497	3.2	0.0408
0.22	0.803	0.72	0.487	3.4	0.0334
0.23	0.795	0.74	0.477	3.6	0.0273
0.24	0.787	0.76	0.468	3.8	0.0224
0.25	0.779	0.78	0.458		
0.26	0.771			4.0	0.0183
0.27	0.763	0.80	0.449	4.2	0.0150
0.28	0.756	0.82	0.440	4.4	0.0123
0.29	0.748	0.84	0.432	4.6	0.0101
		0.86	0.423	4.8	0.0082
0.30	0.741	0.88	0.415		
0.31	0.733			5.0	0.0067
0.32	0.726	0.90	0.407	5.5	0.0041
0.33	0.719	0.92	0.399	6.0	0.0025
0.34	0.712	0.94	0.391	6.5	0.0015
0.35	0.705	0.96	0.383	7.0	0.0009
0.36	0.698	0.98	0.375	7.5	0.0006
0.37	0.691			8.0	0.0003
0.38	0.684			8.5	0.0002
0.39	0.677			9.0	0.0001

(Courtesy of Editors of Handbook of Chemistry and Physics.
Published by Chemical Rubber Company)

Index of Authors

Subject Index

(335)